A GEOMETRIC INTRODUCTION TO LINEAR ALGEBRA

A GEOMETRIC INTRODUCTION TO LINEAR ALGEBRA

DANIEL PEDOE, PROFESSOR OF MATHEMATICS
PURDUE UNIVERSITY, LAFAYETTE, INDIANA

JOHN WILEY AND SONS, INC.
NEW YORK · LONDON · SYDNEY

SECOND PRINTING, FEBRUARY, 1967

Library of Congress Catalog Card Number: 63-20637
Printed in the United States of America

To G. A. J. and M. W. G.

Preface

This book has arisen out of the introductory courses on linear algebra which I have given at Purdue University. It is generally agreed that linear algebra is an excellent subject with which to introduce students to the notion of a mathematical proof, and that it is possible to tell which students should major in mathematics by observing their reactions when they are exposed to a beginning course in linear algebra.

In this book more time is spent on the coordinate geometry of two and three dimensions than is usual in books introducing linear algebra. This is because I am convinced that a geometrical background, such as the first three chapters seek to provide, is essential for a grasp of linear algebra, so that the student will have some idea of the motivation for the ideas that are fully developed from the fourth chapter onward. However, only the notions of coordinate geometry that generalize immediately to space of higher dimensions are discussed. This involves a little repetition, but the advantage to the student is that the notion of a vector in n dimensions is a familiar concept by the time he reaches it.

This book aims to familiarize the reader with the common notions of coordinate geometry, with the various methods that can be used to solve systems of linear equations, involving determinants and matrices, with the advantage on the side of matrices, with matrix manipulation, with the theory of vector spaces, with the notion of the rank of a matrix, and with the reduction of a matrix to echelon form and then to the first rational canonical form. Motivation for the rules of matrix manipulation will be found in the final chapter, on linear mappings. This is a reasonable point at which a further course on linear algebra can begin. Quadratic forms are not considered in this book, since a further course can deal with them adequately.

A fair number of examples are worked in the text, and there are exercises for the student. The book is elementary in the sense that it deals unashamedly with vectors which consist of ordered sets of n real numbers, since these are the vectors that occur in the solution of linear equations with real coefficients. In a further course, however, the student will have no difficulty in seeing that most of the work he has already done extends to fields which are not as familiar to him as the field of real numbers. Indications are given that vectors need not always be ordered finite sets of real numbers, but I do not believe that the most general definition is the one which should be hurled at the student on the very first page.

I hope that this book will help the weaker students and stimulate the stronger ones to read further in linear algebra. With the growth of interest in mathematics in high schools, there is every reason why this book should be studied in the higher grades, since the amount of mathematical preparation needed for its study is slight. The subject of linear algebra is of the utmost importance today, not only in pure mathematics but also in many branches of applied mathematics, including the science of computing. Thus as with differential and integral calculus, the sooner a student is exposed to linear algebra, the better for his mathematical future.

I gratefully acknowledge the criticism of an early version of the text made by Professors Jerison and Drazin. Some improvements in the presentation can be traced to these sources.

D. PEDOE

Lafayette, Indiana
August, 1963

Contents

CHAPTER ONE

Coordinate Geometry of the Plane

Some simple concepts which enter into two and three-dimensional geometry are not only useful in themselves, but help to form a geometrical picture for the more abstract notions of linear algebra which will be developed later. In this chapter we restrict ourselves to the plane, and we assume that the reader has some slight familiarity with the notion of rectangular coordinate axes.

1. Line Segments in the Plane

Let Ox_1, Ox_2 be two perpendicular axes in the plane we are considering, and let $H(h_1, h_2)$ and $K(k_1, k_2)$ be two points in the plane (Fig. 1). If HL_1, KM_1 are perpendiculars onto Ox_1, and HL_2, KM_2 are perpendiculars onto Ox_2, then $L_1H = h_2$, $M_1K = k_2$, $L_2H = h_1$, $M_2K = k_1$, so that

$$\left.\begin{aligned} L_1M_1 &= \text{projection of } HK \text{ onto } Ox_1 = k_1 - h_1, \\ L_2M_2 &= \text{projection of } HK \text{ onto } Ox_2 = k_2 - h_2. \end{aligned}\right\} \tag{1}$$

In writing down the equations (1), note that we regard HK as a *directed line segment*, and both L_1M_1 and L_2M_2 as *signed* distances on Ox_1 and Ox_2 respectively. If, say, the direction from L_1 to M_1 is that of the axis Ox_1, then L_1M_1, as given by equations (1), will be positive. If the direction from L_1 to M_1 is opposite to that of Ox_1, then L_1M_1 will be negative.

Let the directed segment HK make an angle θ_1 with the directed axis Ox_1 and an angle θ_2 with the directed axis Ox_2. We may assume that

$$0 \leqslant \theta_1 \leqslant \pi, \qquad 0 \leqslant \theta_2 \leqslant \pi.$$

Then we also have the equations

$$\left.\begin{aligned} L_1M_1 &= k_1 - h_1 = |HK| \cos \theta_1, \\ L_2M_2 &= k_2 - h_2 = |HK| \cos \theta_2, \end{aligned}\right\} \tag{2}$$

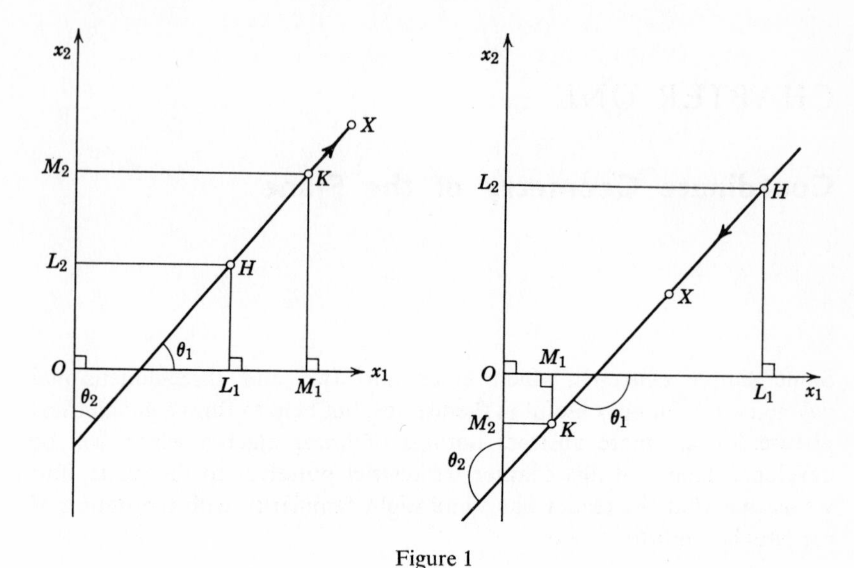

Figure 1

where $|HK|$ is the distance between the points H and K, taken positively, given by the distance formula:

$$|HK| = [(k_1 - h_1)^2 + (k_2 - h_2)^2]^{1/2}.$$

Since the coordinate axes are perpendicular, we know that $\cos \theta_2 = \pm \sin \theta_1$,* but with a view to generalization to the three-dimensional case, we retain the notation of equations (2), noting that the trigonometric formula

$$\cos^2 \theta_1 + \sin^2 \theta_1 = 1$$

becomes

$$\cos^2 \theta_1 + \cos^2 \theta_2 = 1$$

in this case.

If $X(X_1, X_2)$ is any further point on the half-line determined by the directed segment HK, then HX makes the same angle with any directed line we choose that HK does. In particular, HX makes an angle θ_1 with Ox_1 and an angle θ_2 with Ox_2. Hence, substituting $X(X_1, X_2)$ for $K(k_1, k_2)$ in equations (2), we obtain the equations

$$\left.\begin{aligned} X_1 - h_1 &= |HX| \cos \theta_1, \\ X_2 - h_2 &= |HX| \cos \theta_2. \end{aligned}\right\} \quad (3)$$

If we assume that we are given the point H and the direction of the

* Because of the way our angles are defined, we do not always have $\theta_1 + \theta_2 = \pi/2$.

half-line determined by the directed segment HK, so that θ_1 and θ_2 are given, we can eliminate $|HX|$ from these equations and write

$$\frac{X_1 - h_1}{\cos\theta_1} = \frac{X_2 - h_2}{\cos\theta_2}. \tag{4}$$

Since this equation connects the coordinates (X_1, X_2) of any point on the half-line determined by the directed segment HK with the given geometric characteristics of the half-line, we call equation (4) *the equation of the half-line in symmetric form.*

We now show that essentially the same equation is satisfied by points $X(X_1, X_2)$ on the other half-line, beginning at H and proceeding in the direction opposite to HK. If $X(X_1, X_2)$ is on this other half-line, the directed segment HX makes angles $\pi - \theta_1$, $\pi - \theta_2$ with Ox_1 and Ox_2 respectively, and we have

$$X_1 - h_1 = |HX|\cos(\pi - \theta_1),$$
$$X_2 - h_2 = |HX|\cos(\pi - \theta_2).$$

Since $\cos(\pi - \theta) = -\cos\theta$, the symmetric form of the equation of the other half-line is simply

$$\frac{X_1 - h_1}{-\cos\theta_1} = \frac{X_2 - h_2}{-\cos\theta_2}.$$

This equation is the same equation as (4), since the minus signs may be canceled, and we are therefore justified in saying that all points $X(X_1, X_2)$ on the line that passes through $H(h_1, h_2)$, and with direction defined by the angles θ_1 and θ_2 (or $\pi - \theta_1$, $\pi - \theta_2$) satisfy equation (4).

Of course, this is the familiar

$$X_2 = X_1 \tan\theta_1 + \text{constant}$$

of coordinate geometry, but for many purposes the form of equation (4) is more convenient.

We note that it is not the *angles* θ_1, θ_2 (or $\pi - \theta_1$, $\pi - \theta_2$) which are significant for the equation of a line, but the *direction-cosines*, as they are called, namely $\cos\theta_1$ and $\cos\theta_2$. Given these quantities, or merely their ratio, the equation of the line in symmetric form is given by (4).

If we equate each of the fractions given in (4), which vary as (X_1, X_2) describes the line we are considering, to a variable t, thus:

$$\frac{X_1 - h_1}{\cos\theta_1} = \frac{X_2 - h_2}{\cos\theta_2} = t,$$

then on simplification we have the equations

$$\left.\begin{aligned} X_1 &= h_1 + t\cos\theta_1, \\ X_2 &= h_2 + t\cos\theta_2. \end{aligned}\right\} \tag{5}$$

These equations are said to give the *parametric form* of the equation of a line, since the coordinates (X_1, X_2) of a variable point on the line are expressed in terms of a *parameter* (or variable) t.

We have found a geometric interpretation for the parameter t. If we look at equations (3), we see that as $X(X_1, X_2)$ moves along the half-line with direction given by the angles θ_1, θ_2 the parameter $t = |HX|$, and we now also know that as $X(X_1, X_2)$ moves on the half-line with direction given by the angles $\pi - \theta_1$, $\pi - \theta_2$, the parameter $t = -|HX|$. The parameter t may be regarded as a *signed distance*, in the sense that its absolute value represents a distance, and its sign tells us which half-line the point X is on.

If we seek to determine the point on a given line which satisfies an assigned condition, the form of equation (5) can be used to find an equation for t from which t, and hence the corresponding point on the line, may be determined.

Example I

A line is drawn through the point $(-1, 2)$ making an angle of 45° with the axis Ox_1. Find where the line cuts the two coordinate axes. Find also the points on the line which are distant 1 unit from the point $(-1, 1)$.

Since $\cos\theta_1 = \pm 1/\sqrt{2}$, $\cos\theta_2 = \pm 1/\sqrt{2}$, equations (5) become, taking both + signs:

$$X_1 = -1 + t/\sqrt{2},$$
$$X_2 = 2 + t/\sqrt{2}.$$

If this point (X_1, X_2) on the line is also on Ox_1, then $X_2 = 0$. This gives

$$t/\sqrt{2} = -2,$$

so that

$$X_1 = -3.$$

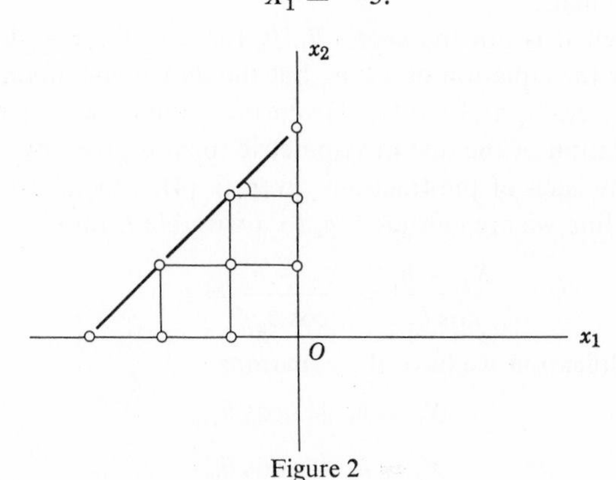

Figure 2

If the point (X_1, X_2) is on Ox_2, then $X_1 = 0$, and $t/\sqrt{2} = 1$, giving $X_2 = 3$. The points where the line cuts the axes are therefore

$$(-3, 0) \text{ and } (0, 3)$$

respectively.

For the second part of the problem we use the formula for the distance between two points to obtain points on the line distant 1 unit from $(-1, 1)$. We find the following equation for t:

$$(-1 + 1 + t/\sqrt{2})^2 + (2 - 1 + t/\sqrt{2})^2 = 1,$$

which gives

$$t(t + \sqrt{2}) = 0.$$

Hence either $t = 0$, which leads to the point $(-1, 2)$ on the line, or $t = -\sqrt{2}$, which produces the point $(-2, 1)$ on the line. The points $(-1, 2)$ and $(-2, 1)$ are both at unit distance from the point $(-1, 1)$. (See Exercises 1, No. 1.)

If the line HK is determined by the two points $H(h_1, h_2)$ and $K(k_1, k_2)$, its equation is obtained from the consideration that the directed segments HK and HX either determine the same angles θ_1, θ_2 with Ox_1, Ox_2 respectively, or angles θ_1, θ_2 for the one directed segment and $\pi - \theta_1$, $\pi - \theta_2$ for the other. In both cases we have

$$\frac{X_1 - h_1}{\cos\theta_1} = \frac{X_2 - h_2}{\cos\theta_2},$$

and

$$\frac{k_1 - h_1}{\cos\theta_1} = \frac{k_2 - h_2}{\cos\theta_2}.$$

From these equations, eliminating the ratio $\cos\theta_1 : \cos\theta_2$, we obtain the equation

$$\frac{X_1 - h_1}{k_1 - h_1} = \frac{X_2 - h_2}{k_2 - h_2} \tag{6}$$

for the equation of the line joining two given points with coordinates (h_1, h_2) and (k_1, k_2) respectively.

An important deduction from the equation

$$\frac{k_1 - h_1}{\cos\theta_1} = \frac{k_2 - h_2}{\cos\theta_2},$$

which may be also written in the form

$$\cos\theta_1 : \cos\theta_2 = k_1 - h_1 : k_2 - h_2$$

is that:

The ratio of the direction-cosines of the angles made by the line HK with the coordinate axes is equal to the ratio of the difference of the corresponding coordinates of H and of K.

As a rule we need not know the actual values of direction-cosines for determining the equation of a line. If we know that the *ratio*

$$\cos\theta_1 : \cos\theta_2 = l_1 : l_2,$$

we can write the equation of the line in the form (4):

$$\frac{X_1 - h_1}{l_1} = \frac{X_2 - h_2}{l_2}.$$

We refer to l_1, l_2 as *direction-ratios.* To obtain direction-*cosines* from direction-*ratios*, we use the equation

$$\cos^2\theta_1 + \cos^2\theta_2 = 1,$$

where we may assume that

$$\cos\theta_1 = kl_1, \qquad \cos\theta_2 = kl_2,$$

so that k is determined by the equation

$$k^2(l_1^2 + l_2^2) = 1.$$

Example 2

The direction-ratios of a given line are $3:-4$. Find the direction-cosines.

The direction-ratios are proportional to the direction-cosines $\cos\theta_1$, $\cos\theta_2$, so that we may write:

$$\cos\theta_1 = 3k, \qquad \cos\theta_2 = -4k.$$

We also have $\cos^2\theta_1 + \cos^2\theta_2 = 1$, which leads to:

$$k^2(9 + 16) = 1,$$

so that

$$k = \pm 1/5,$$

and the direction-cosines are $3/5$, $-4/5$ or $-3/5$, $4/5$.

We remark once again that equation (3) shows us that the parameter t in

$$\frac{X_1 - h_1}{\cos\theta_1} = \frac{X_2 - h_2}{\cos\theta_2} = t$$

is the *signed* distance HX from the fixed point H to the variable point X on the line. If we use direction-ratios, so that $\cos\theta_1 = kl_1$, $\cos\theta_2 = kl_2$, we obtain

$$\frac{X_1 - h_1}{kl_1} = \frac{X_2 - h_2}{kl_2} = t,$$

that is,

$$\frac{X_1 - h_1}{l_1} = \frac{X_2 - h_2}{l_2} = kt.$$

Hence, if we begin with the equations

$$\frac{X_1 - h_1}{l_1} = \frac{X_2 - h_2}{l_2} = T,$$

the parameter T is *not* equal to the signed length HX but is *proportional* to it.

Example 3

Determine the points P on the line which joins the points $(-2, -3)$ and $(3, 4)$ which are such that the line PQ, where Q is $(1, -5)$, makes an angle of 45° with Ox_1.

The parametric equations of the line joining $(-2, -3)$ and $(3, 4)$ are

$$\frac{X_1 - (-2)}{3 - (-2)} = \frac{X_2 - (-3)}{4 - (-3)} = t,$$

which gives us $X_1 = 5t - 2$, $X_2 = 7t - 3$. Let $P = (X_1, X_2)$. The direction-cosines of PQ are $\cos\theta_1$, $\cos\theta_2$, where

$$\frac{5t - 2 - 1}{\cos\theta_1} = \frac{7t - 3 - (-5)}{\cos\theta_2}.$$

Hence $\cos\theta_1 = k(5t - 3)$, $\cos\theta_2 = k(7t + 2)$, and

$$1 = \cos^2\theta_1 + \cos^2\theta_2 = k^2[(5t - 3)^2 + (7t + 2)^2].$$

Since we are told that $\cos\theta_1 = \pm 1/\sqrt{2}$, we have

$$1/2 = \cos^2\theta_1 = k^2(5t - 3)^2$$
$$= \frac{(5t - 3)^2}{(5t - 3)^2 + (7t + 2)^2},$$

so that

$$(5t - 3)^2 = (7t + 2)^2,$$

and

$$5t - 3 = \pm(7t + 2).$$

Hence $2t = -5$, or $12t = 1$, considering both possibilities given by the $\pm$ sign, and the two points are

$$X_1 = -25/2 - 2, \qquad X_2 = -35/2 - 3,$$

and

$$X_1 = 5/12 - 2, \qquad X_2 = 7/12 - 3,$$

that is

$$(-29/2, -41/2) \quad \text{and} \quad (-19/12, -29/12).$$

EXERCISES I

1. Show, in Example 1, that the choice $\cos\theta_1 = -1/\sqrt{2}$, $\cos\theta_2 = +1/\sqrt{2}$ gives a line cutting the coordinate axes in the points (0, 1), (1, 0) respectively, and that the points on the line distant 1 unit from (−1, 1) are (−1, 2) and (0, 1). Are there any other cases?

2. Prove that the point $(a + at^2, 2at)$, where a is constant and t variable, is equally distant from the point $(2a, 0)$ and the Ox_2 axis, for all values of t.

3. Show that the four points

$$(1, 3),\ (3, 5),\ (4, 6) \text{ and } (7, 9)$$

all lie on one line.

4. A line is drawn through the point $P(2, 3)$ parallel to the line $X_2 = \sqrt{3}X_1$ to meet the line $2X_1 + 4X_2 - 27 = 0$ in the point Q. Prove that the length of PQ is $2\sqrt{3} - 1$.

5. Through a point $P(h_1, h_2)$ a line is drawn making an angle θ with Ox_1 to meet the line $aX_1 + bX_2 - 1 = 0$ at Q. A point on PQ is distant PQ/n from P. Prove that as θ varies the locus of such points is given by the equation

$$naX_1 + nbX_2 = (n - 1)ah_1 + (n - 1)bh_2 + 1.$$

2. Position-Ratio of a Point on a Line

If we write equation (6)—the equation of a line joining two given points—in parametric form

$$\frac{X_1 - h_1}{k_1 - h_1} = \frac{X_2 - h_2}{k_2 - h_2} = t, \tag{7}$$

we have

$$\left.\begin{aligned} X_1 &= h_1(1 - t) + k_1 t, \\ X_2 &= h_2(1 - t) + k_2 t. \end{aligned}\right\} \tag{8}$$

We note that since segments on a line are proportional to their projections on an axis [equation (3)],

$$t = HX/HK,$$

so that the parameter t has a simple geometrical interpretation.

Since

$$\begin{aligned} &HX/HK + XK/HK \\ &\qquad = (HX + XK)/HK = HK/HK \\ &\qquad = 1, \end{aligned}$$

if $HX/HK = t$, then $XK/HK = 1 - t$, and $HX/XK = t/(1 - t)$. The form of equation (8) should be noted. If we were given that the point X divides the segment HK in the ratio $\lambda:\mu$, then we have

$$\frac{HX}{\lambda} = \frac{XK}{\mu} = \frac{HX + XK}{\lambda + \mu} = \frac{HK}{\lambda + \mu},$$

so that $t = HX/HK$ in equation (8) becomes

$$t = \lambda/(\lambda + \mu),$$

and equation (8) becomes

$$\left.\begin{aligned} X_1 &= \frac{\mu h_1}{\lambda + \mu} + \frac{\lambda k_1}{\lambda + \mu}, \\ X_2 &= \frac{\mu h_2}{\lambda + \mu} + \frac{\lambda k_2}{\lambda + \mu}. \end{aligned}\right\} \tag{9}$$

In this form, equation (9) is sometimes called the *Joachimsthal ratio-formula* for determining the position of a point on a line when its position-ratio with respect to two given points on the line is known.

The special cases when X *bisects* HK or *trisects* HK are important. If $HX/XK = 1$, so that $\lambda = \mu = 1$, then

$$\left.\begin{aligned} X_1 &= (h_1 + k_1)/2, \\ X_2 &= (h_2 + k_2)/2. \end{aligned}\right\} \tag{10}$$

If $HX/XK = 1/2$, so that $\lambda = 1$, $\mu = 2$, then

$$\left.\begin{aligned} X_1 &= (2h_1 + k_1)/3, \\ X_2 &= (2h_2 + k_2)/3. \end{aligned}\right\} \tag{11}$$

The reader may recognize that equation (9) is the formula for the coordinates of the center of mass of particles of mass μ at H and mass λ at K.

Example I

Show that the three lines which join the vertices of a triangle ABC to the midpoints of the opposite sides are concurrent (all pass through the same point).

Let the coordinates of the vertices be

$$A(a_1, a_2), \qquad B(b_1, b_2), \qquad C(c_1, c_2).$$

Then if α is the midpoint of BC, the coordinates of α are

$$((b_1 + c_1)/2, (b_2 + c_2)/2).$$

The point G on $A\alpha$ which is such that

$$AG/G\alpha = 2/1$$

has coordinates given by

$$\begin{aligned} 3X_1 &= \frac{2(b_1 + c_1)}{2} + a_1 \\ &= a_1 + b_1 + c_1, \\ 3X_2 &= \frac{2(b_2 + c_2)}{2} + a_2 \\ &= a_2 + b_2 + c_2. \end{aligned}$$

The symmetry of these coordinates with respect to the vertices A, B, C of the triangle shows that G also lies on the join of B to the midpoint of CA and on the join of C to the midpoint of AB and trisects, in each case, the segment joining a vertex to the midpoint of the opposite side.

The formulas (9) are valid for all values of the ratio $\lambda : \mu$. When this ratio is positive, we obtain points which lie *between* H and K, and when the ratio is negative, we obtain points which lie *outside* the segment HK.

For example, the point (0, 0) lies outside the segment formed by the points $H = (1, 1)$ and $K = (2, 2)$, and $HO : OK = -1 : 2$. In fact, by (9),

$$\frac{2(1) + (-1)2}{-1 + 2} = 0$$

for both coordinates. Again, the point (3, 3) lies outside the segment HK, and if $X = (3, 3)$, then $HX : XK = -2 : 1$, and

$$\frac{-2(2) + 1(1)}{-2 + 1} = 3$$

for both coordinates again, thus verifying our assertions in these simple cases. The student should trace the motion of the point $X(X_1, X_2)$ given by equation (9) as the ratio $\lambda : \mu$ varies. It will be found that as this ratio tends to -1, the point X moves off to infinity on the line HK, so that *for the finite points we are considering we do not have* $\lambda + \mu = 0$.

EXERCISES 2

1. Prove that the coordinates of the points of trisection of the segment joining $H(1, 2)$ and $K(3, -2)$ are $(5/3, 2/3)$ and $(7/3, -2/3)$ respectively. Prove also that the coordinates of a point X dividing HK externally so that $3HX = KX$ are $(0, 4)$.

2. The segment joining $(-2, -4)$ and $(3, 1)$ is divided into five equal parts. Prove that one of these points of division is the point $(0, -2)$.

3. The coordinates of three points H, X, K are (1, 1), (3, 5) and (6, 11) respectively. Show that X is a point lying between H and K on the segment HK.

4. The join of the point $P(X_1', X_2')$ to $O(0, 0)$ cuts the line $a_1X_1 + a_2X_2 + 1 = 0$ in the point Q. Show that $PQ:OQ = a_1X_1' + a_2X_2' + 1$.

5. $ABCD$ is a parallelogram. Show that the line joining D to the mid-point of AB cuts AC at a point of trisection of AC.

6. P and Q are two points whose coordinates are $(at^2, 2at)$ and $(at^{-2}, -2at^{-1})$ respectively, and S is the point $(a, 0)$, where a is constant, and t varies. Prove that the points P, S and Q are collinear, and that $1/SP + 1/SQ$ is a constant independent of t.

7. If H and K are two given points, and X lies on the line HK with $HX:XK = \lambda:\mu$, trace the changes in the position of X as the ratio $\lambda:\mu$ varies from $-\infty$ to $+\infty$.

3. Angle between Two Lines

Suppose that we have two directed lines, one making angles θ_1, θ_2 with the directed axes Ox_1, Ox_2 and the other making angles φ_1, φ_2. Let the directed segment OA, where O is the origin, have the direction of the first line, and let the directed segment OB have the direction of the second line. Then if $A = (a_1, a_2)$, and $B = (b_1, b_2)$, we have

$$a_1 = |OA| \cos \theta_1, \qquad a_2 = |OA| \cos \theta_2,$$

$$b_1 = |OB| \cos \varphi_1, \qquad b_2 = |OB| \cos \varphi_2.$$

By the distance formula,

$$\begin{aligned}(AB)^2 &= (a_1 - b_1)^2 + (a_2 - b_2)^2 \\ &= (r_1 \cos \theta_1 - r_2 \cos \varphi_1)^2 + (r_1 \cos \theta_2 - r_2 \cos \varphi_2)^2,\end{aligned}$$

writing $r_1 = |OA|$, and $r_2 = |OB|$. But the cosine-formula for the triangle OAB also gives us

$$(AB)^2 = r_1^2 + r_2^2 - 2r_1r_2 \cos \theta,$$

where θ is the angle between the directed segments OA and OB. This is equal to the angle between the original directed lines. On expanding the first expression for $(AB)^2$ and using the formulas

$$\cos^2 \theta_1 + \cos^2 \theta_2 = 1 = \cos^2 \varphi_1 + \cos^2 \varphi_2,$$

we see that

$$\cos \theta = \cos \theta_1 \cos \varphi_1 + \cos \theta_2 \cos \varphi_2. \tag{12}$$

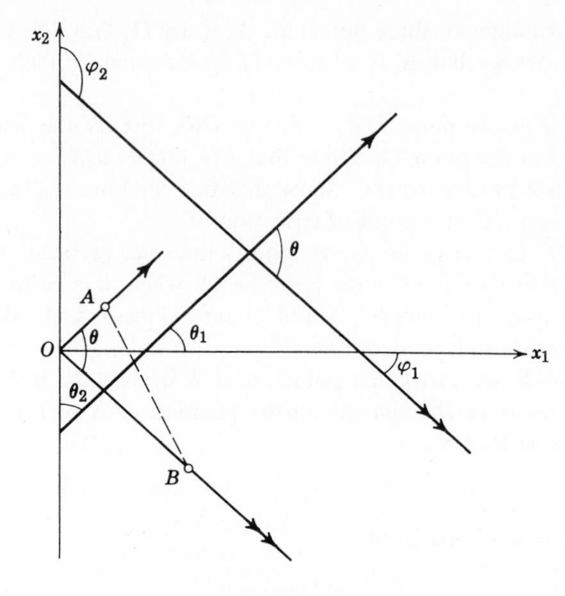

Figure 3

This formula is particularly simple to apply when the lines are perpendicular. Then $\theta = 90°$, and $\cos\theta = 0$, and we have

$$0 = \cos\theta_1 \cos\varphi_1 + \cos\theta_2 \cos\varphi_2.$$

If $\cos\theta_1 = kl_1$, $\cos\theta_2 = kl_2$, $\cos\varphi_1 = k'm_1$, $\cos\varphi_2 = k'm_2$, so that (l_1, l_2) and (m_1, m_2) are the respective direction-ratios of the two lines, then the condition for perpendicularity is

$$0 = kk'(l_1m_1 + l_2m_2),$$

and since neither k nor $k' = 0$, we have

$$0 = l_1m_1 + l_2m_2, \tag{13}$$

as the condition for two lines to be *perpendicular*, or *orthogonal*.

Example I

Find the coordinates of a point which is such that the line joining it to the point (7, 4) is bisected at right angles by the line

$$3X_1 - X_2 - 7 = 0.$$

If the point is (α_1, α_2), the midpoint of the segment has the coordinates

$$\left(\frac{\alpha_1 + 7}{2}, \frac{\alpha_2 + 4}{2}\right),$$

and this point lies on the given line, so that

$$\frac{3(\alpha_1 + 7)}{2} - \frac{\alpha_2 + 4}{2} - 7 = 0,$$

that is

$$3\alpha_1 - \alpha_2 + 3 = 0.$$

The direction-ratios of the join are $7 - \alpha_1 : 4 - \alpha_2$. To apply the condition (13) for orthogonality, we need the direction-ratios of the line $3X_1 - X_2 - 7 = 0$. We may write this equation in the form

$$3X_1 = X_2 + 7,$$

or

$$\frac{X_1}{1} = \frac{X_2 + 7}{3},$$

so that the direction-ratios of this line are $1:3$. The condition for orthogonality is therefore

$$7 - \alpha_1 + 3(4 - \alpha_2) = 0,$$

or

$$\alpha_1 + 3\alpha_2 - 19 = 0.$$

Solving these two equations for (α_1, α_2), we find that $(1, 6)$ are the coordinates of the required point, or *mirror image* of $(7, 4)$ in the line $3X_1 - X_2 - 7 = 0$.

EXERCISES 3

1. Show that the points (a, a) and $(ka, -ka)$ always subtend a right angle at the point $(0, 0)$. Prove also that the triangle with vertices $(3, -2)$, $(-5, 4)$ and $(9, 6)$ is right angled.

2. Find the equations of the lines that pass through the point $(0, 3)$ and are inclined at an angle of $30°$ to the line $\sqrt{3}X_1 - X_2 + 4 = 0$.

3. Prove that the points $(2, -1)$, $(0, 2)$, $(3, 0)$ and $(-1, 1)$ are the vertices of a parallelogram, and find the angle between the diagonals.

4. The Direction-Ratios of a Line

The equation of a line is not always given in the form

$$\frac{X_1 - h_1}{l_1} = \frac{X_2 - h_2}{l_2}, \tag{14}$$

which is called the *symmetrical* form. We have seen the usefulness of this form for obtaining the coordinates of a variable point on the line in terms of a parameter, and this form of equation also demonstrates the direction-ratios $l_1:l_2$ of the line.

The symmetrical form (14) leads immediately to a *linear* equation for the line:

$$l_2(X_1 - h_1) - l_1(X_2 - h_2) = 0,$$

and we see that in this equation:

$$l_1:l_2 = -\text{coefficient of } X_2:\text{coefficient of } X_1.$$

Conversely, suppose we are given a linear equation in the coordinates (X_1, X_2), say

$$a_1X_1 + a_2X_2 + a_3 = 0. \tag{15}$$

Let (h_1, h_2) be any point which satisfies the equation of this locus. Then

$$a_1h_1 + a_2h_2 + a_3 = 0.$$

Subtracting this equation from equation (15), we have

$$a_1(X_1 - h_1) + a_2(X_2 - h_2) = 0,$$

which may be written in the form

$$\frac{X_1 - h_1}{a_2} = \frac{X_2 - h_2}{-a_1}.$$

This equation shows that the points (X_1, X_2) which satisfy equation (15) describe a line with direction-ratios $a_2:-a_1$.

We have therefore shown that a linear equation represents a line, and have established the rule for determining the direction-ratios $l_1:l_2$ of the line:

$$l_1:l_2 = \textit{coefficient of } X_2:-(\textit{coefficient of } X_1). \tag{16}$$

If $b_1X_1 + b_2X_2 + b_3 = 0$ represents a line perpendicular to the line given by (15), since its direction-ratios $m_1:m_2$ are given by the equation

$$m_1:m_2 = b_2:-b_1,$$

the condition (13) for orthogonality becomes

$$a_1b_1 + a_2b_2 = 0.$$

Hence any line perpendicular to $a_1X_1 + a_2X_2 + a_3 = 0$ may be written in the form

$$a_2X_1 - a_1X_2 + b_3 = 0.$$

Since the direction-ratios of this perpendicular line are $a_1:a_2$, we have the important rule:

direction-ratios of normal to line = coefficient of X_1:*coefficient of* X_2.

We illustrate these results by obtaining the formula for the perpendicular distance of the point (h_1, h_2) from the line $a_1X_1 + a_2X_2 + a_3 = 0$.

A line perpendicular to the given line and passing through the point (h_1, h_2) has direction-ratios $a_1 : a_2$ and is therefore given by the equations:

$$\frac{X_1 - h_1}{a_1} = \frac{X_2 - h_2}{a_2} = t.$$

A variable point on this line is

$$\left.\begin{aligned} X_1 &= h_1 + a_1 t, \\ X_2 &= h_2 + a_2 t, \end{aligned}\right\}$$

and this lies on $a_1X_1 + a_2X_2 + a_3 = 0$ if

$$a_1(h_1 + a_1t) + a_2(h_2 + a_2t) + a_3 = 0,$$

so that t satisfies the equation

$$t(a_1^2 + a_2^2) + (a_1h_1 + a_2h_2 + a_3) = 0.$$

This value of t determines the foot of the perpendicular onto the given line. The perpendicular distance of (h_1, h_2) from the line is the distance between (h_1, h_2) and the foot. If this is p, then

$$\begin{aligned} p^2 &= (h_1 - h_1 - a_1t)^2 + (h_2 - h_2 - a_2t)^2 \\ &= t^2(a_1^2 + a_2^2) \\ &= \frac{(a_1h_1 + a_2h_2 + a_3)^2}{(a_1^2 + a_2^2)}, \end{aligned}$$

so that

$$p = \frac{|a_1h_1 + a_2h_2 + a_3|}{(a_1^2 + a_2^2)^{1/2}}. \tag{17}$$

Example I

We may now find the mirror image of (7, 4) in the line $3X_1 - X_2 - 7 = 0$ by another method (cf. Example 1, § 3).

The perpendicular distance of (7, 4) from the line is

$$p = \frac{|3 \cdot 7 - 4 - 7|}{(3^2 + 1^2)^{1/2}} = \frac{10}{\sqrt{10}} = \sqrt{10}.$$

The line through (7, 4) perpendicular to the given line is

$$\frac{X_1 - 7}{3} = \frac{X_2 - 4}{-1}.$$

If we wish to use a parameter which is the *signed distance* from (7, 4) measured along this line, we must use direction-*cosines* in the denominators, giving

$$\frac{X_1 - 7}{3/\sqrt{10}} = \frac{X_2 - 4}{-1/\sqrt{10}} = t,$$

so that

$$X_1 = 7 + 3t/\sqrt{10}, \qquad X_2 = 4 - t/\sqrt{10}.$$

When t is either $+\sqrt{10}$ or $-\sqrt{10}$, (X_1, X_2) is on the line $3X_1 - X_2 - 7 = 0$, since $|t| = p = \sqrt{10}$. Inspection shows that $t = -\sqrt{10}$ gives the foot of the perpendicular onto the line from (7, 4). Then $t = -2\sqrt{10}$ gives the geometrical image:

$$X_1 = 7 - 6 = 1, \qquad X_2 = 4 + 2 = 6,$$

that is, the point (1, 6).

EXERCISES 4

1. Prove that the length of the perpendicular drawn from the point (2, 4) to the line joining the points (3, 1) and (7, 4) is 3 units.

2. Show that the line $X_1 \cos\theta + X_2 \sin\theta - 3 = 0$ is always perpendicular to the line joining (0, 0) to the point $(3 \cos\theta, 3 \sin\theta)$. Deduce that the first-named line always touches a fixed circle, as θ varies.

Give an alternative proof, by finding the length of the perpendicular from (0, 0) onto the first-named line.

3. Prove that the product of the perpendiculars from $(ae, 0)$ and $(-ae, 0)$ onto the line

$$\frac{X_1 \cos\theta}{a} + \frac{X_2 \sin\theta}{b} - 1 = 0$$

is constant and equal to b^2, the relation between a, e and b being $b^2 = a^2(1 - e^2)$.

4. Find the coordinates of the foot of the perpendicular from $(a, 0)$ onto the line $X_1 - \lambda X_2 + a\lambda^2 = 0$, and show that as λ varies all these feet lie on a fixed line.

5. The Intersection of Two Lines

To find the point where two given lines intersect, we must solve the equations which represent the lines simultaneously. Let these equations be

$$\left.\begin{aligned} a_1X_1 + a_2X_2 + a_3 &= 0, \\ b_1X_1 + b_2X_2 + b_3 &= 0. \end{aligned}\right\} \tag{18}$$

We suppose that (X_1', X_2') satisfies both these equations. Then (X_1', X_2') also satisfies the equation

$$p(a_1X_1 + a_2X_2 + a_3) + q(b_1X_1 + b_2X_2 + b_3) = 0,$$

for all values of p and q. If we take $p = b_2, q = -a_2$, this becomes

$$(a_1b_2 - a_2b_1)X_1' + (b_2a_3 - b_3a_2) = 0,$$

the coefficient of X_2' being zero, and if we now choose $p = b_1$ and $q = -a_1$, we have

$$(a_2b_1 - a_1b_2)X_2' + (a_3b_1 - a_1b_3) = 0,$$

the coefficient of X_1' being zero.

We write the solution in the form

$$\frac{X_1'}{a_2b_3 - a_3b_2} = \frac{-X_2'}{a_1b_3 - a_3b_1} = \frac{1}{a_1b_2 - a_2b_1}. \tag{19}$$

In this form, the solution of the equations is easy to remember. If we use the notation

$$\begin{vmatrix} a_2 & a_3 \\ b_2 & b_3 \end{vmatrix} = a_2b_3 - a_3b_2,$$

and call the symbol on the left a *determinant* of two rows and columns, the equations (19) may be written in the form

$$\frac{X_1'}{\begin{vmatrix} a_2 & a_3 \\ b_2 & b_3 \end{vmatrix}} = \frac{-X_2'}{\begin{vmatrix} a_1 & a_3 \\ b_1 & b_3 \end{vmatrix}} = \frac{1}{\begin{vmatrix} a_1 & a_2 \\ b_1 & b_2 \end{vmatrix}}. \tag{20}$$

The determinants in the denominators are extracted systematically from the *array*, or *matrix*

$$\begin{bmatrix} a_1 & a_2 & a_3 \\ b_1 & b_2 & b_3 \end{bmatrix} \tag{21}$$

of the coefficients of the two equations, by deleting the vertical entries (or *column*) corresponding to X_1, then X_2 (with a change of sign), and finally the constant term. We shall develop the theory of determinants, and matrices, later. Meanwhile, the student is urged to use the form given by (20) when solving two simultaneous linear equations.

If we look back at the equation which gives the value of X_1', we see that if $a_1b_2 - a_2b_1 = 0$, we are left with

$$b_2a_3 - b_3a_2 = 0.$$

If the left-hand side of this equation is *not* zero, we have an apparent paradox, which arises from the assumption that the two lines do intersect. But if $a_1b_2 - a_2b_1 = 0$, then $a_2{:}-a_1 = b_2{:}-b_1$, so that both lines have the same direction-ratios; that is, they are *parallel*, and therefore do not intersect. But if we also have $b_2a_3 - b_3a_2 = 0$, there is no contradiction.

However, if we have

$$a_2b_3 - a_3b_2 = a_1b_3 - a_3b_1 = a_1b_2 - a_2b_1 = 0,$$

formula (20) is meaningless. We show that this happens if, and only if, the two lines given by (18) are *identical*.

We suppose, in the first instance, that the one equation is a *multiple* of the other. By this we mean that

$$a_1X_1 + a_2X_2 + a_3 = k(b_1X_1 + b_2X_2 + b_3) \qquad k \neq 0.$$

Then $$a_1 = kb_1, \qquad a_2 = kb_2, \qquad a_3 = kb_3,$$

and $$a_2b_3 - a_3b_2 = k(b_2b_3 - b_3b_2) = 0;$$

similarly $$a_1b_3 - a_3b_1 = a_1b_2 - a_2b_1 = 0.$$

Here it is clear that any solution of one equation is also a solution of the other, since if

$$a_1X_1' + a_2X_2' + a_3 = 0, \qquad b_1X_1' + b_2X_2' + b_3 = k^{-1}(0) = 0,$$

and conversely. The two equations have the same set of solutions and represent identical lines.

Conversely, suppose that we are given that

$$a_2b_3 - a_3b_2 = a_1b_3 - a_3b_1 = a_1b_2 - a_2b_1 = 0,$$

and we know that for the line $a_1X_1 + a_2X_2 + a_3 = 0$ none of the coefficients a_1, a_2, a_3 is zero. If $b_1 = 0$, the equations given show immediately that $b_2 = 0$ (third equation), that $b_3 = 0$ (first equation), and that $b_1 = 0$ (second equation). Since we naturally assume that at least one of the coefficients b_1, b_2, b_3 is not zero, we cannot have $b_1 = 0$. But if $b_1 \neq 0$, we cannot have either $b_2 = 0$ or $b_3 = 0$, since if any one of the three coefficients is zero, the vanishing of the other two is implied. Hence none of b_1, b_2, b_3 is zero, and we may therefore write the equations in the form

$$\frac{a_2}{b_2} = \frac{a_3}{b_3}, \quad \frac{a_1}{b_1} = \frac{a_3}{b_3}, \quad \frac{a_1}{b_1} = \frac{a_2}{b_2},$$

which leads to

$$\frac{a_1}{b_1} = \frac{a_2}{b_2} = \frac{a_3}{b_3}.$$

If we put these equal fractions equal to $k \neq 0$, we have

$$a_1 = kb_1, \qquad a_2 = kb_2, \qquad a_3 = kb_3,$$

and
$$a_1X_1 + a_2X_2 + a_3 = k(b_1X_1 + b_2X_2 + b_3),$$

so that the two equations represent identical lines.

We have assumed that none of the coefficients a_1, a_2, a_3 is zero. The student should have no difficulty in showing that the two equations represent identical lines if a_1 or a_2 is zero, or if $a_1 = a_3 = 0$, or $a_2 = a_3 = 0$.

We now return to the equation

$$p(a_1X_1 + a_2X_2 + a_3) + q(b_1X_1 + b_2X_2 + b_3) = 0 \tag{22}$$

and remark that it is the equation of a line. It passes through any point (X_1', X_2') that is common to the two lines given by (18). Since the ratio $p{:}q$ is at our disposal, we can make the line given by (22) satisfy one further condition. If the lines given by (18) are parallel, the line given by (22) is also parallel to them.

Example I

Find the equation of the line which passes through the point (1, 1) and the intersection of the lines $18X_1 + 17X_2 - 1 = 0$ and $3X_1 + 45X_2 + 19 = 0$.

We need not solve these equations to find the point of intersection. The equation

$$18X_1 + 17X_2 - 1 + k(3X_1 + 45X_2 + 19) = 0$$

represents a line passing through the common intersection of the two given lines. This line passes through (1, 1) if

$$18 + 17 - 1 + k(3 + 45 + 19) = 0,$$

that is if
$$34 + k(67) = 0,$$

so that the required line is

$$67(18X_1 + 17X_2 - 1) - 34(3X_1 + 45X_2 + 19) = 0.$$

EXERCISES 5

1. Show that the equations of the lines through the intersection of the two lines $2X_1 - X_2 + 5 = 0 = X_1 + 3X_2 - 6$ which are respectively perpendicular to and parallel to the line $5X_1 + 8X_2 - 10 = 0$ are $56X_1 - 35X_2 + 157 = 0$ and $5X_1 + 8X_2 - 13 = 0$.

2. Prove that the equations of the two lines which pass through the intersection of the lines $X_1 - X_2 + 2 = 0 = 2X_1 - X_2 + 3$ and are such that the perpendicular on each from the point $(-1, -1)$ is of length 6/5 units are $4X_1 - 3X_2 + 7 = 0$ and $4X_1 + 3X_2 + 1 = 0$.

3. Prove that the locus of the orthocenter of the triangle whose sides are $X_1 - pX_2 + ap^2 = 0$, $X_1 - qX_2 + aq^2 = 0$, and $X_1 - rX_2 + ar^2 = 0$, where p, q, and r vary, but are all distinct, is the line $X_1 + a = 0$. (The orthocenter is the common intersection of perpendiculars from the vertices of a triangle onto the opposite sides).

[The perpendicular through the intersection of the first two sides has the equation $rX_1 + X_2 - a(p + q + pqr) = 0$.]

CHAPTER TWO

Vectors in Two Dimensions

6. Directed Line Segments and Vectors

We have considered directed line segments HK in Chapter 1. If we consider the directed segment HK to be a displacement, or *carrier*, of the point H to the point K, it is then appropriate to call it a *vector*, this being the original meaning of the term, introduced by Sir W. R. Hamilton (1805–65).

We do not wish to stress unduly the physical notion of a vector, which is often defined as any quantity having both magnitude and direction (is an elephant moving northeast a vector?). In our later development of the subject, other aspects will concern us. We discuss these aspects for directed line segments in a plane.

First of all, a special notation is appropriate. We indicate that we are considering the line segment HK as a *directed* line segment or *vector* by using the symbol $\overrightarrow{HK}$. The points H and K are the endpoints of this vector, and H is called the *origin* of the vector.

If we discuss vectors, we must define a relation of *equality*. We say that $\overrightarrow{HK} = \overrightarrow{H'K'}$ if, and only if, the lines HK and $H'K'$ are parallel, the lengths HK and $H'K'$ are equal, and the direction of motion from H to K is the same as that from H' to K'.

This can be expressed far more simply in terms of coordinates. If the points H and K have coordinates (h_1, h_2) and (k_1, k_2) respectively, and the points H' and K' have coordinates (h_1', h_2') and (k_1', k_2') respectively, the vector $\overrightarrow{HK}$ is defined effectively by the ordered pair of numbers $(k_1 - h_1, k_2 - h_2)$ and the vector $\overrightarrow{H'K'}$ is likewise defined by the ordered pair $(k_1' - h_1', k_2' - h_2')$. Then $\overrightarrow{HK} = \overrightarrow{H'K'}$ if, and only if

$$(k_1' - h_1', k_2' - h_2') = (k_1 - h_1, k_2 - h_2),$$

which implies the two equations

$$k_1' - h_1' = k_1 - h_1, \qquad k_2' - h_2' = k_2 - h_2.$$

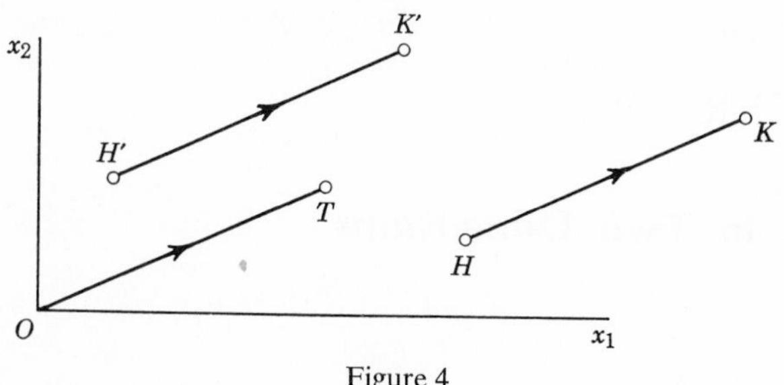

Figure 4

In other words, two vectors are regarded as equal if, and only if, their projections on Ox_1 are equal, and their projections on Ox_2 are equal, these projections being regarded as algebraic (that is as signed) quantities.

Vectors for which the origin is not fixed, or assigned, are called *non-localized* vectors. There is a great advantage in considering *localized* vectors, with the origin at O, the origin of coordinates. Every non-localized vector is equal to a vector with its origin at O. Thus $\overrightarrow{HK}$ is equal to the vector $\overrightarrow{OT}$ (Fig. 4) given by the ordered pair $(k_1 - h_1, k_2 - h_2)$. Since O is $(0, 0)$, the coordinates of T are $(k_1 - h_1, k_2 - h_2)$.

We introduce a special notation for vectors localized at the origin of coordinates. Such vectors will be denoted by single letters such as **X**, **Y**, **Z**, **T** in **boldface** type. Since any such vector, say **X**, is determined by an ordered pair of numbers, we denote an ordered pair of numbers equivalent to a vector, say the pair (p_1, p_2), by the same pair in *square* brackets, thus: $[p_1, p_2]$.

Hence $[p_1, p_2]$ denotes the vector with origin $(0, 0)$ and endpoint (p_1, p_2).

There are certain operations we wish to carry out with localized vectors. Let us consider *addition*.

Let $\overrightarrow{OA} = \mathbf{X} = [a_1, a_2]$, and $\overrightarrow{OB} = \mathbf{Y} = [b_1, b_2]$ be any two localized

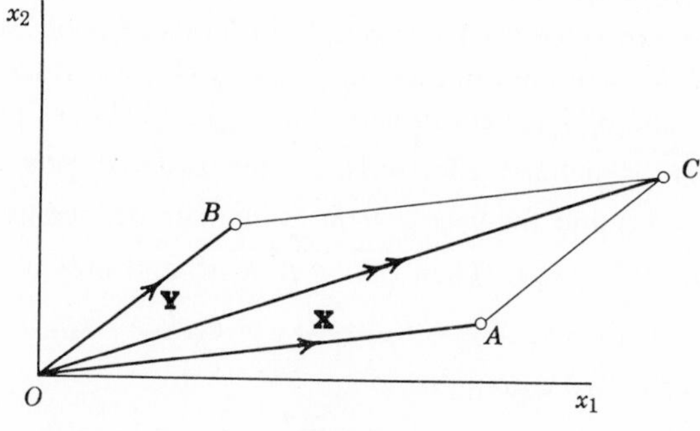

Figure 5

vectors. The coordinates of A are (a_1, a_2), and the coordinates of B are (b_1, b_2). We define the sum $\mathbf{X} + \mathbf{Y}$ of the two vectors to be the localized vector

$$[a_1 + b_1, a_2 + b_2].$$

Hence the endpoint C of the localized vector $\mathbf{X} + \mathbf{Y}$ has coordinates $(a_1 + b_1, a_2 + b_2)$.

This definition is equivalent to the *parallelogram law* for the addition of vectors (Fig. 5). If we complete the parallelogram, two of whose adjacent sides are OA and OB, the diagonal OC of this parallelogram has for its projection on the axes

$$\text{projection of } OA + \text{projection of } AC,$$

or

$$\text{projection of } OB + \text{projection of } BC,$$

so that C is indeed the point with coordinates $(a_1 + b_1, a_2 + b_2)$.

With this law of addition it is clear that

$$\mathbf{X} + \mathbf{Y} = [a_1 + b_1, a_2 + b_2] = [b_1 + a_1, b_2 + a_2] = \mathbf{Y} + \mathbf{X}.$$

We say that vector addition is *commutative*. It is useful to define a zero localized vector, denoted by $\mathbf{0}$, and we define

$$\mathbf{0} = [0, 0].$$

Then

$$\mathbf{X} + \mathbf{0} = \mathbf{0} + \mathbf{X} = \mathbf{X}.$$

The *negative* $-\mathbf{X}$ of a vector $\mathbf{X} = [a_1, a_2]$ is $-\mathbf{X} = [-a_1, -a_2]$,

and

$$\begin{aligned} \mathbf{X} + (-\mathbf{X}) &= [a_1 - a_1, a_2 - a_2] \\ &= [0, 0] = \mathbf{0}. \end{aligned}$$

The sum $\mathbf{X} + (-\mathbf{Y}) = [a_1 - b_1, a_2 - b_2]$ is written $\mathbf{X} - \mathbf{Y}$, so that we may talk of *subtracting* the localized vector $\mathbf{Y}$ from the localized vector $\mathbf{X}$.

The addition of three or more localized vectors may be obtained either algebraically or geometrically, by using the parallelogram law. If $\mathbf{Z} = [c_1, c_2]$, we have

$$\begin{aligned} (\mathbf{X} + \mathbf{Y}) + \mathbf{Z} &= [(a_1 + b_1), (a_2 + b_2)] + [c_1, c_2] \\ &= [(a_1 + b_1) + c_1, [a_2 + b_2) + c_2] \\ &= [a_1 + (b_1 + c_1), a_2 + (b_2 + c_2)] \\ &= [a_1, a_2] + [(b_1 + c_1), (b_2 + c_2)] \\ &= \mathbf{X} + (\mathbf{Y} + \mathbf{Z}). \end{aligned}$$

We express this last result by the statement that vector addition is *associative*.

A vector $\mathbf{X} = [a_1, a_2]$ may be multiplied by a real number s (called a *scalar*) in the sense that we *define*

$$s\mathbf{X} = [sa_1, sa_2],$$

and obtain a *scalar product* $s\mathbf{X}$ from $\mathbf{X}$ which, in the geometrical representation, is in the same, or the opposite direction to $\mathbf{X}$, and is equal to $\mathbf{X}$ if $s = 1$.

We see at once that

$$\begin{aligned}(s + t)\mathbf{X} &= [(s + t)a_1, (s + t]a_2] \\ &= [sa_1, sa_2] + [ta_1, ta_2] \\ &= s\mathbf{X} + t\mathbf{X},\end{aligned}$$

and

$$\begin{aligned}s(\mathbf{X} + \mathbf{Y}) &= s[a_1 + b_1, a_2 + b_2] \\ &= [s(a_1 + b_1), s(a_2 + b_2)] \\ &= [sa_1, sa_2] + [sb_1, sb_2] \\ &= s\mathbf{X} + s\mathbf{Y}.\end{aligned}$$

Summing up, we have proved the following properties of localized vectors under the laws of addition and scalar multiplication defined previously, and we list them as a theorem.

Theorem I. *Let* $\mathbf{X}, \mathbf{Y}, \mathbf{Z}$ *be localized vectors and* s, t *real numbers. Then*

(i) $$\mathbf{X} + \mathbf{Y} = \mathbf{Y} + \mathbf{X},$$

(ii) $$(\mathbf{X} + \mathbf{Y}) + \mathbf{Z} = \mathbf{X} + (\mathbf{Y} + \mathbf{Z}),$$

(iii) $$(st)\mathbf{X} = s(t\mathbf{X}),$$

(iv) $$(s + t)\mathbf{X} = s\mathbf{X} + t\mathbf{X},$$

(v) $$s(\mathbf{X} + \mathbf{Y}) = s\mathbf{X} + s\mathbf{Y},$$

(vi) $$1 \cdot \mathbf{X} = \mathbf{X}.$$

The use of a single symbol to represent an ordered pair of numbers, together with the laws of operation given in Theorem 1, simplifies some of our previous work. Consider the equation of a line given in § 2, equation (7), which leads to equation (8):

$$\left.\begin{aligned}X_1 &= h_1(1 - t) + k_1t, \\ X_2 &= h_2(1 - t) + k_2t.\end{aligned}\right\}$$

If we use vector notation, with $\mathbf{X} = [X_1, X_2]$, $\mathbf{H} = [h_1, h_2]$ and $\mathbf{K} = [k_1, k_2]$, these two equations may be expressed by the one vector equation

$$\mathbf{X} = (1 - t)\mathbf{H} + t\mathbf{K}. \tag{23}$$

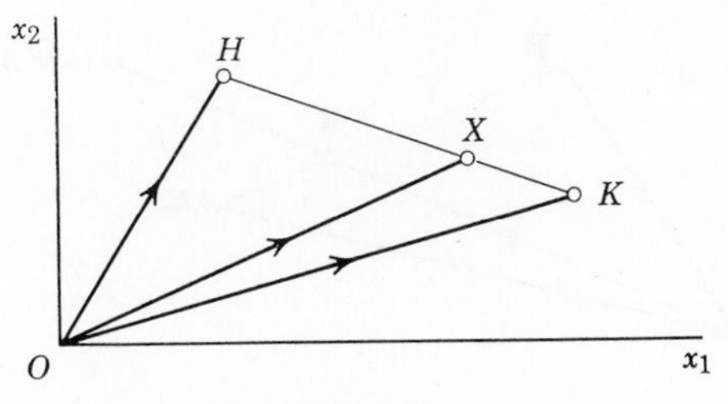

Figure 6

The geometrical picture of this equation is given in Fig. 6. The endpoint of the vector **X** divides the segment formed by the endpoints of the vectors **H** and **K** in the ratio $t:1-t$. We shall show in the next section that equation (23) is a special case of a more general result, based on the Joachimsthal ratio-equations (§ 2, equation (9)).

EXERCISES 6

1. Perform the operations indicated, and obtain the resulting vector:

(*a*) $$3[1, 4] + [0, 2],$$

(*b*) $$-6[7, 8] + 2[5, 9],$$

(*c*) $$p[-3, 4] + q[0, 0].$$

2. Provide proofs for properties (iii) and (vi) listed in Theorem 1.

3. What are the vector equations of the lines joining the following pairs of points?

(*a*) $$(5, -6), \qquad (1, 3),$$

(*b*) $$(0, 8), \qquad (-2, 9)?$$

7. Linear Dependence of Vectors

If the endpoint of the vector $\mathbf{X} = [X_1, X_2]$ divides the endpoints of the vectors $\mathbf{H} = [h_1, h_2]$ and $\mathbf{K} = [k_1, k_2]$ in the ratio $\lambda:\mu$, the ratio formula, equation (9) of § 2,

$$\left.\begin{aligned} X_1 &= \frac{\mu h_1}{\lambda + \mu} + \frac{\lambda k_1}{\lambda + \mu}, \\ X_2 &= \frac{\mu h_2}{\lambda + \mu} + \frac{\lambda k_2}{\lambda + \mu} \end{aligned}\right\}$$

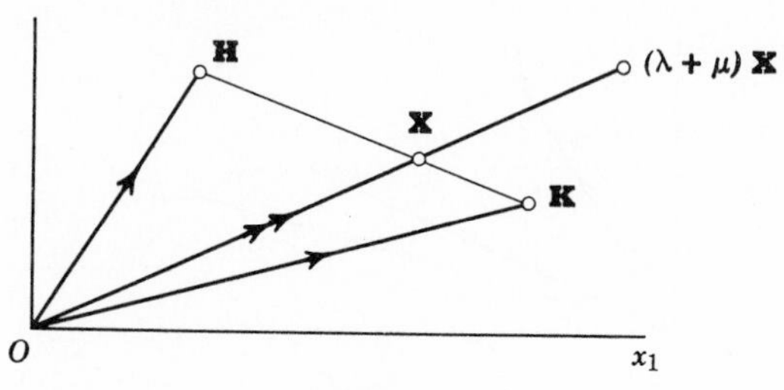

Figure 7

can be expressed by the vector equation

$$\mathbf{X} = \frac{\mu\mathbf{H}}{\lambda + \mu} + \frac{\lambda\mathbf{K}}{\lambda + \mu},$$

or

$$\lambda\mathbf{K} + \mu\mathbf{H} = (\lambda + \mu)\mathbf{X}. \tag{24}$$

A geometrical picture of this formula is given in Fig. 7. The difference in the situations in Figs. 6 and 7 should be noted. Since $(1 - t) + t = 1$, equation (23) gives a sum of linear multiples of the vectors **H** and **K** equal to a vector **X** with endpoint on the line HK. But if $\lambda + \mu \neq 1$, then $\lambda\mathbf{K} + \mu\mathbf{H} = (\lambda + \mu)\mathbf{X}$, where **X** is a vector with its endpoint on the line HK, dividing the segment HK in the ratio $\lambda:\mu$, but $(\lambda + \mu)\mathbf{X}$ does not have its endpoint on the line HK.

It will have been noted that we have dropped the prefix *localized* when talking of vectors. Unless the contrary is stated, all the vectors we consider will be localized.

Example I

We prove once more, but in vector notation, the theorem that the medians of a triangle are concurrent (cf. § 2, Example 1).

Let the vertices A, B, C of the triangle be given by the vectors **A**, **B**, **C**. Then if α is the midpoint of BC,

$$\mathbf{B} + \mathbf{C} = 2\overrightarrow{O\alpha}.$$

If G is the point which divides $A\alpha$ in the ratio $2:1$,

$$1 \cdot \mathbf{A} + 2\overrightarrow{O\alpha} = 3\overrightarrow{OG},$$

which leads to

$$3\overrightarrow{OG} = \mathbf{A} + \mathbf{B} + \mathbf{C}.$$

Once again, the symmetry of this result shows that the three medians all pass through G.

EXERCISES 7.1

1. If $\mathbf{H} = [h_1, h_2]$, and $\mathbf{K} = [k_1, k_2]$, show that $\mathbf{K} - \mathbf{H}$ is equal to the non-localized vector $\overrightarrow{HK}$, where $H = (h_1, h_2)$ and $K = (k_1, k_2)$ (use the parallelogram law.)

2. Show that the line HK is parallel to $H'K'$ if and only if $\mathbf{H} - \mathbf{K} = s(\mathbf{H}' - \mathbf{K}')$, where $s \neq 0$.

3. If α, β are the respective midpoints of the sides BC and CA of a triangle ABC, show that the line $\alpha\beta$ is parallel to AB, and that the length of the segment $\alpha\beta$ is half that of the side AB (a vectorial proof is required).

We say that equation (24), which may be written in the form

$$\lambda \mathbf{K} + \mu \mathbf{H} - (\lambda + \mu)\mathbf{X} = \mathbf{0},$$

expresses the *linear dependence* of the set of vectors $\mathbf{K}$, $\mathbf{H}$ and $\mathbf{X}$. The notion is of fundamental importance in the sequel, and, although we shall not be making use of the general notions just yet, we give the general definition.

Definition 1. *The set of vectors* $\mathbf{X}_1, \mathbf{X}_2, \ldots, \mathbf{X}_n$ *is said to be a linearly dependent set if numbers* $a_1, a_2, \ldots, a_n$, *not all zero, exist so that*

$$a_1\mathbf{X}_1 + a_2\mathbf{X}_2 + \cdots + a_n\mathbf{X}_n = \mathbf{0}.$$

In the example of linear dependence just cited, the set of vectors $\mathbf{K}$, $\mathbf{H}$ and $\mathbf{X}$ is linearly dependent, and the numbers (scalars) multiplying them are λ, μ, and $-(\lambda + \mu)$ respectively. As we are using the real number system, the numbers $a_1, a_2, \ldots,$ in the definition are real numbers.

If, say, a_1 is not zero, we may write

$$\mathbf{X}_1 = -a_1^{-1}a_2\mathbf{X}_2 - a_1^{-1}a_3\mathbf{X}_3 - \cdots - a_1^{-1}a_n\mathbf{X}_n,$$

so that the vector $\mathbf{X}_1$ is expressed as a linear sum of scalar multiples of the vectors $\mathbf{X}_2, \mathbf{X}_3, \ldots, \mathbf{X}_n$. This leads to Definition 2.

Definition 2. *If a vector* $\mathbf{Y}$ *may be expressed as a linear sum of scalar multiples of vectors* $\mathbf{Y}_1, \mathbf{Y}_2, \ldots, \mathbf{Y}_m$, *thus*

$$\mathbf{Y} = b_1\mathbf{Y}_1 + b_2\mathbf{Y}_2 + \cdots + b_m\mathbf{Y}_m,$$

we say that $\mathbf{Y}$ *is linearly dependent on the set of vectors* $\mathbf{Y}_1, \mathbf{Y}_2, \ldots, \mathbf{Y}_m$.

It follows from Definition 2 that

$$(-1)\mathbf{Y} + b_1\mathbf{Y}_1 + b_2\mathbf{Y}_2 + \cdots + b_m\mathbf{Y}_m = \mathbf{0},$$

so that if $\mathbf{Y}$ is linearly dependent on the set $\mathbf{Y}_1, \mathbf{Y}_2, \ldots, \mathbf{Y}_m$, the augmented set consisting of $\mathbf{Y}, \mathbf{Y}_1, \mathbf{Y}_2, \ldots, \mathbf{Y}_m$ is a linearly dependent set. But we cannot deduce from the fact that the set $\mathbf{Y}, \mathbf{Y}_1, \mathbf{Y}_2, \ldots, \mathbf{Y}_m$ is a linearly dependent set that the vector $\mathbf{Y}$ is linearly dependent on the set of vectors $\mathbf{Y}_1, \mathbf{Y}_2, \ldots, \mathbf{Y}_m$. For the information given is that

$$c\mathbf{Y} + c_1\mathbf{Y}_1 + c_2\mathbf{Y}_2 + \cdots + c_m\mathbf{Y}_m = \mathbf{0},$$

where not all the numbers $c, c_1, c_2, \ldots, c_m$ are zero. If $c \neq 0$, we may express $\mathbf{Y}$ as a sum of scalar multiples of $\mathbf{Y}_1, \mathbf{Y}_2, \ldots, \mathbf{Y}_m$. But c may be zero.

Another implication of Definition 1 must be noted here. Since $1 \cdot \mathbf{0} = \mathbf{0}$, the zero vector is always linearly dependent.

Again, if $\mathbf{X}_1, \mathbf{X}_2, \ldots, \mathbf{X}_n$ is any set of vectors, the equation

$$0 \cdot \mathbf{X}_1 + 0 \cdot \mathbf{X}_2 + \cdots + 0 \cdot \mathbf{X}_n + 1 \cdot \mathbf{0} = \mathbf{0}$$

shows that *any set of vectors containing the zero vector is a linearly dependent set.*

Definition 3. *A set of vectors is linearly independent if it is not dependent.*

This definition sometimes worries students. To prove that a given set of vectors $\mathbf{X}_1, \mathbf{X}_2, \ldots, \mathbf{X}_n$ is an *independent* set, we assume a relation of *dependence*

$$a_1\mathbf{X}_1 + a_2\mathbf{X}_2 + \cdots + a_n\mathbf{X}_n = \mathbf{0},$$

and prove that *all* the scalars $a_1, a_2, \ldots, a_n$ must be zero.

We show that the vectors

$$\mathbf{e}_1 = [1, 0], \qquad \mathbf{e}_2 = [0, 1]$$

are independent. If they were dependent, we could find real numbers a_1, a_2 not both zero such that

$$a_1\mathbf{e}_1 + a_2\mathbf{e}_2 = \mathbf{0}.$$

This implies $\qquad a_1[1, 0] + a_2[0, 1] = [a_1, a_2] = [0, 0],$

from which $a_1 = a_2 = 0$. Hence, since $\mathbf{e}_1$ and $\mathbf{e}_2$ are not dependent, they are independent.

Since any vector $\mathbf{X} = [X_1, X_2]$ can be written in the form

$$\mathbf{X} = X_1[1, 0] + X_2[0, 1] = X_1\mathbf{e}_1 + X_2\mathbf{e}_2,$$

any vector is *linearly dependent* on the two fixed vectors $\mathbf{e}_1, \mathbf{e}_2$.

We consider another example. If two vectors, neither of which is the zero vector, are linearly dependent, one must be a scalar multiple of the other.

Let the vectors be $\mathbf{H} = [h_1, h_2]$ and $\mathbf{K} = [k_1, k_2]$. By hypothesis,

$$a\mathbf{H} + b\mathbf{K} = \mathbf{0},$$

where at least one of the numbers a, b is not zero. In fact, neither can be zero, for if, say $a = 0$, then since $b \neq 0$, we would have $\mathbf{K} = \mathbf{0}$, which we have excluded. Hence we may write $\mathbf{H} = c\mathbf{K}$, where $c \neq 0$.

From this result it follows immediately that if both h_1 and h_2 are not zero, the vectors $[h_1, h_2]$ and $[sh_1, th_2]$, where $s \neq t$, are *linearly independent.*

Theorem 2. *Any three two-dimensional vectors are linearly dependent.*

First proof. If one of the three vectors is the zero vector, the theorem is trivial, so we may suppose that none of the three vectors

$$\mathbf{A} = [a_1, a_2], \qquad \mathbf{B} = [b_1, b_2], \quad \text{and} \quad \mathbf{C} = [c_1, c_2]$$

is the zero vector. If the endpoints of the vectors are

$$A = (a_1, a_2), \qquad B = (b_1, b_2) \quad \text{and} \quad C = (c_1, c_2)$$

we also assume that the line AB is defined and does not pass through O, the origin. Then the line OC, if it is not parallel to AB, will cut AB in a point C'. Let this point C' be such that

$$AC' : C'B = \lambda : \mu,$$

where either λ or μ can be zero, but they cannot be zero simultaneously. By equation (24), § 7,

$$\mu\mathbf{A} + \lambda\mathbf{B} = (\lambda + \mu)\overrightarrow{OC'}.$$

Therefore, if $\overrightarrow{OC'} = \rho\mathbf{C}$, this equation becomes

$$\mu\mathbf{A} + \lambda\mathbf{B} - \rho(\lambda + \mu)\mathbf{C} = \mathbf{0},$$

which proves that the vectors **A**, **B**, and **C** are dependent, since not more than one of λ, μ can be zero.

We leave the special cases of this theorem, omitted above, to be proved as an exercise.

EXERCISES 7.2

1. Show that if the line AB passes through the origin, or if $\mathbf{A} = \mathbf{B}$, the relation of linear dependence may be written in the form

$$\mathbf{A} - k\mathbf{B} + 0 \cdot \mathbf{C} = \mathbf{0}.$$

2. Show that if the line AB is parallel to OC, the relation of linear dependence may be written in the form

$$\mathbf{A} - \mathbf{B} + k\mathbf{C} = \mathbf{0}.$$

Second Proof. With an eye on later developments, we give a second proof of this theorem. Using the same notation, we wish to prove the existence of scalars λ, μ, ν, not all zero, such that

$$\lambda\mathbf{A} + \mu\mathbf{B} + \nu\mathbf{C} = \mathbf{0}.$$

This vector equation leads to the two equations

$$\left.\begin{aligned} \lambda a_1 + \mu b_1 + \nu c_1 = 0, \\ \lambda a_2 + \mu b_2 + \nu c_2 = 0. \end{aligned}\right\} \tag{25}$$

These two equations for λ, μ, ν are said to be *homogeneous* equations, since if (λ', μ', ν') is a solution, so also is $(k\lambda', k\mu', k\nu')$. Of course $\lambda' = 0$, $\mu' = 0$, $\nu' = 0$ is always a solution, but this is the one solution we are *not* interested in, and it is referred to as the *trivial solution.*

If the two equations are essentially identical (see the discussion on p. 18) that is if

$$(\lambda a_1 + \mu b_1 + \nu c_1) = k(\lambda a_2 + \mu b_2 + \nu c_2),$$

so that

$$\frac{a_1}{a_2} = \frac{b_1}{b_2} = \frac{c_1}{c_2},$$

then all solutions of one satisfy the other, and we need only solve the one equation,

$$\lambda a_1 + \mu b_1 + \nu c_1 = 0.$$

If, say, $a_1 \neq 0$, we can put $\mu = \theta$, $\nu = \phi$, and then

$$\lambda = -a_1^{-1}(\theta b_1 + \phi c_1),$$

and we obtain an infinity of solutions by varying θ and ϕ. We need only one non-trivial solution to prove our theorem.

If the two equations are not essentially identical, then not all of the quantities

$$b_1c_2 - b_2c_1, \qquad a_1c_2 - a_2c_1, \qquad a_1b_2 - a_2b_1$$

are zero, and

$$\lambda' = b_1c_2 - b_2c_1, \qquad \mu' = -(a_1c_2 - a_2c_1), \qquad \nu' = a_1b_2 - a_2b_1$$

satisfy both equations and give a non-trivial solution.

For the origin of this *deus ex machina* the equations (19) of § 5 should be consulted, with due regard to the difference in notation. The foregoing is a solution via *determinantal theory*, or direct elimination, as in § 5. The solution of the two equations (25) is given by the formula

$$\frac{\lambda}{\begin{vmatrix} b_1 & c_1 \\ b_2 & c_2 \end{vmatrix}} = \frac{-\mu}{\begin{vmatrix} a_1 & c_1 \\ a_2 & c_2 \end{vmatrix}} = \frac{\nu}{\begin{vmatrix} a_1 & b_1 \\ a_2 & b_2 \end{vmatrix}},$$

and it is this result which we may use to prove our theorem.

Third Proof. This proof will not appear to be essentially different from the method used for obtaining the determinantal formula above, but in its development later, this method is quite distinct.

We now stress the fact that any solution of the equations (25) is also a solution of the equations obtained by the following operations:

1. Writing the equations in a different order.
2. Multiplying an equation by a non-zero scalar.
3. Adding a multiple of one equation to the other equation.

It is clear that any two equations obtained from the original two by operations 1 and 2 can always be transformed back into the original two by means of operations of type 1 and 2. If two equations are obtained by means of operation 3, say

$$\lambda a_2 + \mu b_2 + \nu c_2 = 0,$$

and $$\lambda a_1 + \mu b_1 + \nu c_1 + k(\lambda a_2 + \mu b_2 + \nu c_2) = 0,$$

we can obtain the two original equations by retaining the first one and subtracting k times the first equation from the second equation.

Since the solutions of our two original equations satisfy the two obtained by any application of operations 1, 2, and 3, and since the two derived equations can be transformed back into the two original ones by application of operations 1, 2, and 3, we see that the original two equations and the derived two equations *have the same solutions.*

Our intention is to use the operations 1, 2, and 3 to obtain two equations which are easier to solve.

Suppose that $a_1 \neq 0$. Then we subtract

$$a_2 a_1^{-1}(\lambda a_1 + \mu b_1 + \nu c_1) = 0$$

from $$\lambda a_2 + \mu b_2 + \nu c_2 = 0$$

and obtain two equations

$$\lambda a_1 + \mu b_1 + \nu c_1 = 0,$$

$$\mu e_1 + \nu f_1 = 0,$$

(where e_1, or f_1, or both can be zero) which have the same solutions as the original two equations.

If $e_1 = f_1 = 0$, we have only the first equation to solve, and we proceed as on p. 30. If $e_1 = 0$, then if $f_1 \neq 0$ we have $\nu = 0$, and we choose any value of (λ, μ), not both zero, for which

$$\lambda a_1 + \mu b_1 = 0.$$

If $e_1 f_1 \neq 0$, we may take

$$\mu = -f_1\theta, \qquad \nu = e_1\theta,$$

and then the first equation gives

$$\lambda = a_1^{-1}(b_1 f_1 - c_1 e_1)\theta,$$

and we have a non-trivial solution of the two equations, involving a parameter θ.

Our reasons for giving this third proof are that essentially the same method will be used later for solving sets of linear equations (Chapter 5).

Example 2

Solve the equations

$$\lambda + 2\mu + 3\nu = 0,$$

$$3\lambda + 7\mu - \nu = 0.$$

Two equations with the same solutions as the original two are obtained by subtracting 3 times the first equation from the second equation, which gives us:

$$\lambda + 2\mu + 3\nu = 0,$$

$$\mu - 10\nu = 0,$$

and we may take $\mu = 10\theta$, $\nu = \theta$, whence $\lambda = -23\theta$, and a solution is $(\lambda, \mu, \theta) = (-23\theta, 10\theta, \theta)$.

EXERCISES 7.3

1. Solve the equations $\begin{aligned} 2\lambda + \mu + 5\nu &= 0, \\ 4\lambda + 2\mu + \nu &= 0. \end{aligned}$
2. Solve the equations $\begin{aligned} 9\lambda + 3\mu + \nu &= 0, \\ 18\lambda + 6\mu + 2\nu &= 0. \end{aligned}$
3. Solve the equations $\begin{aligned} 7\lambda + 5\mu + 4\nu &= 0, \\ 6\lambda + 3\mu + 2\nu &= 0. \end{aligned}$
4. Show (without quoting Theorem 2) that the vectors [1, 3], [2, 5], and [3, 7] are linearly dependent.

8. The Inner Product of Two Vectors

If $\mathbf{A} = [a_1, a_2]$ is a localized vector, we define the *length*, or *modulus* of the vector $\mathbf{A}$, written $\|\mathbf{A}\|$, as

$$\|\mathbf{A}\| = [a_1^2 + a_2^2]^{1/2}.$$

This is, of course, the length of OA, where $A = (a_1, a_2)$.

Similarly, if $\mathbf{B} = [b_1, b_2]$,

$$\|\mathbf{B}\| = (b_1^2 + b_2^2)^{1/2}.$$

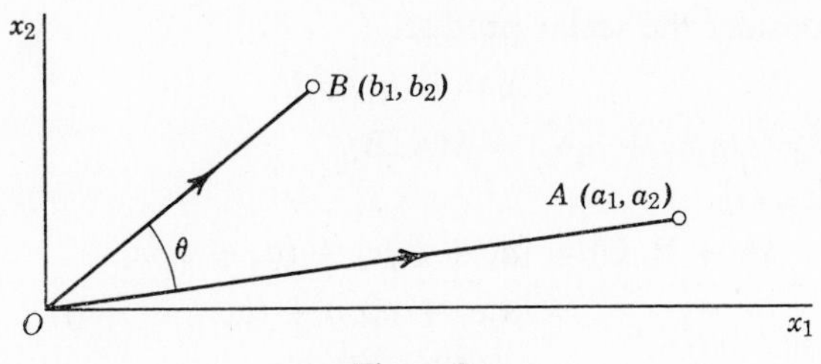

Figure 8

The direction-cosines of the vector $\overrightarrow{OA}$ are

$$\frac{a_1}{(a_1^2 + a_2^2)^{1/2}}, \quad \frac{a_2}{(a_1^2 + a_2^2)^{1/2}},$$

which may also be written in the form

$$\frac{a_1}{\|\mathbf{A}\|}, \quad \frac{a_2}{\|\mathbf{A}\|},$$

and the direction-cosines of the vector $\overrightarrow{OB}$ are

$$\frac{b_1}{\|\mathbf{B}\|}, \quad \frac{b_2}{\|\mathbf{B}\|}.$$

If we therefore apply the formula (equation (12), § 3) for the angle between two lines, which is

$$\cos \theta = \cos \theta_1 \cos \varphi_1 + \cos \theta_2 \cos \varphi_2,$$

to find the angle between **A** and **B**, we have

$$\cos \theta = \frac{a_1 b_1 + a_2 b_2}{\|\mathbf{A}\| \, \|\mathbf{B}\|},$$

or

$$\|\mathbf{A}\| \, \|\mathbf{B}\| \cos \theta = a_1 b_1 + a_2 b_2. \tag{26}$$

Definition. *If* $\mathbf{A} = [a_1, a_2]$ *and* $\mathbf{B} = [b_1, b_2]$, *the* INNER PRODUCT (*sometimes called the* DOT PRODUCT) *of* **A** *and* **B** *is defined as the expression* $a_1 b_1 + a_2 b_2$, *and is written* $(\mathbf{A}, \mathbf{B})$.

We see by equation (26) that

$$(\mathbf{A}, \mathbf{B}) = \|\mathbf{A}\| \, \|\mathbf{B}\| \cos \theta. \tag{27}$$

If we take $\mathbf{B} = \mathbf{A}$, then

$$(\mathbf{A}, \mathbf{A}) = (a_1^2 + a_2^2) = \|\mathbf{A}\|^2. \tag{28}$$

It is clear that

$$\begin{aligned}(\mathbf{A}, \mathbf{B}) &= a_1 b_1 + a_2 b_2 \\ &= b_1 a_1 + b_2 a_2 = (\mathbf{B}, \mathbf{A}).\end{aligned}$$

Also if we consider the scalar product

$$k\mathbf{A} = [ka_1, ka_2],$$

then $(k\mathbf{A}, \mathbf{B}) = k(a_1b_1 + a_2b_2) = k(\mathbf{A}, \mathbf{B})$,
and if $\mathbf{C} = [c_1, c_2]$,

$$\begin{aligned}(\mathbf{A} + \mathbf{B}, \mathbf{C}) &= (a_1 + b_1)c_1 + (a_2 + b_2)c_2 \\ &= (a_1c_1 + a_2c_2) + (b_1c_1 + b_2c_2) \\ &= (\mathbf{A}, \mathbf{C}) + (\mathbf{B}, \mathbf{C}).\end{aligned}$$

We have therefore obtained the following properties of the inner product of two vectors:

Theorem 3. *The inner product has the properties:*

(i) $$(\mathbf{A}, \mathbf{B}) = (\mathbf{B}, \mathbf{A}),$$

(ii) $$k(\mathbf{A}, \mathbf{B}) = (k\mathbf{A}, \mathbf{B}),$$

(iii) $$(\mathbf{A} + \mathbf{B}, \mathbf{C}) = (\mathbf{A}, \mathbf{C}) + (\mathbf{B}, \mathbf{C}).$$

When

$$(\mathbf{A}, \mathbf{B}) = a_1b_1 + a_2b_2 = \|\mathbf{A}\|\ \|\mathbf{B}\| \cos\theta = 0,$$

we say that the vectors **A** and **B** are *orthogonal.* If neither **A** nor **B** is zero, it then follows that $\cos\theta = 0$, and the vectors are at right angles to each other.

We may use the properties of the inner product to find the equation of a line in vector form [cf. equation (23), § 6]. We suppose that we are given $H = (h_1, h_2)$, a point on the line, and the direction-ratios $l_1 : l_2$ of the *normal* to the line. Then if $\mathbf{H} = [h_1, h_2]$, and $\mathbf{X} = [X_1, X_2]$, where (X_1, X_2) is any point on the line, $\mathbf{X} - \mathbf{H}$ is parallel to the line, and therefore orthogonal to $\mathbf{L} = [l_1, l_2]$. Hence

$$(\mathbf{X} - \mathbf{H}, \mathbf{L}) = 0,$$

and using the distributive property of the inner product [Theorem 3, (iii)], we have

$$(\mathbf{X}, \mathbf{L}) - (\mathbf{H}, \mathbf{L}) = 0, \tag{29}$$

for a vector equation of the line.

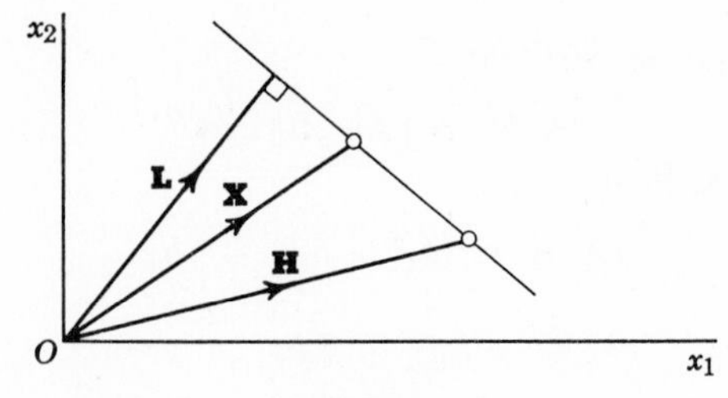

Figure 9

In coordinates this reads

$$X_1 l_1 + X_2 l_2 - (h_1 l_1 + h_2 l_2) = 0.$$

Example I

We use the properties of the inner product of two vectors to prove that the perpendiculars from the vertices of a triangle ABC on to the opposite sides all pass through a point.

Suppose that the perpendicular from A to BC intersects the perpendicular from B to CA at O. Let $\overrightarrow{OA} = \mathbf{A}$, $\overrightarrow{OB} = \mathbf{B}$, and $\overrightarrow{OC} = \mathbf{C}$, and assume that none of these is the zero vector.

We know that $\mathbf{B} - \mathbf{C}$ is parallel to BC. Since OA is perpendicular to BC,

$$(\mathbf{A}, \mathbf{B} - \mathbf{C}) = 0.$$

Similarly

$$(\mathbf{B}, \mathbf{C} - \mathbf{A}) = 0.$$

These equations give

$$(\mathbf{A}, \mathbf{B}) = (\mathbf{A}, \mathbf{C}),$$

and

$$(\mathbf{B}, \mathbf{A}) = (\mathbf{B}, \mathbf{C}),$$

so that

$$(\mathbf{A}, \mathbf{B}) = (\mathbf{B}, \mathbf{A}) = (\mathbf{A}, \mathbf{C}) = (\mathbf{B}, \mathbf{C}).$$

Hence

$$(\mathbf{C}, \mathbf{A} - \mathbf{B}) = (\mathbf{C}, \mathbf{A}) - (\mathbf{C}, \mathbf{B}) = 0,$$

since

$$(\mathbf{C}, \mathbf{A}) = (\mathbf{A}, \mathbf{C}) = (\mathbf{B}, \mathbf{C}) = (\mathbf{C}, \mathbf{B}),$$

and therefore $\mathbf{C} = \overrightarrow{OC}$ is perpendicular to AB, neither $\mathbf{C}$ nor $\mathbf{A} - \mathbf{B}$ being the zero vector.

EXERCISES 8.1

1. Using vectorial methods, prove that the perpendicular bisectors of the sides of a triangle ABC all pass through one point.

2. If A, B, C, and D are any four points in the plane, and A' is the midpoint of BC, B' the midpoint of CA and C' the midpoint of AB, prove that the sum of the three inner products

$$(\overrightarrow{A'D}, \overrightarrow{BC}) + (\overrightarrow{B'D}, \overrightarrow{CA}) + (\overrightarrow{C'D}, \overrightarrow{AB}) = 0.$$

Deduce the result of Exercise 1 by taking A, B, C as the vertices of a triangle and D as the intersection of the perpendicular bisectors of BC and CA respectively.

There is a simple geometrical interpretation of the inner product of two vectors which is often useful.

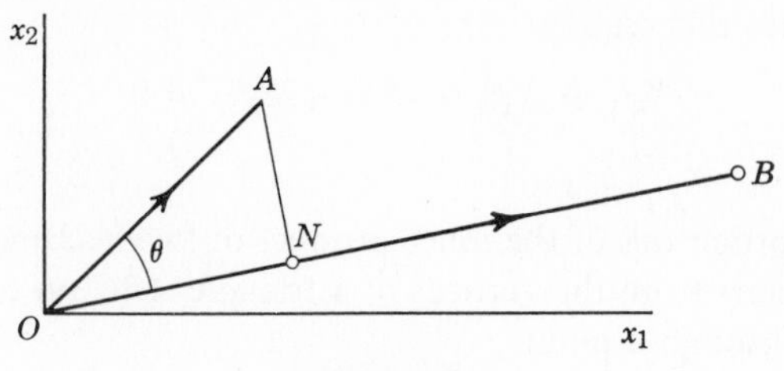

Figure 10

If N be the foot of the perpendicular from A on to OB, then

$$ON = |OA| \cos \theta,$$

and

$$\begin{aligned} ON \cdot |OB| &= |OA| \cdot |OB| \cos \theta \\ &= \|\mathbf{A}\| \, \|\mathbf{B}\| \cos \theta \\ &= (\mathbf{A}, \mathbf{B}). \end{aligned}$$

We use this interpretation to find once again the length of the perpendicular from the point (h_1, h_2) onto the line $a_1X_1 + a_2X_2 + a_3 = 0$ [equation (17), § 4].

If HN is the perpendicular from H onto the line, and $X = (X_1, X_2)$ is any point on the line, then $\overrightarrow{HX}$ is equal to the vector $\mathbf{X} - \mathbf{H}$; and if $\mathbf{A} = [a_1, a_2]$, then $\mathbf{A}$ is parallel to the normal to the line $\pm\overrightarrow{HN}$. Hence

$$\pm(\mathbf{X} - \mathbf{H}, \mathbf{A}) = |HN| \cdot \|\mathbf{A}\|$$

by the geometrical interpretation just given, so that

$$|HN| = \pm \frac{(\mathbf{X} - \mathbf{H}, \mathbf{A})}{\sqrt{a_1^{\,2} + a_2^{\,2}}}\,.$$

The numerator of this fraction is

$$\begin{aligned} \pm(\mathbf{X} - \mathbf{H}, \mathbf{A}) &= \pm(\mathbf{X}, \mathbf{A}) \mp (\mathbf{H}, \mathbf{A}) \\ &= \pm\{(X_1 - h_1)a_1 + (X_2 - h_2)a_2\}. \end{aligned}$$

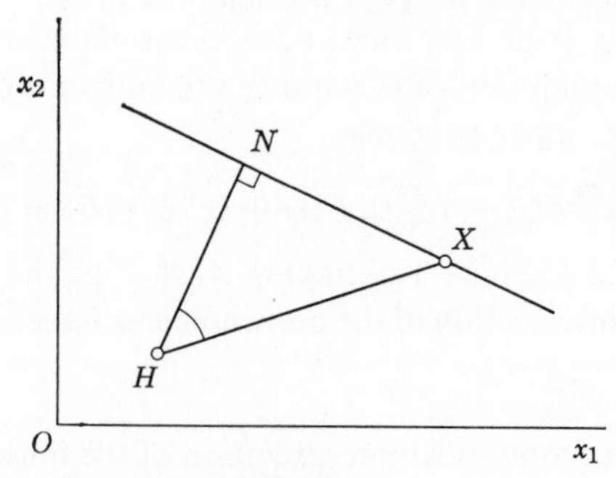

Figure 11

But since (X_1, X_2) is on the given line,

$$X_1a_1 + X_2a_2 = -a_3,$$

so that finally

$$\text{perpendicular} = |HN| = \mp \frac{(a_1h_1 + a_2h_2 + a_3)}{\sqrt{a_1^2 + a_2^2}}.$$

EXERCISES 8.2

1. Show that if, in the foregoing proof, $\overrightarrow{HN}$ is in the same direction as the normal $\mathbf{A} = [a_1, a_2]$ to the line, then $a_1h_1 + a_2h_2 + a_3$ is negative, so that we must accept the minus sign in the formula for $|HN|$.

2. If A, B are the endpoints of two independent vectors $\mathbf{A}$, $\mathbf{B}$, deduce from the equations

$$(\mathbf{B} - \mathbf{A}, \mathbf{B} - \mathbf{A}) = \|\mathbf{B} - \mathbf{A}\|^2 = \|\mathbf{B}\|^2 + \|\mathbf{A}\|^2 - 2(\mathbf{A}, \mathbf{B})$$

the cosine formula for the triangle AOB,

$$AB^2 = OA^2 + OB^2 - 2OA \cdot OB \cos \widehat{AOB}.$$

CHAPTER THREE

Coordinate Geometry of Three Dimensions

We shall now show that many of the notions and formulas discussed in the geometry of the plane extend very readily to three-dimensional space. Of course, besides lines there are now new entities, planes, to reckon with.

9. The Axes, and Lines through the Origin

We choose an origin O in three-dimensional space and then draw through O three directed axes Ox_1, Ox_2, and Ox_3 which are mutually orthogonal. If X is any point in the space, we drop perpendiculars XL_1, XL_2, and XL_3 onto the planes Ox_2x_3, Ox_3x_1, and Ox_1x_2 respectively. Then the distances L_1X, L_2X, and L_3X give the coordinates X_1, X_2, X_3 of the point X. The coordinate X_1 is positive if L_1X and Ox_1 are in the same direction, negative if L_1X and Ox_1 are in opposite directions. The same is true for the other coordinates, X_2 and X_3. Of course, if $L_1X = 0$, we take $X_1 = 0$, and then X lies in the plane Ox_2x_3. We may say at once, then, that the *equation* of the plane Ox_2x_3 is $X_1 = 0$. Similarly the equation of Ox_3x_1 is $X_2 = 0$, and the equation of Ox_1x_2 is $X_3 = 0$.

In three dimensions we at once note a fundamental difference from what goes on in two dimensions. We have linear equations which represent *planes*. We shall soon see that all planes are given by linear equations. What about lines?

At all points of the line Ox_1, both X_2 and X_3 are zero. We say that the equations of Ox_1 are $X_2 = 0$ *and* $X_3 = 0$. In fact Ox_1 is the intersection of the planes Ox_3x_1 and Ox_1x_2, and these planes are given by $X_2 = 0$ and $X_3 = 0$. Similarly, Ox_2 has the equations $X_3 = 0$ and $X_1 = 0$, and Ox_3 has the equations $X_1 = 0$ and $X_2 = 0$.

It would appear then that a line needs two linear equations to determine it, and we shall see that this is so.

Every point X has three coordinates (X_1, X_2, X_3) and is uniquely determined if the values of these three coordinates are assigned. Each

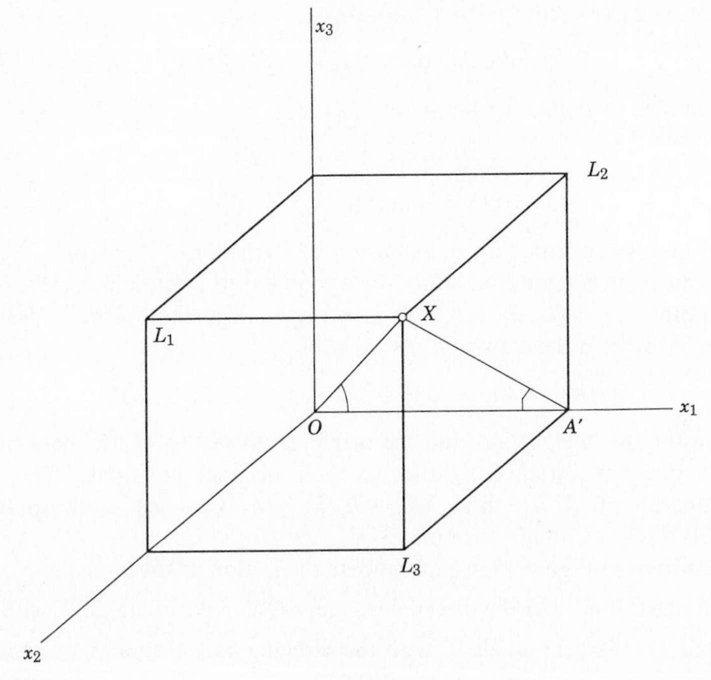

Figure 12

coordinate may be either positive or negative, so that we have the following possible combinations of signs:

$$\left.\begin{matrix} (+\,+\,+) & (+\,+\,-) & (+\,-\,+) & (+\,-\,-) \\ (-\,+\,+) & (-\,+\,-) & (-\,-\,+) & (-\,-\,-). \end{matrix}\right\}$$

Each combination corresponds to a region of space, and since the crossing of a coordinate plane, say Ox_2x_3, changes the sign of X_1, we may assert that the three coordinate planes Ox_2x_3, Ox_3x_1, and Ox_1x_2 divide the space into eight distinct regions. In two dimensions the coordinate axes divide the plane into four regions. The addition of the axis Ox_3 doubles the possibilities, since the third coordinate may be positive or negative.

The simple Fig. 12 contains a lot of information. The plane L_2XL_3 is orthogonal to Ox_1. Hence every line in this plane is orthogonal to Ox_1. In particular, if the plane L_2XL_3 intersects Ox_1 in A', the line XA' is orthogonal to Ox_1.

Since $XL_2A'L_3$ is a rectangle,

$$(XA')^2 = (L_2X)^2 + (L_3X)^2 = X_2^{\,2} + X_3^{\,2},$$

so that we have the important formula

$$\text{Perpendicular onto } Ox_1 = (X_2^2 + X_3^2)^{1/2}, \tag{30}$$

with similar formulas for the other axes.

Again, $$(OX)^2 = (OA')^2 + (XA')^2,$$

that is, $$(OX)^2 = X_1^2 + X_2^2 + X_3^2, \tag{31}$$

which may be regarded as an extension of Pythagoras' theorem.

We move away from the origin for a moment to remark that if we have two points $H = (h_1, h_2, h_3)$ and $K = (k_1, k_2, k_3)$, the formula for the distance between these two points must be

$$(HK)^2 = (h_1 - k_1)^2 + (h_2 - k_2)^2 + (h_3 - k_3)^2. \tag{31)*$$

To see this we merely imagine the origin O moved to H, the coordinate planes being maintained parallel to their original positions. The new coordinates of K are now $(k_1 - h_1, k_2 - h_2, k_3 - h_3)$, and applying formula (31), we obtain formula (31)*.

Returning to Figure 12, we investigate the notion of the *direction-cosines* of a directed line. Let the directed segment $\overrightarrow{OX}$ make an angle θ_1 with the directed axis $\overrightarrow{Ox_1}$, an angle θ_2 with the directed axis $\overrightarrow{Ox_2}$, and an angle θ_3 with the directed axis $\overrightarrow{Ox_3}$. In each case we may choose the angles so that

$$0 \leqslant \theta_1 \leqslant \pi, \qquad 0 \leqslant \theta_2 \leqslant \pi, \qquad 0 \leqslant \theta_3 \leqslant \pi.$$

Since XA' is perpendicular to Ox_1,

$$\overrightarrow{OA'} = X_1 = |OX| \cos \theta_1.$$

Similarly we have the formulas

$$X_2 = |OX| \cos \theta_2, \qquad X_3 = |OX| \cos \theta_3.$$

Substituting in formula (31), we have

$$(OX)^2 = X_1^2 + X_2^2 + X_3^2 = (OX)^2(\cos^2 \theta_1 + \cos^2 \theta_2 + \cos^2 \theta_3),$$

from which it follows that

$$\cos^2 \theta_1 + \cos^2 \theta_2 + \cos^2 \theta_3 = 1. \tag{32}$$

This is the fundamental relation satisfied by direction-cosines in three dimensions, and this is again an extension of the result for two dimensions. But whereas in two dimensions we know that $\sin \theta_1 = \pm\cos \theta_2$, there are no such simple relations in three dimensions. The direction-cosines, however, serve to determine uniquely a line through the origin.

In fact, if we are given $\cos\theta_1$, $\cos\theta_2$ and $\cos\theta_3$ for a half-line through the origin, we have the equations

$$\frac{X_1}{\cos\theta_1} = \frac{X_2}{\cos\theta_2} = \frac{X_3}{\cos\theta_3} = |OX|, \tag{33}$$

and thus all points on the half-line have the coordinates

$$X_1 = t\cos\theta_1, \qquad X_2 = t\cos\theta_2, \qquad X_3 = t\cos\theta_3,$$

where $t = |OX|$ is a variable parameter. If, as in the interpretation of equation (5), § 1, we consider t as a *signed distance*, by allowing it to assume both positive and negative values we obtain all points on the line determined by the given half-line.

Example I

Determine the lines through O which make equal angles with the axes.

For such lines

$$\cos\theta_1 = \pm\cos\theta_2 = \pm\cos\theta_3,$$

so that, using the fundamental relation

$$\cos^2\theta_1 + \cos^2\theta_2 + \cos^2\theta_3 = 1,$$

we have

$$3\cos^2\theta_1 = 1,$$

and the possibilities are

$$\cos\theta_1 = \pm 1/\sqrt{3}, \qquad \cos\theta_2 = \pm 1/\sqrt{3}, \qquad \cos\theta_3 = \pm 1/\sqrt{3}.$$

We only obtain four (not eight) distinct lines, since the lines

$$\frac{X_1}{l_1} = \frac{X_2}{l_2} = \frac{X_3}{l_3}, \qquad \frac{X_1}{-l_1} = \frac{X_2}{-l_2} = \frac{X_3}{-l_3}$$

are the same lines.

Hence the direction-ratios of the four distinct lines are:

$$(1:1:1), \quad (1:1:-1), \quad (1:-1:1), \quad (-1:1:1).$$

EXERCISES 9

1. Find the angles $\theta_1, \theta_2, \theta_3$ ($0 \leqslant \theta_i \leqslant \pi$) made by the lines joining O to the points

(*a*) $(\sqrt{2}, 1, 1)$,
(*b*) $(-1, 2, 2)$,
(*c*) $(2, -3, 6)$.

2. A line through O makes angles of 60° with Ox_1 and 45° with Ox_2. Find the angle it makes with Ox_3.

3. Prove that the point (3, −1, 2) is the center of a sphere which passes through the four points

$$(2, 1, 4), \quad (5, 1, 1), \quad (4, -3, 0), \quad \text{and} \quad (1, -3, 3)$$

and find its radius.

4. Show that the four points

$$(1, -1, -1), \quad (-1, 1, -1), \quad (-1, -1, 1), \quad \text{and} \quad (1, 1, 1)$$

form the vertices of a regular tetrahedron, of edge $2\sqrt{2}$ units long.

10. Angle between Two Lines

Let $\overrightarrow{OA}$ and $\overrightarrow{OB}$ be two directed lines through O, with respective direction-cosines $\cos\theta_1$, $\cos\theta_2$, $\cos\theta_3$, and $\cos\varphi_1$, $\cos\varphi_2$, $\cos\varphi_3$. If $A = (a_1, a_2, a_3)$ and $B = (b_1, b_2, b_3)$,

$$\text{then,}\quad a_1 = |OA|\cos\theta_1, \qquad a_2 = |OA|\cos\theta_2, \qquad a_3 = |OA|\cos\theta_3,$$
$$b_1 = |OB|\cos\varphi_1, \qquad b_2 = |OB|\cos\varphi_2, \qquad b_3 = |OB|\cos\varphi_3.$$

By the distance formula (31)*,

$$\begin{aligned}(AB)^2 &= (a_1 - b_1)^2 + (a_2 - b_2)^2 + (a_3 - b_3)^2\\ &= (|OA|\cos\theta_1 - |OB|\cos\varphi_1)^2\\ &\quad + (|OA|\cos\theta_2 - |OB|\cos\varphi_2)^2 + (|OA|\cos\theta_3 - |OB|\cos\varphi_3)^2.\end{aligned}$$

But by the cosine-formula for the triangle OAB,

$$(AB)^2 = |OA|^2 + |OB|^2 - 2\,|OA|\cdot|OB|\cos\theta,$$

where θ is the angle between $\overrightarrow{OA}$ and $\overrightarrow{OB}$. A comparison of the two equations for $(AB)^2$ gives us the following:

$$\begin{aligned}(OA)^2(\cos^2\theta_1 + \cos^2\theta_2 + \cos^2\theta_3) + (OB)^2(\cos^2\varphi_1 + \cos^2\varphi_2 + \cos^2\varphi_3)\\ - 2\,|OA|\,|OB|\,(\cos\theta_1\cos\varphi_1 + \cos\theta_2\cos\varphi_2 + \cos\theta_3\cos\varphi_3)\\ = (OA)^2 + (OB)^2 - 2\,|OA|\,|OB|\cos\theta.\end{aligned}$$

By the fundamental identity for direction-cosines [equation (32)], we are left with

$$\cos\theta = \cos\theta_1\cos\varphi_1 + \cos\theta_2\cos\varphi_2 + \cos\theta_3\cos\varphi_3. \tag{34}$$

This is a direct generalization of formula (12), § 3, for the angle between lines in the plane.

Example I

Three edges of a cube lie along the coordinate axes. Find the angles between the diagonals through O of the faces of the cube which pass through O.

We may use Fig. 12, taking $X = (a, a, a)$. We wish to determine the angle between OL_2 and OL_1. Since L_2 is $(a, 0, a)$, the direction-cosines of OL_2 are

$$(1/\sqrt{2}, 0, 1/\sqrt{2}),$$

and since L_1 is $(0, a, a)$, the direction-cosines of OL_1 are

$$(0, 1/\sqrt{2}, 1/\sqrt{2}).$$

Application of formula (34) therefore gives us

$$\cos\theta = (1/\sqrt{2})(0) + (0)(1/\sqrt{2}) + (1/\sqrt{2})^2,$$

so that

$$\cos\theta = 1/2,$$

and $\widehat{L_1OL_2} = 60°$. In fact, the triangle OL_1L_2 is equilateral, since $OL_1 = L_1L_2 = OL_2$.

As in the plane, formula (34) is important when the two lines are perpendicular, or orthogonal to each other. Then $\theta = 90°$, $\cos\theta = 0$, and the formula becomes

$$0 = \cos\theta_1\cos\varphi_1 + \cos\theta_2\cos\varphi_2 + \cos\theta_3\cos\varphi_3.$$

Here again we may use direction-*ratios* instead of direction-*cosines.* If

$$\cos\theta_1 = kl_1, \qquad \cos\theta_2 = kl_2, \qquad \cos\theta_3 = kl_3,$$

we say that $l_1:l_2:l_3$ are the direction-*ratios* of the line OA. If similarly

$$\cos\varphi_1 = k'm_1, \qquad \cos\varphi_2 = k'm_2, \qquad \cos\varphi_3 = k'm_3,$$

then $m_1:m_2:m_3$ are the direction-ratios of the line OB. The condition for orthogonality becomes

$$0 = kk'(l_1m_1 + l_2m_2 + l_3m_3),$$

or

$$0 = l_1m_1 + l_2m_2 + l_3m_3, \tag{35}$$

and in this form we shall use it frequently.

Example 2

Show that the lines through O with direction-ratios

$$1:2:2, \qquad -14:2:5, \qquad 2:-11:10$$

form a set of orthogonal axes.

We do not need to obtain direction-cosines to prove this result. Since

$$1(-14) + 2(2) + 2(5) = 0,$$

the first two lines are orthogonal. Since

$$(-14)(2) + 2(-11) + 5(10) = 0,$$

the second and third are orthogonal, and finally since

$$1(2) + 2(-11) + 2(10) = 0,$$

the first and third are orthogonal.

EXERCISES 10

1. The line OP lies in the plane Ox_3x_1 and bisects the angle between Ox_3 and Ox_1, and the line OQ lies in the plane Ox_1x_2 and bisects the external angle between the lines Ox_1 and Ox_2. Determine the angle between OP and OQ.
2. In Fig. 12 suppose that the coordinates of X are (a, b, c). Determine the angle between OX and OL_3, and between OL_2 and OL_1.
3. Determine the direction-ratios of a line which is perpendicular to each of the two lines with respective direction-ratios

$$3:-2:4 \quad \text{and} \quad 1:3:-2.$$

Determine also the direction-cosines of this line.

11. Line Segments in Space

Two lines in space of three dimensions may intersect, in which case they define a plane, or they may be parallel, when they still define a plane, or they may be *skew*, which means that they do not intersect, but they are not parallel, and they do not lie in a plane, since this would imply that they are parallel, or intersect. We wish to talk about the *angle* between directed lines which may be skew, and we do this by drawing through any point V lines parallel to the pair of directed lines. Then the angle between the pair of directed lines through V is said to be the angle between

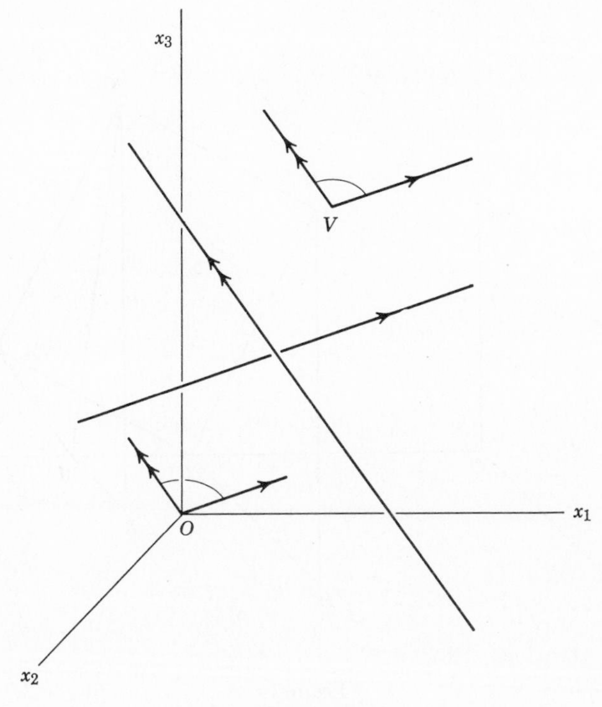

Figure 13

the original directed lines. It is clear that the position of the point V does not affect the value of the angle, so that the definition is a reasonable one.

Now let $H = (h_1, h_2, h_3)$ and $K = (k_1, k_2, k_3)$ be any two points in space, and drop perpendiculars HL from H and KM from K onto the axis Ox_1. Let θ_1 be the angle between the directed segment $\overrightarrow{HK}$ and the directed axis $\overrightarrow{Ox_1}$. We wish to prove that

$$\overrightarrow{LM} = |HK| \cos \theta_1,$$

that is

$$k_1 - h_1 = |HK| \cos \theta_1. \tag{36}$$

Let HH' and KK' be perpendiculars from H and K respectively onto the Ox_1x_2 plane. Then the plane HLH' is orthogonal to Ox_1, and therefore $H'L$ is perpendicular to Ox_1. Similarly, $K'M$ is perpendicular to Ox_1.

Through L draw LN equal and parallel to HK, so that $\overrightarrow{LN} = \overrightarrow{HK}$. Consider the plane KMN.

Since KN is parallel to HL, $HKNL$ being a parallelogram, KN is orthogonal to Ox_1. But KM is orthogonal to Ox_1. Therefore the *plane* KMN is orthogonal to Ox_1, and so MN is orthogonal to Ox_1.

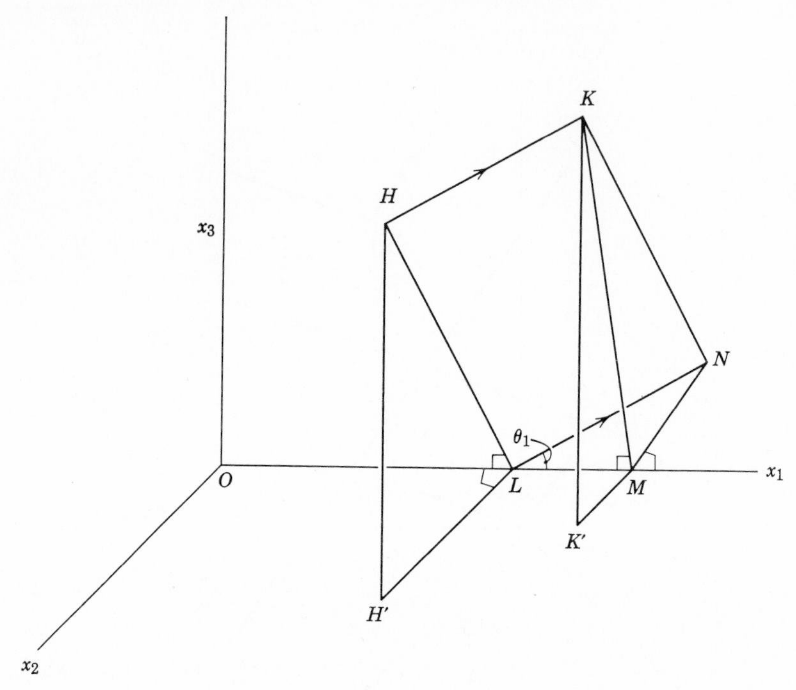

Figure 14

Since the angle between $\overrightarrow{LM}$ and $\overrightarrow{LN} = \overrightarrow{HK}$ is θ_1, we now have at once

$$\overrightarrow{LM} = |LN| \cos \theta_1 = |HK| \cos \theta_1,$$

and $\overrightarrow{LM} = k_1 - h_1$, since $OM = k_1$ and $OL = h_1$. Hence formula (36) is established. We shall see that it is the basis for much which follows, just as the corresponding formula in two dimensions [(1) of § 1] led to the developments given in Chapter 1.

If $\overrightarrow{HK}$ makes an angle θ_2 with $\overrightarrow{Ox_2}$, and θ_3 with $\overrightarrow{Ox_3}$, reasoning similar to the foregoing gives us

$$k_2 - h_2 = |HK| \cos \theta_2,$$

and

$$k_3 - h_3 = |HK| \cos \theta_3.$$

If we draw a line through the origin O parallel to the directed segment $\overrightarrow{HK}$, it will make angles θ_1 with $\overrightarrow{Ox_1}$, θ_2 with $\overrightarrow{Ox_2}$, and θ_3 with $\overrightarrow{Ox_3}$. Hence the fundamental formula (32) for lines through the origin applies, and we have

$$\cos^2 \theta_1 + \cos^2 \theta_2 + \cos^2 \theta_3 = 1.$$

From this formula there follows at once the distance formula (31)*:

$$(HK)^2 = (k_1 - h_1)^2 + (k_2 - h_2)^2 + (k_3 - h_3)^2.$$

Another deduction from the foregoing equations is

$$\frac{\cos \theta_1}{k_1 - h_1} = \frac{\cos \theta_2}{k_2 - h_2} = \frac{\cos \theta_3}{k_3 - h_3},$$

which we can express by the rule:

ratio of direction-cosines = ratio of coordinate differences,

again an immediate generalization of the situation in two dimensions (see § 1).

If (X_1, X_2, X_3) is any point on the half-line determined by the directed segment $\overrightarrow{HK}$, we have

$$\frac{X_1 - h_1}{\cos \theta_1} = \frac{X_2 - h_2}{\cos \theta_2} = \frac{X_3 - h_3}{\cos \theta_3} = |HX|,$$

which we can immediately extend to

$$\frac{X_1 - h_1}{\cos \theta_1} = \frac{X_2 - h_2}{\cos \theta_2} = \frac{X_3 - h_3}{\cos \theta_3} = HX, \tag{37}$$

where now (X_1, X_2, X_3) is any point on the line HK, and HX is the *signed* distance of X from H. The argument giving the extension is exactly the same as that in § 1, p. 4.

Another form for the equation of the line HK is

$$\frac{X_1 - h_1}{k_1 - h_1} = \frac{X_2 - h_2}{k_2 - h_2} = \frac{X_3 - h_3}{k_3 - h_3}. \tag{38}$$

We use the form (37) when the line is characterized by a point (h_1, h_2, h_3) on it, and the direction-cosines $\cos \theta_1, \cos \theta_2, \cos \theta_3$ of the line. The second form (38) is used when the line is determined by two points.

The direction-*cosines* of the line are proportional to the coordinate differences

$$k_1 - h_1 : k_2 - h_2 : k_3 - h_3.$$

In other words, the coordinate differences give the direction-*ratios* of the line, which are sufficient for many purposes, especially when orthogonality is involved. If actual direction-*cosines* of the line are required, they are obtained from the direction ratios $k_1 - h_1$, $k_2 - h_2$, and $k_3 - h_3$ by dividing by $|HK|$, so that the direction-*cosines* are

$$\frac{k_1 - h_1}{|HK|}, \quad \frac{k_2 - h_2}{|HK|}, \quad \frac{k_3 - h_3}{|HK|},$$

since by formula (31)* these quantities squared add up to 1.

A word must be said about the possibility of denominators in equations (37) or (38) being zero. If a segment is perpendicular to the Ox_1 axis, say, then $\cos\theta_1 = 0$, and the equations (37), written formally, become

$$\frac{X_1 - h_1}{0} = \frac{X_2 - h_2}{\cos\theta_2} = \frac{X_3 - h_3}{\cos\theta_3} = HX.$$

We interpret them to mean

$$X_1 - h_1 = 0,$$

together with

$$\frac{X_2 - h_2}{\cos\theta_2} = \frac{X_3 - h_3}{\cos\theta_3} = HK,$$

and we see at once that both these equations are correct, the first because the segment lies in the plane $X_1 = h_1$, and the second equation is correct from our previous working if neither $\cos\theta_2$ nor $\cos\theta_3$ is zero. The coordinates of a variable point on the line are now

$$(h_1, h_2 + t\cos\theta_2, h_3 + t\cos\theta_3).$$

If both $\cos\theta_1$ and $\cos\theta_2$ are zero, the formal equations

$$\frac{X_1 - h_1}{0} = \frac{X_2 - h_2}{0} = \frac{X_3 - h_3}{\cos\theta_3} = HX$$

are interpreted to mean

$$X_1 - h_1 = 0 = X_2 - h_2, \qquad X_3 - h_3 = HX\cos\theta_3,$$

where the fundamental relation between direction-cosines shows that $\cos\theta_3 = \pm 1$. All points on the line are then of the form

$$(h_1, h_2, h_3 + t),$$

where t can be positive or negative. Such a line is parallel to Ox_3, and the equations $X_1 - h_1 = 0 = X_2 - h_2$ are sufficient to define it, since the equation $X_3 - h_3 = t$ merely says that X_3 can assume any real value.

Example I

Show that the point (2, 0, 3) is common to the lines which join (7, −6, 1) to (17, −18, −3) and (1, 4, −5) to (3, −4, 11).

The equation of the first line is

$$\frac{X_1 - 7}{7 - 17} = \frac{X_2 - (-6)}{-6 - (-18)} = \frac{X_3 - 1}{1 - (-3)},$$

that is
$$\frac{X_1 - 7}{-10} = \frac{X_2 + 6}{12} = \frac{X_3 - 1}{4},$$

and substituting the point (2, 0, 3) in these equations, each fraction = 1/2, so that (2, 0, 3) is on the first line.

The equation of the second line is

$$\frac{X_1 - 1}{1 - 3} = \frac{X_2 - 4}{4 - (-4)} = \frac{X_3 - (-5)}{-5 - 11},$$

that is

$$\frac{X_1 - 1}{-2} = \frac{X_2 - 4}{8} = \frac{X_3 + 5}{-16},$$

and substituting (2, 0, 3) makes each of these fractions = −1/2, so that (2, 0, 3) is also on the second line.

To illustrate the powerful technique we have acquired in handling problems in three dimensions, let us consider another problem.

Example 2

An antenna mast whose vertical axis meets the ground at O is supported by two straight ropes which lie in vertical planes through the axis. These ropes are attached to the axis at heights of 50 feet and 60 feet, and are attached to the ground at points whose bearings from O are N. and S.E. respectively, and these points are at 60 feet and 80 feet from the axis. Show that the acute angle between the ropes is nearly 87°.

We take Ox_1 in a northerly direction, Ox_2 pointing east, and Ox_3 along the axis of the mast. The ends of the ropes have the following coordinates:

$$(60, 0, 0) \quad \text{and} \quad (0, 0, 50),$$

$$\left(\frac{-80}{\sqrt{2}}, \frac{80}{\sqrt{2}}, 0\right) \quad \text{and} \quad (0, 0, 60).$$

The direction-ratios of the ropes are respectively

$$60:0:-50$$

and

$$-40\sqrt{2}:40\sqrt{2}:-60,$$

and their direction-cosines are

$$\frac{60}{10\sqrt{61}}, \quad 0, \quad \frac{-50}{10\sqrt{61}},$$

and

$$\frac{-40\sqrt{2}}{100}, \quad \frac{40\sqrt{2}}{100}, \quad \frac{-60}{100}.$$

Therefore, using the formula (34), p. 42 we have

$$\cos\theta = \frac{-2400\sqrt{2} + 3000}{100(10\sqrt{61})} = \frac{30 - 24\sqrt{2}}{10\sqrt{61}}$$
$$\sim -0\cdot 05,$$

which gives $\theta \sim 93^\circ$, so that the acute angle $\sim 180^\circ - 93^\circ = 87^\circ$.

EXERCISES II

1. Show that the points (5, −5, 4), (3, −4, 0), and (5, 4, 1) form a right-angled triangle, and prove that the point (7, 3, 5) completes the rectangle.

2. Show that the lines

$$\frac{X_1 - 2}{5} = \frac{X_2 - 3}{6} = \frac{X_3 - 4}{7} \quad \text{and} \quad \frac{X_1 - 5}{2} = \frac{X_2 - 6}{3} = \frac{X_3 - 7}{4}$$

intersect in the point (7, 9, 11). More generally, prove that the lines

$$\frac{X_1 - a}{a'} = \frac{X_2 - b}{b'} = \frac{X_3 - c}{c'} \quad \text{and} \quad \frac{X_1 - a'}{a} = \frac{X_2 - b'}{b} = \frac{X_3 - c'}{c}$$

intersect in the point $(a + a', b + b', c + c')$.

3. Show that if the line joining the points (a, b, c) and (a', b', c') passes through O, then $|aa' + bb' + cc'| = dd'$, where d and d' are the distances of the points from O.

4. Show that the equation of the line through the points (h, h_2, h_3) and (h, k_2, k_3) may be written in the form

$$X_1 - h = 0, \quad \frac{X_2 - h_2}{(k_2 - h_2)} = \frac{X_3 - h_3}{(k_3 - h_3)},$$

and that these equations may be regarded as a formal interpretation of equations (38) in the special case $k_1 = h_1$.

Find the equations of the lines through the point (1, 2, 3) which are respectively perpendicular to Ox_1 and to Ox_2.

5. Show that the equation of the line through the points (a, b, c) and (a, b, c') where $c \neq c'$, may be written

$$X_1 - a = 0 = X_2 - b.$$

What is the equation of the line through the point (1, 2, 0) which is parallel to Ox_3?

12. Position-Ratio of a Point on a Line

The development of § 2 generalizes immediately to three dimensions, since segments on a line are proportional to their projections on an axis (equation (36)), as in two dimensions (equation (3)).

The equation of a line joining two points [(38)]

$$\frac{X_1 - h_1}{k_1 - h_1} = \frac{X_2 - h_2}{k_2 - h_2} = \frac{X_3 - h_3}{k_3 - h_3}$$

is called the *symmetric form* of the equation. There are other ways of writing the equations. If we put each of these equal fractions equal to t, we have the *parametric form* of the equations of a line joining two points:

$$\left.\begin{aligned} X_1 &= h_1(1 - t) + k_1 t, \\ X_2 &= h_2(1 - t) + k_2 t, \\ X_3 &= h_3(1 - t) + k_3 t. \end{aligned}\right\} \tag{39}$$

We note that $t = HX/HK$, by the remark that segments on a line are proportional to their projections on an axis, and as in § 2, we deduce that

$$HX/XK = t/(1 - t).$$

If we are given that the point X divides the segment HK in the ratio $\lambda:\mu$, then, as in § 2,

$$t = \lambda/(\lambda + \mu),$$

and equation (39) becomes

$$X_i = \frac{\mu h_i}{\lambda + \mu} + \frac{\lambda k_i}{\lambda + \mu} \qquad (i = 1, 2, 3). \tag{40}$$

The three equations given by (40) determine the coordinates of a point of a line in terms of the *position-ratio* $\lambda:\mu$ of the point with respect to two given points $H = (h_1, h_2, h_3)$ and $K = (k_1, k_2, k_3)$. If $\lambda:\mu$ is positive, the point X lies between H and K. If $\lambda:\mu$ is negative, the point X lies *outside* the segment HK.

Once again, the coordinates of the midpoint of a segment HK are found by taking $\lambda:\mu = 1:1$, and they are

$$X_i = \frac{h_i + k_i}{2} \qquad (i = 1, 2, 3).$$

A point of trisection, dividing HK in the ratio $1:2$ is

$$X_i = \frac{2h_i + k_i}{3} \qquad (i = 1, 2, 3).$$

Example 1

Show that the lines joining the vertices A, B, C, D of a tetrahedron to the centroids of the opposite faces all pass through one point.

The centroid of the triangle formed by $B = (b_1, b_2, b_3)$, $C = (c_1, c_2, c_3)$, and $D = (d_1, d_2, d_3)$ has the coordinates

$$\frac{b_1 + c_1 + d_1}{3}, \quad \frac{b_2 + c_2 + d_2}{3}, \quad \frac{b_3 + c_3 + d_3}{3}.$$

If this point is α, the point G dividing $A\alpha$ in the ratio $3:1$ has the coordinates

$$\frac{3\left(\dfrac{b_1 + c_1 + d_1}{3}\right) + a_1}{4}, \quad \frac{3\left(\dfrac{b_2 + c_2 + d_2}{3}\right) + a_2}{4}, \quad \frac{3\left(\dfrac{b_3 + c_3 + d_3}{3}\right) + a_3}{4},$$

that is

$$\frac{(a_1 + b_1 + c_1 + d_1)}{4}, \quad \frac{(a_2 + b_2 + c_2 + d_2)}{4}, \quad \frac{(a_3 + b_3 + c_3 + d_3)}{4},$$

and the symmetry of this result shows that G lies on the four lines joining a vertex to the centroid of the opposite face.

EXERCISES 12

1. Show that in a tetrahedron the joins of midpoints of opposite edges meet in a point which bisects each of them.
2. Show that the foot of the perpendicular from the origin on to the line joining $(11, 0, -1)$ and $(-9, 4, 5)$ is the point $(1, 2, 2)$.
3. Show that the perpendicular distance from $(-1, 3, 9)$ to the line

$$\frac{X_1 - 13}{5} = \frac{X_2 + 8}{-8} = \frac{X_3 - 31}{1}$$

is 21 units.

13. The Equation of a Plane

A plane is determined as the locus of lines which pass through a given point $H = (h_1, h_2, h_3)$ and are orthogonal to a given direction in space, a line with direction-ratios $l_1:l_2:l_3$, say. If $X = (X_1, X_2, X_3)$ is any point in the plane, HX is orthogonal to the given normal to the plane, and since the direction-ratios of HX are

$$X_1 - h_1 : X_2 - h_2 : X_3 - h_3,$$

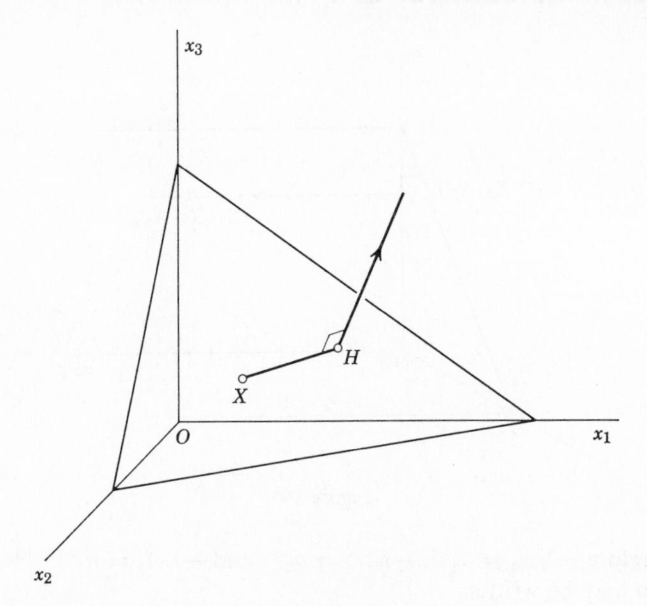

Figure 15

the orthogonality condition, equation (35), gives us

$$l_1(X_1 - h_1) + l_2(X_2 - h_2) + l_3(X_3 - h_3) = 0. \qquad (41)$$

This is the equation of the plane, and it is linear in X_1, X_2, X_3. We remark that *the ratio of the coefficients of* X_1, X_2, $X_3 = l_1\!:\!l_2\!:\!l_3$, *which gives us the normal to the plane.*

Conversely, a linear equation represents a plane. For if the equation is

$$l_1X_1 + l_2X_2 + l_3X_3 + l_4 = 0,$$

and (h_1, h_2, h_3) is any point on this locus, then

$$l_1h_1 + l_2h_2 + l_3h_3 + l_4 = 0.$$

Subtraction gives

$$l_1(X_1 - h_1) + l_2(X_2 - h_2) + l_3(X_3 - h_3) = 0,$$

and this shows that the join XH is orthogonal to the fixed line with direction-ratios $l_1\!:\!l_2\!:\!l_3$, so that the points X lie in a definite plane.

Various special forms of the equation of a plane may be noted:

1. *The intercept form:* If the plane cuts intercepts a_1, a_2, a_3 on the coordinate axes, the points $(a_1, 0, 0)$, $(0, a_2, 0)$, and $(0, 0, a_3)$ satisfy the equation

$$l_1X_1 + l_2X_2 + l_3X_3 + l_4 = 0,$$

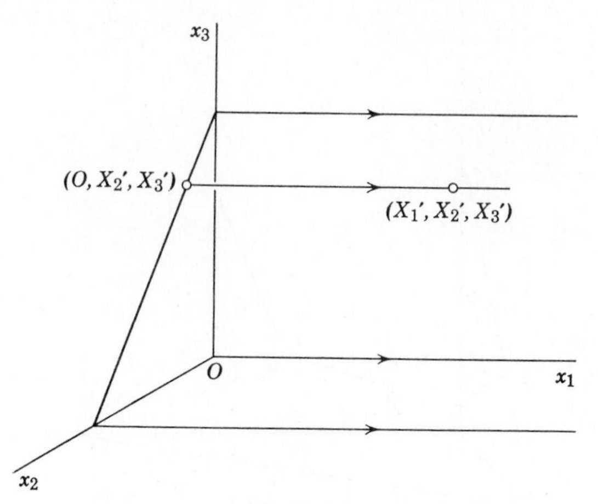

Figure 16

and therefore $-l_1:l_4 = a_1^{-1}$, $-l_2:l_4 = a_2^{-1}$, and $-l_3:l_4 = a_3^{-1}$. Hence the equation may be written

$$\frac{X_1}{a_1} + \frac{X_2}{a_2} + \frac{X_3}{a_3} - 1 = 0. \tag{42}$$

2. *Plane parallel to an axis:* If the plane is parallel to Ox_1, the normal to the plane will be orthogonal to Ox_1, and therefore $l_1 = 0$. The equation is then

$$l_2X_2 + l_3X_3 + l_4 = 0. \tag{43}$$

In the plane $X_1 = 0$, this equation represents a line, and if $(0, X_2', X_3')$ is any point on this line, the point (X_1', X_2', X_3'), for any value of X_1', lies in the plane. This is illustrated in Fig. 16. Since X_1 does not appear in equation (43), there is no restriction on its value.

This form will appear often, in connection with the equations of a line (§ 14), and it is important to understand how to interpret it.

Example I

Find the geometrical (mirror) image of the point $H = (h_1, h_2, h_3)$ in the plane $a_1X_1 + a_2X_2 + a_3X_3 + a_4 = 0$.

If the normal to the plane through H meets the plane at N, the image is a point H' on HN such that $HN = NH'$.

The equation of the normal through H is

$$\frac{X_1 - h_1}{a_1} = \frac{X_2 - h_2}{a_2} = \frac{X_3 - h_3}{a_3} = t,$$

and we know that t is proportional to the (signed) distance HX. When X is at N,

$$a_1(h_1 + a_1t) + a_2(h_2 + a_2t) + a_3(h_3 + a_3t) + a_4 = 0,$$

and this gives the parameter t_N for N:

$$t_N = \frac{-(a_1h_1 + a_2h_2 + a_3h_3 + a_4)}{a_1^2 + a_2^2 + a_3^2},$$

so that the parameter $t_{H'}$ for H' is $2t_N$, and the point H' is

$$(h_1 + 2a_1t_N, h_2 + 2a_2t_N, h_3 + 2a_3t_N).$$

This worked example also gives us the perpendicular distance of H from the plane:

$$\begin{aligned}(HN)^2 &= (h_1 + a_1t_N - h_1)^2 + (h_2 + a_2t_N - h_2)^2 + (h_3 + a_3t_N - h_3)^2 \\ &= (t_N)^2(a_1^2 + a_2^2 + a_3^2),\end{aligned}$$

so that

$$\text{Perpendicular} = \frac{|a_1h_1 + a_2h_2 + a_3h_3 + a_4|}{\sqrt{(a_1^2 + a_2^2 + a_3^2)}}. \tag{44}$$

This is also an immediate generalization of the result for two dimensions [equation (17), § 4].

Example 2

Show that the line $X_1 - 1 = -9X_2 + 18 = -3X_3 - 9$ is parallel to the plane $3X_1 - 3X_2 + 10X_3 - 26 = 0$. Verify that the mirror image of the line in the plane is given by the equations

$$X_1 - 4 = -9X_2 - 9 = -3X_3 + 21.$$

To obtain the direction-ratios of the given line we must first write it in the symmetrical form [equation (38)]. We have

$$\frac{X_1 - 1}{1} = \frac{X_2 - 2}{-1/9} = \frac{X_3 - (-3)}{-1/3},$$

so that the direction-ratios are $1:-1/9:-1/3$. The normal to the plane has direction-ratios $3:-3:10$, and since $3(1) - 3(-1/9) + 10(-1/3) = 0$, the given line is orthogonal to the normal, and therefore parallel to the given plane.

The reputed mirror image is

$$\frac{X_1 - 4}{1} = \frac{X_2 - (-1)}{-1/9} = \frac{X_3 - 7}{-1/3},$$

and also has direction-ratios $1:-1/9:-1/3$, so that it is parallel to the object-line. One point on the first line is $(1, 2, -3)$, and the signed perpendicular distance of this point from the given plane is

$$\frac{3(1) - 3(2) + 10(-3) - 26}{\sqrt{(3^2 + 3^2 + 10^2)}} = \frac{-\sqrt{118}}{2},$$

whereas the signed distance of the point $(4, -1, 7)$ on the second line is

$$\frac{3(4) - 3(-1) + 10(7) - 26}{\sqrt{118}} = \frac{+\sqrt{118}}{2},$$

the difference in sign indicating that the two points are at equal distances on *opposite* sides of the plane. Finally, since the direction-ratios of the join of $(1, 2, -3)$ and $(4, -1, 7)$ are $3:-3:10$, so that the join is parallel to the normal to the given plane, the statement that the second line is the mirror image of the first in the plane is verified.

EXERCISES 13

1. Find the equations of the line through $(1, 2, 3)$ which cuts the line $X_1 + 1 = 2X_2 - 4 = X_3 + 4$ and is parallel to the plane

$$X_1 + 5X_2 + X_3 = 0.$$

2. The vertices of a tetrahedron are $A(0, 0, 0)$, $B(3, 0, 0)$, $C(2, 3, 0)$, and $D(1, 1, 1)$. Find the angle between the planes ACD, ABC and the perpendicular distance of B from the plane ACD.

3. Two edges, AB, CD of a tetrahedron $ABCD$ are perpendicular. Prove that the distance between the midpoints of AC and BD is equal to the distance between the midpoints of AD and BC.

14. Planes and Lines

The symmetrical form for the equations of a line which passes through the point $H = (h_1, h_2, h_3)$ and has direction-ratios $l_1:l_2:l_3$ is (cf. equations (37))

$$\frac{X_1 - h_1}{l_1} = \frac{X_2 - h_2}{l_2} = \frac{X_3 - h_3}{l_3}. \tag{45}$$

This set of equations is equivalent to two linear equations. If we take the first two terms in (45) we have

$$l_2(X_1 - h_1) - l_1(X_2 - h_2) = 0, \tag{46}$$

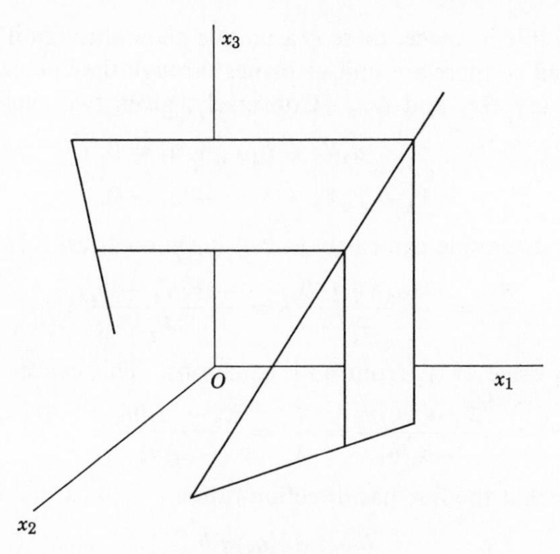

Figure 17

and if we take the second and third term we have

$$l_3(X_2 - h_2) - l_2(X_3 - h_3) = 0. \tag{47}$$

The equations (46) and (47) were deduced from (45), and conversely from (46) and (47) we easily obtain (45); by equating the common term $(X_2 - h_2)$, thus:

$$\frac{X_2 - h_2}{l_2} = \frac{X_1 - h_1}{l_1}$$

and
$$\frac{X_2 - h_2}{l_2} = \frac{X_3 - h_3}{l_3},$$

so that
$$\frac{X_1 - h_1}{l_1} = \frac{X_2 - h_2}{l_2} = \frac{X_3 - h_3}{l_3}.$$

Hence every point $X = (X_1, X_2, X_3)$ which satisfies the equation (45) also satisfies equations (46) and (47), and every common solution $X = (X_1, X_2, X_3)$ of (46) and (47) also satisfies equations (45). This is the meaning of our statement that the equations (45) are *equivalent* to two linear equations, (46) and (47).

Two planes intersect in a line, and geometrically we have merely found two special planes which pass through the line. In fact, the plane given by (46) contains no term in X_3, and is therefore parallel to Ox_3, and the plane given by (47) contains no term in X_1, and is therefore parallel to Ox_1 (see Fig. 17).

Given any line in space, there is a unique plane through it parallel to a given line, and so there are unique planes through the line parallel to two of the axes, say Ox_1 and Ox_3. Conversely, given two such planes, say

$$a_2X_2 + a_3X_3 + a_4 = 0,$$

and

$$b_1X_1 + b_2X_2 \qquad + b_4 = 0,$$

the line they determine can easily be put in symmetrical form thus:

$$\frac{X_2}{1} = \frac{-(a_3X_3 + a_4)}{a_2} = \frac{-(b_1X_1 + b_4)}{b_2},$$

equating the value of X_1 from both equations. This can be tidied up as

$$\frac{X_1 + b_4/b_1}{-b_2/b_1} = \frac{X_2}{1} = \frac{X_3 + a_4/a_3}{-a_2/a_3},$$

which shows that the line has direction-ratios

$$b_2a_3 : -b_1a_3 : a_2b_1,$$

and passes through the point

$$(-b_4/b_1, 0, -a_4/a_3).$$

We point out that equation (45) can also be written

$$\frac{X_1 - h_1}{l_1} + t = \frac{X_2 - h_2}{l_2} + t = \frac{X_3 - h_3}{l_3} + t,$$

which is

$$\frac{X_1 - (h_1 - l_1t)}{l_1} = \frac{X_2 - (h_2 - l_2t)}{l_2} = \frac{X_3 - (h_3 - l_3t)}{l_3}.$$

This shows that although the direction-ratios of a line are fixed, in the symmetrical form of equations *any* point on the line can be used instead of $H = (h_1, h_2, h_3)$. Hence, when we derive the symmetrical form from the equations of two planes, we may obtain equations which look different and yet are correct, according to our method of procedure.

Example I

Put the equations of the line given by the two planes $X_2 - X_3 + 3 = 0$ and $2X_1 + 3X_2 + 1 = 0$ in symmetric form.

Equating the value of X_2 from both equations, we have

$$X_2 = X_3 - 3 = \frac{-(2X_1 + 1)}{3},$$

or

$$\frac{X_1 + 1/2}{-3/2} = \frac{X_2}{1} = \frac{X_3 - 3}{1},$$

which gives a point $(-1/2, 0, 3)$ on the line, and direction-ratios $-3/2:1:1 = -3:2:2$.

If we equated the values of $X_2 + 3$ from both equations, we should obtain

$$X_2 + 3 = X_3 = \frac{-(2X_1 - 8)}{3},$$

giving

$$\frac{X_1 - 4}{-3/2} = \frac{X_2 + 3}{1} = \frac{X_3}{1},$$

a line with the same direction-ratios, passing through the point $(4, -3, 0)$. The line is the same in both cases.

One final remark is necessary. Suppose that the two planes defining the line are not parallel to an axis, and have the equations

$$a_1X_1 + a_2X_2 + a_3X_3 + a_4 = 0,$$

$$b_1X_1 + b_2X_2 + b_3X_3 + b_4 = 0.$$

By a familiar argument, any point on the common line of intersection also satisfies the equation

$$p(a_1X_1 + a_2X_2 + a_3X_3 + a_4) + q(b_1X_1 + b_2X_2 + b_3X_3 + b_4) = 0, \qquad (48)$$

for all values of p and q. But this equation represents a plane. This plane therefore *contains* the line, and by choosing suitable values of p and q we can find planes through the line which are parallel, respectively, to Ox_1 and Ox_3, and then proceed to find a symmetrical form for the equation.

Example 2

Find in symmetrical form the equations of the line of intersection of the planes

$$3X_1 - 2X_2 + X_3 - 1 = 0 = 5X_1 + 4X_2 - 6X_3 - 2.$$

The plane

$$2(3X_1 - 2X_2 + X_3 - 1) + (5X_1 + 4X_2 - 6X_3 - 2) = 11X_1 - 4X_3 - 4 = 0$$

contains the line. So does the plane

$$5(3X_1 - 2X_2 + X_3 - 1) - 3(5X_1 + 4X_2 - 6X_3 - 2) = -22X_2 + 23X_3 + 1 = 0.$$

Hence a symmetrical form is (equating the value of X_3)

$$X_3 = \frac{11X_1 - 4}{4} = \frac{22X_2 - 1}{23},$$

or

$$\frac{X_1 - 4/11}{4/11} = \frac{X_2 - 1/22}{23/22} = \frac{X_3}{1}$$

so that the direction-ratios are 8:23:22, and (4/11, 1/22, 0) is a point on the line.

Practically, the quickest way to find the symmetrical form of the equations of a line from the equations of two planes passing through the line is to determine the direction-ratios of the line. In the last example, if $l_1:l_2:l_3$ are these direction-ratios, then

$$3l_1 - 2l_2 + l_3 = 0,$$

$$5l_1 + 4l_2 - 6l_3 = 0,$$

since the line is perpendicular to the normal to each of the planes in which it lies. These equations give

$$l_1:l_2:l_3 = 8:23:22$$

immediately, and to determine a point on the line we may put $X_3 = 0$ in the equations and solve

$$3X_1 - 2X_2 - 1 = 0,$$

$$5X_1 + 4X_2 - 2 = 0,$$

which gives us

$$\frac{X_1}{8} = \frac{X_2}{1} = \frac{1}{22},$$

so that (8/22, 1/22, 0) is a point on the line, and the symmetrical form of equation is

$$\frac{X_1 - 8/22}{8} = \frac{X_2 - 1/22}{23} = \frac{X_3}{22},$$

as previously.

This point of view is discussed again, in a more general context, in the next section.

EXERCISES 14

1. Prove that the equation of the plane passing through the origin and the line of intersection of the planes

$$3X_1 - X_2 + 2X_3 - 4 = 0 = X_1 + X_2 + X_3 - 1$$

is $X_1 + 5X_2 + 2X_3 = 0$. Prove also that the equation of the plane through the origin perpendicular to this line of intersection is

$$3X_1 + X_2 - 4X_3 = 0.$$

2. Find the equation of the plane which contains the line

$$\tfrac{1}{2}(X_1 - 1) = -(X_2 + 1) = \tfrac{1}{4}(X_3 - 3)$$

and is perpendicular to the plane

$$X_1 + 2X_2 + X_3 - 12 = 0.$$

Deduce that the direction-ratios of the orthogonal projection of the given line on to the given plane are $4 : -7 : 10$.

15. The Intersection of Two Planes

We may consider the solution of the two linear equations

$$\left.\begin{aligned} a_1X_1 + a_2X_2 + a_3X_3 + a_4 &= 0, \\ b_1X_1 + b_2X_2 + b_3X_3 + b_4 &= 0 \end{aligned}\right\} \qquad (49)$$

from another point of view, which will be generalized later.

Each equation represents a plane, and to each plane there is a parallel plane through the origin, with equation given simply by omitting the constant term. Thus the respective parallel planes through (0, 0, 0) are

$$\left.\begin{aligned} a_1X_1 + a_2X_2 + a_3X_3 &= 0, \\ b_1X_1 + b_2X_2 + b_3X_3 &= 0. \end{aligned}\right\} \qquad (50)$$

These are homogeneous equations, and if (X_1', X_2', X_3') satisfies them, so does (kX_1', kX_2', kX_3') for any value of k. Geometrically speaking, the two planes given by (50), if distinct, determine a line of points passing through the origin.

We know that (50) has the solution [cf. § 5, (19), p. 17]

$$X_1' : X_2' : X_3' = (a_2b_3 - a_3b_2) : -(a_1b_3 - a_3b_1) : (a_1b_2 - a_2b_1) \qquad (51)$$

if the planes are distinct, and we may then say that

$$(kX_1', kX_2', kX_3') = (k(a_2b_3 - a_3b_2), -k(a_1b_3 - a_3b_1), k(a_1b_2 - a_2b_1)),$$

since it gives the coordinates of a variable point on the line of solutions, is the *general* solution of equations (50).

There is a connection between the solutions of the non-homogeneous equations (49), and the solutions of the homogeneous derived equations (50). Let

$$Y = (Y_1, Y_2, Y_3), \qquad Z = (Z_1, Z_2, Z_3)$$

be two distinct solutions of equations (49). Then

$$a_1 Y_1 + a_2 Y_2 + a_3 Y_3 + a_4 = 0 = a_1 Z_1 + a_2 Z_2 + a_3 Z_3 + a_4,$$

$$b_1 Y_1 + b_2 Y_2 + b_3 Y_3 + b_4 = 0 = b_1 Z_1 + b_2 Z_2 + b_3 Z_3 + b_4,$$

and so

$$a_1(Y_1 - Z_1) + a_2(Y_2 - Z_2) + a_3(Y_3 - Z_3) = 0,$$

$$b_1(Y_1 - Z_1) + b_2(Y_2 - Z_2) + b_3(Y_3 - Z_3) = 0.$$

That is, $Y - Z = (Y_1 - Z_1, Y_2 - Z_2, Y_3 - Z_3)$ satisfies the homogeneous equations given by (50). Hence

$$Y - Z = (kX_1', kX_2', kX_3'),$$

for some particular value of k, where $X' = (X_1', X_2', X_3')$ is given by equations (51), and therefore

$$Y = (Y_1, Y_2, Y_3) = (Z_1, Z_2, Z_3) + (kX_1', kX_2', kX_3') = Z + kX'.$$

Here Y, a solution of the non-homogeneous equations (49), is expressed as a sum of a solution Z of the non-homogeneous equations plus a solution kX' of the homogeneous equations given by (50). Conversely, it is clear that if Z is any solution of equations (49) (the non-homogeneous), and kX' is any solution of the homogeneous equations (50), then $Y = Z + kX'$ also satisfies the non-homogeneous equations (49).

We deduce that we cannot obtain a more general solution of the equations (49) (non-homogeneous) than by taking any particular fixed solution $Z = (Z_1, Z_2, Z_3)$ of these equations and adding to it the most general solution $kX' = (kX_1', kX_2', kX_3')$ of the *homogeneous* equations given by (50).

Geometrically, the two planes intersect in a line. We may find the direction-ratios of this line by considering parallel planes through the origin. Then *any* point on the line will do to fix it and to obtain the symmetric equations (in the foregoing notation):

$$\frac{X_1 - Z_1}{X_1'} = \frac{X_2 - Z_2}{X_2'} = \frac{X_3 - Z_3}{X_3'} = k,$$

which gives the parametric form for the solutions

$$(Z_1 + kX_1', Z_2 + kX_2', Z_3 + kX_3')$$

as found earlier.

Example I

Solve the equations

$$3X_1 - 2X_2 + X_3 - 1 = 0 = 5X_1 + 4X_2 - 6X_3 - 2 = 0.$$

The homogeneous equations are

$$3X_1 - 2X_2 + X_3 = 0,$$
$$5X_1 + 4X_2 - 6X_3 = 0,$$

and give

$$X_1 : X_2 : X_3 = (12 - 4) : -(-18 - 5) : (12 + 10) = 8 : 23 : 22$$

that is, $X_1' = 8k$, $X_2' = 23k$, $X_3' = 22k$ is the general solution of the homogeneous set. A particular solution of the non-homogeneous equations is given by taking $X_1 = 0$, when we have $-2X_2 + X_3 - 1 = 0 = 4X_2 - 6X_3 - 2$, so that $X_2 = -1$ and $X_3 = -1$. Hence

$$X_1 = 8k, \qquad X_2 = 23k - 1, \qquad X_3 = 22k - 1$$

is the general solution of the equations.

In symmetric form, the solutions are:

$$\frac{X_1}{8} = \frac{X_2 + 1}{23} = \frac{X_3 + 1}{22} = k,$$

and when we solve the homogeneous equations we are, in fact, finding the direction-ratios of the line of intersection of the two planes, as was illustrated at the end of § 14.

EXERCISES 15

1. Show that the equation of the line of intersection of the two planes given by the equations

$$X_1 + X_3 - 2 = 0 = X_1 + X_2 - 4$$

may be written in the form

$$\frac{X_1 - 1}{-1} = \frac{X_2 - 3}{1} = \frac{X_3 - 1}{1}.$$

2. Show that any point on the line of intersection of the two planes given by the equations

$$X_1 + X_2 + X_3 - 8 = 0 = X_1 - X_3$$

may be written in the form $(-k + 2, 2k + 2, -k + 2)$, where k is a variable parameter.

CHAPTER FOUR

Vectors in Three Dimensions

16. Vectors and Linear Dependence

We have, of course been using vectors, calling them *directed segments*, in our discussion of three-dimensional space. Everything that was said in § 6 about vectors in two dimensions generalizes to vectors in three dimensions. Of course vectors in three dimensions with origin at (0, 0, 0)* are given by three and not two entries, thus:

$$\mathbf{X} = [X_1, X_2, X_3].$$

The addition of the localized vectors $\mathbf{X}$ and $\mathbf{Y} = [Y_1, Y_2, Y_3]$ is defined by the equation

$$\mathbf{X} + \mathbf{Y} = [X_1 + Y_1, X_2 + Y_2, X_3 + Y_3].$$

The parallelogram law for the addition of vectors in three dimensions is valid. If we look at Fig. 5, and suppose the parallelogram $OBCA$ to be sticking out of the plane Ox_1x_2, not lying in it, the proof depends on the evident statement that

$$\text{projection of } \overrightarrow{OA} + \text{projection of } \overrightarrow{AC} \\ = \text{projection of } \overrightarrow{OC},$$

the projection being onto any axis. The coordinates of the endpoint C of the diagonal are therefore $(X_1 + Y_1, X_2 + Y_2, X_3 + Y_3)$, so that $\overrightarrow{OC}$ does represent the sum $\mathbf{X} + \mathbf{Y}$.

Scalar multiplication of the vector $\mathbf{X}$ by any real number s is defined as:

$$s\mathbf{X} = [sX_1, sX_2, sX_3].$$

Once again, the facts contained in the following theorem are easily verified for vectors in three dimensions:

* Such vectors are also called *bound* vectors, and *non-localized* vectors are also called *free* vectors.

Theorem 4. *If* **X**, **Y**, **Z** *are localized vectors, and* s, t *real numbers, then*

(i) $$\mathbf{X} + \mathbf{Y} = \mathbf{Y} + \mathbf{X},$$

(ii) $$(\mathbf{X} + \mathbf{Y}) + \mathbf{Z} = \mathbf{X} + (\mathbf{Y} + \mathbf{Z}),$$

(iii) $$(st)\mathbf{X} = s(t\mathbf{X}),$$

(iv) $$(s + t)\mathbf{X} = s\mathbf{X} + t\mathbf{X},$$

(v) $$s(\mathbf{X} + \mathbf{Y}) = s\mathbf{X} + s\mathbf{Y},$$

(vi) $$1 \cdot \mathbf{X} = \mathbf{X}.$$

The equation of a line in three dimensions, using vector notation, is of exactly the same form as in two dimensions [equation (23), § 6], namely

$$\mathbf{X} = (1 - t)\mathbf{H} + t\mathbf{K}, \quad \text{where}$$

$H = (h_1, h_2, h_3)$ and $K = (k_1, k_2, k_3)$ are two points on the line. This follows immediately from equations (39), which may be written

$$X_i = (1 - t)h_i + tk_i \qquad (i = 1, 2, 3),$$

and then in vector form as

$$[X_1, X_2, X_3] = (1 - t)[h_1, h_2, h_3] + t[k_1, k_2, k_3].$$

A vector **X** is said to *depend linearly* on vectors $\mathbf{X}_1, \mathbf{X}_2, \ldots, \mathbf{X}_n$ if we may write **X** as a linear sum of multiples of these vectors, thus:

$$\mathbf{X} = a_1\mathbf{X}_1 + a_2\mathbf{X}_2 + \cdots + a_n\mathbf{X}_n.$$

The vector equation of a line expresses the fact that a vector with endpoint on the line is linearly dependent on any two vectors whose endpoints determine the line; but it should be noted that the multiplying scalars $1 - t$ and t are special, since their sum is 1. To determine what happens if the multiplying factors are not special in this sense, consider the vector **X** with endpoint at a division of the segment HK in the ratio $\lambda : \mu$. From equations (40) of § 12, we have

$$\mathbf{X} = \frac{\mu\mathbf{H}}{\lambda + \mu} + \frac{\lambda\mathbf{K}}{\lambda + \mu},$$

so that

$$\mu\mathbf{H} + \lambda\mathbf{K} = (\lambda + \mu)\mathbf{X}. \tag{52}$$

A similar equation is true in two dimensions [equation (24), § 7], and Fig. 7, which illustrates the two-dimensional case, also serves for the three-dimensional case, it being understood that the points H and K do not necessarily lie in the plane Ox_1x_2. But in three dimensions we give the equation (52) a different emphasis, and state the new point of view as a theorem.

Theorem 5. *All vectors which depend linearly on the vectors* **H** *and* **K** *lie in the plane* OHK*, where* O *is the origin of the vectors and* H, K *are the endpoints of the vectors* **H** *and* **K**.

Proof. Any vector which depends linearly on **H** and **K** may be written in the form $\mu\mathbf{H} + \lambda\mathbf{K}$, and equation (52) shows that this vector is $(\lambda + \mu)\mathbf{X}$, where X divides HK in the ratio $\lambda:\mu$, so that **X**, and therefore also $(\lambda + \mu)\mathbf{X}$, lies in the plane OHK. If $\lambda + \mu = 0$, $\mu(\mathbf{H} - \mathbf{K})$ is parallel to HK (Exercises 16.1, No. 4), and still lies in the plane OHK.

Example 1

We prove once more, but in vector notation, that the lines joining the vertices of a tetrahedron $ABCD$ to the centroids of the opposite faces are concurrent (cf. Example, § 12).

Let the vertices be given by the vectors **A**, **B**, **C**, and **D**. The centroid of the face BCD is the vector $\frac{1}{3}(\mathbf{B} + \mathbf{C} + \mathbf{D})$, and the vector **G** whose endpoint divides the join of this centroid to A in the ratio $1:3$ is given by the equation

$$\begin{aligned} 4\mathbf{G} &= 1 \cdot \mathbf{A} + 3(\tfrac{1}{3})(\mathbf{B} + \mathbf{C} + \mathbf{D}) \\ &= \mathbf{A} + \mathbf{B} + \mathbf{C} + \mathbf{D}. \end{aligned}$$

The symmetry of this result proves the theorem.

EXERCISES 16.1

1. Perform the operations indicated, and obtain the resulting vector:
   (*a*) $3[1, 4, 2] + [0, 2, 6]$,
   (*b*) $-6[7, 8, 0] + 2[5, 9, -1]$,
   (*c*) $p[-3, 4, 1/2] + q[0, 0, 0]$.
2. Provide proofs for all the properties of vectors listed in Theorem 4.
3. What are the vector equations of the lines joining the following pairs of points?
   (*a*) $(5, -6, 2)$, $(1, 3, 4)$,
   (*b*) $(0, 8, 10)$, $(-2, 9, 7)$.
4. If $\mathbf{H} = [h_1, h_2, h_3]$ and $\mathbf{K} = [k_1, k_2, k_3]$, show, from the parallelogram law, that the vector $\mathbf{K} - \mathbf{H}$ is equal to the non-localized vector $\overrightarrow{HK}$, where H and K are the respective endpoints of the two vectors.
5. Show that the line HK is parallel to the line $H'K'$ if and only if $\mathbf{H} - \mathbf{K} = s(\mathbf{H}' - \mathbf{K}')$, where $s \neq 0$.
6. If $ABCD$ is a tetrahedron, show that the lines joining the midpoints of opposite edges, such as AB and CD, all pass through a point.

Our definition of linear dependence for a set of three-dimensional vectors agrees with that given for vectors in two dimensions (Definition 1, § 7).

Definition 1. *The set of vectors* $\mathbf{X}_1, \mathbf{X}_2, \ldots, \mathbf{X}_n$ *is said to be a linearly dependent set if real numbers* $a_1, a_2, \ldots, a_n$, *not all zero, exist so that*

$$a_1\mathbf{X}_1 + a_2\mathbf{X}_2 + \cdots + a_n\mathbf{X}_n = \mathbf{0}.$$

The zero vector in three dimensions is $\mathbf{0} = [0, 0, 0]$, and once again we see that *any set of vectors containing the zero vector is a linearly dependent set.* This follows from the equation

$$0 \cdot \mathbf{X}_1 + 0 \cdot \mathbf{X}_2 + \cdots + 0 \cdot \mathbf{X}_n + 1 \cdot \mathbf{0} = \mathbf{0}.$$

Definition 2. *A set of vectors is linearly independent if it is not dependent.*

In three dimensions we can easily find three vectors which are linearly *independent*, so that Theorem 2, § 7 is characteristic of vectors in two dimensions. In fact the vectors

$$\mathbf{e}_1 = [1, 0, 0], \qquad \mathbf{e}_2 = [0, 1, 0], \qquad \mathbf{e}_3 = [0, 0, 1]$$

are independent. For if

$$a_1\mathbf{e}_1 + a_2\mathbf{e}_2 + a_3\mathbf{e}_3 = \mathbf{0},$$

it follows that

$$[a_1, a_2, a_3] = [0, 0, 0].$$

As another illustration of the ideas of dependence and independence we prove Theorem 5*.

Theorem 5*. *If a set of three vectors is linearly dependent, the vectors are coplanar.*

Proof. Since two lines through the origin O determine a plane, the theorem is trivial if any one, or more, of the vectors is the zero vector, or if one of the set, which we denote by $\mathbf{A}$, $\mathbf{B}$, $\mathbf{C}$, is a scalar multiple of another vector of the set. If, say, $\mathbf{A} = s\mathbf{B}$, then the vectors $\mathbf{A}$ and $\mathbf{B}$ lie along the same line through O, and this line, together with the line determined by $\mathbf{C}$, gives the plane in which the three vectors lie. It follows that in the given relation of dependence

$$\lambda\mathbf{A} + \mu\mathbf{B} + \nu\mathbf{C} = \mathbf{0},$$

none of the constants λ, μ, ν can be zero, since if, say $\lambda = 0$, we cannot have either μ or ν zero, since none of $\mathbf{A}$, $\mathbf{B}$ or $\mathbf{C}$ is zero, and we would have

$$\mathbf{B} = k\mathbf{C},$$

which is excluded. We may therefore write

$$\mathbf{A} = q\mathbf{B} + r\mathbf{C},$$

and, by Theorem 5, the vector $\mathbf{A}$ lies in the plane determined by $\mathbf{B}$ and $\mathbf{C}$.

Theorem 5.** *If three vectors are coplanar, they form a linearly dependent set.*

Proof. Since any set of vectors containing the zero vector is a dependent set, we may assume that none of the vectors **A**, **B**, **C** is the zero vector. If the lines along which the vectors lie are not distinct, one vector is a scalar multiple of another, say $\mathbf{A} = s\mathbf{B}$, if the lines along which **A** and **B** lie coincide. The relation of dependence is then simply

$$\mathbf{A} - s\mathbf{B} + 0 \cdot \mathbf{C} = \mathbf{0}.$$

We therefore arrive at the case in which the three vectors lie along three distinct coplanar lines. If B, C are the endpoints of **B**, **C**, suppose that the line OA along which **A** lies intersects the line BC at the point A', where A' divides the segment BC in the ratio $\lambda{:}\mu$. Then by equation (52),

$$\mu\mathbf{B} + \lambda\mathbf{C} = (\lambda + \mu)\overrightarrow{OA'},$$

and if $\overrightarrow{OA'} = \rho\mathbf{A}$, we have the relation of dependence

$$-\rho(\lambda + \mu)\mathbf{A} + \mu\mathbf{B} + \lambda\mathbf{C} = \mathbf{0},$$

where since λ and μ cannot both be zero, not all the constant multipliers are zero.

If OA is parallel to the line BC, then $\mathbf{B} - \mathbf{C} = k\mathbf{A}$, for some value of k, and the relation of dependence may be written

$$-k\mathbf{A} + \mathbf{B} - \mathbf{C} = \mathbf{0}.$$

The three theorems numbered 5, 5* and 5** are related theorems, and the proofs have been given in some detail to illustrate the notions of linear dependence and independence. The theorem in three dimensions which corresponds to Theorem 2, § 7 is Theorem 6.

Theorem 6. *Any four vectors in three dimensions are linearly dependent.*

Proof. Once again, we exclude the zero vector from the set. Let the four vectors be **A**, **B**, **C**, and **D**, with respective endpoints A, B, C, and D.

If any three of the vectors, say **A**, **B**, and **C** are coplanar, then these three vectors are linearly dependent, by Theorem 5**, and the relation

$$a\mathbf{A} + b\mathbf{B} + c\mathbf{C} = \mathbf{0},$$

where not all the constants a, b, and c are zero, involves the relation

$$a\mathbf{A} + b\mathbf{B} + c\mathbf{C} + 0 \cdot \mathbf{D} = \mathbf{0}.$$

We may therefore assume that the vectors **A**, **B**, and **C** are not coplanar. The plane ABC does not pass through the origin O, since if it did, the vectors **A**, **B**, and **C** would be coplanar. The line OD therefore cuts the plane

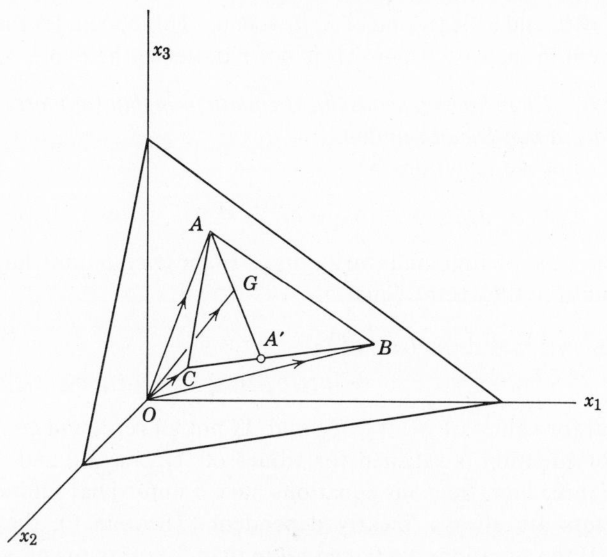

Figure 18

ABC in a point $G \neq O$, or is parallel to it. If OD is not parallel to the plane ABC, we use the division-ratio formula (52) to obtain a linear relation between the vectors **A**, **B**, **C**, and **D**.

Let AG intersect BC in the point A', and suppose that $CA':A'B = \mu:\nu$. Then by equation (52)

$$\mu\mathbf{B} + \nu\mathbf{C} = (\mu + \nu)\overrightarrow{OA'}.$$

The ration $A'G:GA$ is determinate, and we can determine λ so that

$$A'G:GA = \lambda:\mu + \nu,$$

where μ and ν are as already determined. We can now write

$$(\mu + \nu)\overrightarrow{OA'} + \lambda\overrightarrow{OA} = (\lambda + \mu + \nu)\overrightarrow{OG},$$

which leads to

$$\lambda\mathbf{A} + \mu\mathbf{B} + \nu\mathbf{C} = (\lambda + \mu + \nu)\overrightarrow{OG}. \tag{53}$$

Equation (53), of course, may be regarded as an extension of equation (52). The point G is the centroid of particles of mass λ at A, μ at B, and ν at C.

We cannot have $\lambda + \mu + \nu = 0$, since equation (53) then shows that **A**, **B**, and **C** are linearly dependent, and, contrary to our initial assumption, they would be coplanar, by Theorem 5*. Hence we can write

$$(\lambda + \mu + \nu)\overrightarrow{OG} = -\rho\mathbf{D},$$

where $\rho \neq 0$, and (53) becomes

$$\lambda\mathbf{A} + \mu\mathbf{B} + \nu\mathbf{C} + \rho\mathbf{D} = \mathbf{0},$$

where $\rho \neq 0$, and at least one of λ, μ, $\nu \neq 0$. This concludes the proof of the theorem in the case when OD is not parallel to the plane ABC.

Corollary. *Three homogeneous linear equations in four (or more) unknowns always have a non-trivial solution.*

Proof. Let the equations be

$$a_{i1}X_1 + a_{i2}X_2 + a_{i3}X_3 + a_{i4}X_4 = 0 \qquad (i = 1, 2, 3),$$

taking the case of four unknowns first. If these equations have a non-trivial solution, the vector equation

$$[a_{11}, a_{21}, a_{31}]X_1 + [a_{12}, a_{22}, a_{32}]X_2 \\ + [a_{13}, a_{23}, a_{33}]X_3 + [a_{14}, a_{24}, a_{34}]X_4 = \mathbf{0},$$

is satisfied for values of X_1, X_2, X_3, and X_4 not all zero, and conversely, if the vector equation is satisfied for values of X_1, X_2, X_3, and X_4 not all zero, the three homogeneous equations have a non-trivial solution. Since four vectors are always linearly dependent (Theorem 6), the corollary follows. If the equations contained more than four unknowns, say X_5 and X_6, take $X_5 = X_6 = 0$, and we then have the case already dealt with.

EXERCISES 16.2

1. Show that Theorem 6 is still true when the vector $\mathbf{D}$ is parallel to the plane ABC, and that the relation of dependence is then of the form

$$\lambda(\mathbf{A} - \mathbf{C}) + \mu(\mathbf{B} - \mathbf{C}) + \nu\mathbf{D} = \mathbf{0}.$$

Investigate also the necessary modification of the proof if AG is parallel to BC.

2. Writing $\mathbf{G} = \overrightarrow{OG}$, give an alternative proof of Theorem 6 from the consideration that the vectors $\mathbf{A} - \mathbf{G}$, $\mathbf{B} - \mathbf{G}$, and $\mathbf{C} - \mathbf{G}$ are coplanar.

3. Deduce from the proof of Theorem 6 that if the endpoint of a vector $\mathbf{X}$ lies in the plane ABC, we may write $\mathbf{X} = a\mathbf{A} + b\mathbf{B} + c\mathbf{C}$, where $a + b + c = 1$. Deduce from Exercise 1 that if $\mathbf{X}$ is parallel to the plane, we may write $\mathbf{X} = a\mathbf{A} + b\mathbf{B} + c\mathbf{C}$, but $a + b + c = 0$.

17. Determinants of Orders 2 and 3

We continue the proof of Theorem 6, that any four vectors in three dimensions are linearly dependent, in a new section, since the second method of proof introduces determinants of order 3.

To prove that $\mathbf{A} = [a_1, a_2, a_3]$, $\mathbf{B} = [b_1, b_2, b_3]$, $\mathbf{C} = [c_1, c_2, c_3]$, and $\mathbf{D} = [d_1, d_2, d_3]$ are always linearly dependent, we must establish the existence (changing our notation) of x, y, z, t, not all zero, such that

$$x\mathbf{A} + y\mathbf{B} + z\mathbf{C} + t\mathbf{D} = \mathbf{0}.$$

This equation is equivalent to the three equations:

$$\left.\begin{aligned} u &\equiv xa_1 + yb_1 + zc_1 + td_1 = 0, \\ v &\equiv xa_2 + yb_2 + zc_2 + td_2 = 0, \\ w &\equiv xa_3 + yb_3 + zc_3 + td_3 = 0, \end{aligned}\right\} \tag{54}$$

that is, three homogeneous linear equations in four unknowns, x, y, z, t, and we wish to prove that such a set of equations always has a non-trivial solution, that is, a solution other than $x = y = z = t = 0$.

The solutions of these three equations also satisfy the equation

$$\lambda u + \mu v + \nu w = 0, \tag{55}$$

for any values of λ, μ, ν. Let us see whether we can choose λ, μ, ν so that in equation (55) the coefficients of y and of z are both zero. This is the case if

$$\left.\begin{aligned} \lambda b_1 + \mu b_2 + \nu b_3 = 0, \\ \lambda c_1 + \mu c_2 + \nu c_3 = 0. \end{aligned}\right\} \tag{56}$$

We know how to solve these equations [cf. equation (19), § 5 p. 17] and we write

$$\lambda = \begin{vmatrix} b_2 & b_3 \\ c_2 & c_3 \end{vmatrix}, \quad -\mu = \begin{vmatrix} b_1 & b_3 \\ c_1 & c_3 \end{vmatrix}, \quad \nu = \begin{vmatrix} b_1 & b_2 \\ c_1 & c_2 \end{vmatrix}.$$

With these values of λ, μ, ν, equation (55) becomes

$$x\left\{a_1\begin{vmatrix} b_2 & b_3 \\ c_2 & c_3 \end{vmatrix} - a_2\begin{vmatrix} b_1 & b_3 \\ c_1 & c_3 \end{vmatrix} + a_3\begin{vmatrix} b_1 & b_2 \\ c_1 & c_2 \end{vmatrix}\right\}$$
$$+ t\left\{d_1\begin{vmatrix} b_2 & b_3 \\ c_2 & c_3 \end{vmatrix} - d_2\begin{vmatrix} b_1 & b_3 \\ c_1 & c_3 \end{vmatrix} + d_3\begin{vmatrix} b_1 & b_2 \\ c_1 & c_2 \end{vmatrix}\right\} = 0.$$

We can now solve for the ratio $x:t$, and by repeating the process and choosing λ, μ, ν suitably on each occasion, we can solve for the ratios $y:t$ and $z:t$, and thus find a solution $x:y:z:t$ of equations (54).

The solution for $x:t$ given earlier suggests defining a *determinant* of three rows and columns (a determinant of *order* 3) thus:

$$\begin{vmatrix} a_1 & a_2 & a_3 \\ b_1 & b_2 & b_3 \\ c_1 & c_2 & c_3 \end{vmatrix} = a_1\begin{vmatrix} b_2 & b_3 \\ c_2 & c_3 \end{vmatrix} - a_2\begin{vmatrix} b_1 & b_3 \\ c_1 & c_3 \end{vmatrix} + a_3\begin{vmatrix} b_1 & b_2 \\ c_1 & c_2 \end{vmatrix}. \tag{57}$$

We observe that the coefficients of a_1, a_2, a_3 in the *expansion* (as it is called) of this determinant, are obtained by striking out the row and column in the determinant which contains the a_1, the a_2 or the a_3, and writing down the determinant of the second order which remains, with a change of sign as we move along the row, thus:

$$\begin{vmatrix} a_1 & a_2 & a_3 \\ b_1 & b_2 & b_3 \\ c_1 & c_2 & c_3 \end{vmatrix} = \begin{vmatrix} b_2 & b_3 \\ c_2 & c_3 \end{vmatrix},$$

$$\begin{vmatrix} a_1 & a_2 & a_3 \\ b_1 & b_2 & b_3 \\ c_1 & c_2 & c_3 \end{vmatrix} = -\begin{vmatrix} b_1 & b_3 \\ c_1 & c_3 \end{vmatrix},$$

$$\begin{vmatrix} a_1 & a_2 & a_3 \\ b_1 & b_2 & b_3 \\ c_1 & c_2 & c_3 \end{vmatrix} = (-1)(-1)\begin{vmatrix} b_1 & b_2 \\ c_1 & c_2 \end{vmatrix}.$$

Example I

We calculate the determinant:

$$\begin{vmatrix} a & h & g \\ h & b & f \\ g & f & c \end{vmatrix} = a\begin{vmatrix} b & f \\ f & c \end{vmatrix} - h\begin{vmatrix} h & f \\ g & c \end{vmatrix} + g\begin{vmatrix} h & b \\ g & f \end{vmatrix}$$

$$= a(bc - f^2) - h(hc - fg) + g(hf - bg)$$

$$= abc + 2fgh - af^2 - bg^2 - ch^2.$$

EXERCISES 17.1

1. Show that

$$\begin{vmatrix} 0 & r & -q \\ -r & 0 & p \\ q & -p & 0 \end{vmatrix} = 0.$$

2. Show that

$$\begin{vmatrix} a & b & c \\ -1 & x & 0 \\ 0 & -1 & x \end{vmatrix} = ax^2 + bx + c.$$

3. Show that

$$\begin{vmatrix} 1 & -2 & 3 \\ 0 & 4 & 6 \\ 5 & 1 & 0 \end{vmatrix} = -126.$$

With this definition of a determinant of order 3, the equation for the ratio of $x:t$ becomes

$$x\begin{vmatrix} a_1 & a_2 & a_3 \\ b_1 & b_2 & b_3 \\ c_1 & c_2 & c_3 \end{vmatrix} + t\begin{vmatrix} d_1 & d_2 & d_3 \\ b_1 & b_2 & b_3 \\ c_1 & c_2 & c_3 \end{vmatrix} = 0.$$

To conform to the pattern of the array of coefficients in equation (54), we write this equation in another form, after pointing out the following rule:

Rule I. A determinant is unchanged if we interchange rows and columns.

This means that

$$\begin{vmatrix} a_1 & a_2 & a_3 \\ b_1 & b_2 & b_3 \\ c_1 & c_2 & c_3 \end{vmatrix} = \begin{vmatrix} a_1 & b_1 & c_1 \\ a_2 & b_2 & c_2 \\ a_3 & b_3 & c_3 \end{vmatrix}.$$

In fact, the right-hand determinant, by definition, is

$$\begin{aligned} & a_1\begin{vmatrix} b_2 & c_2 \\ b_3 & c_3 \end{vmatrix} - b_1\begin{vmatrix} a_2 & c_2 \\ a_3 & c_3 \end{vmatrix} + c_1\begin{vmatrix} a_2 & b_2 \\ a_3 & b_3 \end{vmatrix} \\ &= a_1(b_2c_3 - b_3c_2) - b_1(a_2c_3 - a_3c_2) + c_1(a_2b_3 - a_3b_2) \\ &= a_1(b_2c_3 - b_3c_2) - a_2(b_1c_3 - b_3c_1) + a_3(b_1c_2 - b_2c_1) \\ &= a_1\begin{vmatrix} b_2 & b_3 \\ c_2 & c_3 \end{vmatrix} - a_2\begin{vmatrix} b_1 & b_3 \\ c_1 & c_3 \end{vmatrix} + a_3\begin{vmatrix} b_1 & b_2 \\ c_1 & c_2 \end{vmatrix}. \end{aligned}$$

We may therefore write the equation for $x:t$ in the form

$$x\begin{vmatrix} a_1 & b_1 & c_1 \\ a_2 & b_2 & c_2 \\ a_3 & b_3 & c_3 \end{vmatrix} + t\begin{vmatrix} d_1 & b_1 & c_1 \\ d_2 & b_2 & c_2 \\ d_3 & b_3 & c_3 \end{vmatrix} = 0,$$

and we can now confidently write

$$y\begin{vmatrix} a_1 & b_1 & c_1 \\ a_2 & b_2 & c_2 \\ a_3 & b_3 & c_3 \end{vmatrix} + t\begin{vmatrix} a_1 & d_1 & c_1 \\ a_2 & d_2 & c_2 \\ a_3 & d_3 & c_3 \end{vmatrix} = 0,$$

and

$$z\begin{vmatrix} a_1 & b_1 & c_1 \\ a_2 & b_2 & c_2 \\ a_3 & b_3 & c_3 \end{vmatrix} + t\begin{vmatrix} a_1 & b_1 & d_1 \\ a_2 & b_2 & d_2 \\ a_3 & b_3 & d_3 \end{vmatrix} = 0,$$

since the pattern for the solution becomes clear from the array (or *matrix*) of the coefficients in equation (54):

$$\begin{bmatrix} a_1 & b_1 & c_1 & d_1 \\ a_2 & b_2 & c_2 & d_2 \\ a_3 & b_3 & c_3 & d_3 \end{bmatrix}.$$

If the reader is not convinced that the foregoing solutions for $y:t$ and $z:t$ are correct, he should soon feel happier, for we shall return to these solutions again very shortly. We now work a numerical example.

Example 2

Solve the equations

$$\begin{aligned} u &\equiv x + 5y + 2z - 9t = 0, \\ v &\equiv x + y + 7z - 6t = 0, \\ w &\equiv \phantom{x + {}} -3y + 4z + 2t = 0, \end{aligned}$$

Let λ, μ, ν be chosen so that in $\lambda u + \mu v + \nu w$ the coefficients of y and z are both zero. This gives us

$$\begin{aligned} 5\lambda + \mu - 3\nu &= 0, \\ 2\lambda + 7\mu + 4\nu &= 0, \end{aligned}$$

so that

$$\lambda = \begin{vmatrix} 1 & -3 \\ 7 & 4 \end{vmatrix}, \quad \mu = -\begin{vmatrix} 5 & -3 \\ 2 & 4 \end{vmatrix}, \quad \nu = \begin{vmatrix} 5 & 1 \\ 2 & 7 \end{vmatrix},$$

that is $\qquad \lambda = 25, \quad \mu = -26, \quad \nu = 33.$

We check that these values do fulfill the desired purpose, and find that

$$x(25 - 26) + t(-9 \cdot 25 + 26 \cdot 6 + 2 \cdot 33) = 0,$$

so that $\qquad -x - 3t = 0.$

We now begin again and determine λ, μ, ν so that in $\lambda u + \mu v + \nu w$ the coefficients of x and z are both zero. This requirement produces the equations

$$\begin{aligned} \lambda + \mu \phantom{{}+ 4\nu} &= 0, \\ 2\lambda + 7\mu + 4\nu &= 0, \end{aligned}$$

and $\lambda = 1 \cdot 4$, $\mu = -(1 \cdot 4)$, and $\nu = (1 \cdot 7 - 2 \cdot 1)$,

that is $$\lambda = 4, \qquad \mu = -4, \qquad \nu = 5,$$

and we find that

$$y[5 \cdot 4 + 1(-4) - 3(5)] + t[-9 \cdot 4 - 6(-4) + 2(5)] = 0,$$

that is $$y - 2t = 0.$$

Finally, we determine λ, μ, ν so that the coefficients of x and y in

$$\lambda u + \mu w + \nu w$$

are zero, and find that

$$\begin{aligned} \lambda + \mu \qquad &= 0, \\ 5\lambda + \mu - 3\nu &= 0, \end{aligned}$$

so that $$\lambda = 1(-3), \qquad \mu = -(-3), \qquad \nu = 1 \cdot 1 - 5 \cdot 1,$$

$$\lambda = -3, \qquad \mu = 3, \qquad \nu = -4,$$

and we find that

$$z(-6 + 21 - 16) + t(27 - 18 - 8) = 0,$$

that is $$-z + t = 0.$$

Hence $x:y:z:t = -3:2:1:1$, and we verify immediately that these values satisfy the original equations.

We have not used the three-rowed determinants in working this example, but verify that we obtain the same result if we do so. We have

$$x\begin{vmatrix} 1 & 5 & 2 \\ 1 & 1 & 7 \\ 0 & -3 & 4 \end{vmatrix} + t\begin{vmatrix} -9 & 5 & 2 \\ -6 & 1 & 7 \\ 2 & -3 & 4 \end{vmatrix} = 0,$$

which produces the equation

$$-x + (-3t) = 0.$$

Then we have

$$y\begin{vmatrix} 1 & 5 & 2 \\ 1 & 1 & 7 \\ 0 & -3 & 4 \end{vmatrix} + t\begin{vmatrix} 1 & -9 & 2 \\ 1 & -6 & 7 \\ 0 & 2 & 4 \end{vmatrix} = 0,$$

that is, $$-y + 2t = 0,$$

and finally,

$$z\begin{vmatrix} 1 & 5 & 2 \\ 1 & 1 & 7 \\ 0 & -3 & 4 \end{vmatrix} + t\begin{vmatrix} 1 & 5 & -9 \\ 1 & 1 & -6 \\ 0 & -3 & 2 \end{vmatrix} = 0,$$

which gives us

$$-z + t = 0,$$

and therefore the previous formulas involving three-rowed determinants lead to the same result.

EXERCISES 17.2

1. Solve the equations

$$2x + 4y + z - 5t = 0,$$
$$x + y + z - 6t = 0,$$
$$2x + 3y + z - 6t = 0.$$

2. Solve the equations (using three-rowed determinants),

$$x + 4y + 11z - 7t = 0,$$
$$2x + 8y + 16z - 8t = 0,$$
$$x + 6y + 17z - 9t = 0.$$

We give a few more simple rules for the manipulation of determinants, verify that they hold for determinants of order 3, and we shall then return to the problem of the solution of three linear equations with which this section began.

Rule 2. The interchange of two rows of a determinant merely changes the sign of the determinant.

This means that, for example,

$$\begin{vmatrix} a_1 & a_2 & a_3 \\ c_1 & c_2 & c_3 \\ b_1 & b_2 & b_3 \end{vmatrix} = -\begin{vmatrix} a_1 & a_2 & a_3 \\ b_1 & b_2 & b_3 \\ c_1 & c_2 & c_3 \end{vmatrix}.$$

Since the left-hand determinant is

$$a_1(c_2b_3 - b_2c_3) - a_2(c_1b_3 - c_3b_1) + a_3(c_1b_2 - c_2b_1)$$
$$= -a_1(b_2c_3 - b_3c_2) + a_2(b_1c_3 - b_3c_1) - a_3(b_1c_2 - b_2c_1),$$

this rule is verified for the interchange of the second and third rows. The same is true for the interchange of any other two rows.

By Rule 1 we may now also give Rule 3.

Rule 3. The interchange of two columns of a determinant merely changes its sign.

We now deduce Rule 4.

Rule 4. If two rows (or columns) of a determinant have identical entries, the determinant is zero.

Suppose that the second and third rows are identical in

$$\Delta = \begin{vmatrix} a_1 & a_2 & a_3 \\ b_1 & b_2 & b_3 \\ b_1 & b_2 & b_3 \end{vmatrix}.$$

Since interchanging rows 2 and 3 produces no visible effect, and yet the sign of Δ is changed, we have

$$\Delta = -\Delta,$$

$$2\Delta = 0,$$

and since the numbers we are using are real numbers, we deduce that $\Delta = 0$.

Rule 5. If a multiple of row i is added to row $j\,(i \neq j)$, the resulting determinant is still $= \Delta$, the original determinant.

If we add k(row 3) to row 1 we have the determinant

$$\begin{vmatrix} a_1 + kc_1 & a_2 + kc_2 & a_3 + kc_3 \\ b_1 & b_2 & b_3 \\ c_1 & c_2 & c_3 \end{vmatrix},$$

which is

$$(a_1 + kc_1)(b_2c_3 - b_3c_2) - (a_2 + kc_2)(b_1c_3 - b_3c_1) + (a_3 + kc_3)(b_1c_2 - b_2c_1).$$

If we pick out the terms not containing k and those containing k, this determinant is clearly

$$\begin{vmatrix} a_1 & a_2 & a_3 \\ b_1 & b_2 & b_3 \\ c_1 & c_2 & c_3 \end{vmatrix} + k \begin{vmatrix} c_1 & c_2 & c_3 \\ b_1 & b_2 & b_3 \\ c_1 & c_2 & c_3 \end{vmatrix},$$

and the coefficient of k is a determinant with row 3 identical to row 1, and this is zero, by Rule 4. Hence the determinant is unchanged in value.

To prove the other cases when, for example, k (row 3) is added to row 2, it is desirable to be able to expand a determinant by moving along other rows than the first. Our definition of determinant, so far, has involved an expansion in terms of the elements of the first row, these elements being multiplied by determinants of order 2 with suitable signs attached. Thus

$$\Delta = \begin{vmatrix} a_1 & a_2 & a_3 \\ b_1 & b_2 & b_3 \\ c_1 & c_2 & c_3 \end{vmatrix} = a_1A_1 + a_2A_2 + a_3A_3,$$

where

$$A_1 = \begin{vmatrix} b_2 & b_3 \\ c_2 & c_3 \end{vmatrix}, \qquad A_2 = -\begin{vmatrix} b_1 & b_3 \\ c_1 & c_3 \end{vmatrix}, \qquad A_3 = \begin{vmatrix} b_1 & b_2 \\ c_1 & c_2 \end{vmatrix}.$$

These *signed* subdeterminants (or signed *minors* of Δ) are called the *cofactors* of the elements they multiply.

We note that

$$b_1A_1 + b_2A_2 + b_3A_3 = 0,$$

and

$$c_1A_1 + c_2A_2 + c_3A_3 = 0,$$

since each expression arises from a determinant in which two rows are identical, namely

$$\begin{vmatrix} b_1 & b_2 & b_3 \\ b_1 & b_2 & b_3 \\ c_1 & c_2 & c_3 \end{vmatrix}, \quad \text{and} \quad \begin{vmatrix} c_1 & c_2 & c_3 \\ b_1 & b_2 & b_3 \\ c_1 & c_2 & c_3 \end{vmatrix}.$$

To expand Δ by moving along elements of row 3, we interchange row 3 and row 1, so that we have

$$\begin{aligned} -\Delta &= \begin{vmatrix} c_1 & c_2 & c_3 \\ b_1 & b_2 & b_3 \\ a_1 & a_2 & a_3 \end{vmatrix} \\ &= c_1\begin{vmatrix} b_2 & b_3 \\ a_2 & a_3 \end{vmatrix} - c_2\begin{vmatrix} b_1 & b_3 \\ a_1 & a_3 \end{vmatrix} + c_3\begin{vmatrix} b_1 & b_2 \\ a_1 & a_2 \end{vmatrix} \\ &= -c_1\begin{vmatrix} a_2 & a_3 \\ b_2 & b_3 \end{vmatrix} + c_2\begin{vmatrix} a_1 & a_3 \\ b_1 & b_3 \end{vmatrix} - c_3\begin{vmatrix} a_1 & a_2 \\ b_1 & b_2 \end{vmatrix}, \end{aligned}$$

interchanging rows in the determinants of order 2, so that

$$\Delta = c_1C_1 + c_2C_2 + c_3C_3,$$

where C_1 is obtained by striking out from Δ the row and column containing c_1, $-C_2$ is obtained by striking out from Δ the row and column containing

c_2 (note the change of sign), and C_3 is obtained from Δ by striking out the row and column containing c_3.

However, if we expand Δ by moving along row 2 so that

$$\Delta = b_1B_1 + b_2B_2 + b_3B_3,$$

we see that the determinant left behind when we strike out the row and column containing b_1 is $-B_1$, that the determinant which corresponds to b_2 is now $+B_2$, and that corresponding to b_3 is $-B_3$. All this is simply summed up in Rule 6.

Rule 6. The cofactor of the element in row i and column j is $(-1)^{i+j}$ (determinant left behind on striking out row i and column j).

The signs attached to elements in the first row, beginning with the element in the first column, are respectively $+, -, +$; those attached to elements in the second row are $-, +, -$; and those attached to elements in the third row are again $+, -, +$.

These rules hold for determinants of any order (p. 196). We also note that Rule 5 holds if "column" is used instead of "row," and we may expand a determinant by moving down any column, using Rule 6 to determine the sign which must be attached to the corresponding minor determinant.

The method of expansion of a determinant in terms of the elements of any row or column makes it plain that if we multiply the elements of any row (or column) by k, the resulting determinant is multiplied by k. We state this as follows:

Rule 7. If the elements of any one row or column of a determinant are multiplied by k, the resulting determinant $\Delta' = k\Delta$, where Δ is the original determinant.

We apply these rules to solve the following equations which were considered at the beginning of this section:

$$\left.\begin{aligned} u &\equiv xa_1 + yb_1 + zc_1 + td_1 = 0, \\ v &\equiv xa_2 + yb_2 + zc_2 + td_2 = 0, \\ w &\equiv xa_3 + yb_3 + zc_3 + td_3 = 0. \end{aligned}\right\} \tag{54}$$

Let

$$\Delta = \begin{vmatrix} a_1 & b_1 & c_1 \\ a_2 & b_2 & c_2 \\ a_3 & b_3 & c_3 \end{vmatrix},$$

and suppose that A_1, A_2, A_3 are the cofactors of a_1, a_2, a_3 respectively in Δ. Then

$$a_1A_1 + a_2A_2 + a_3A_3 = \Delta, \quad \text{whereas}$$
$$b_1A_1 + b_2A_2 + b_3A_3 = c_1A_1 + c_2A_2 + c_3A_3 = 0,$$

since each of these latter expressions is the expansion of a determinant with two identical columns, and such a determinant is zero (Rule 4). Hence

$$uA_1 + vA_2 + wA_3 = x\Delta + t(d_1A_1 + d_2A_2 + d_3A_3) = 0,$$

and

$$d_1A_1 + d_2A_2 + d_3A_3 = \begin{vmatrix} d_1 & b_1 & c_1 \\ d_2 & b_2 & c_2 \\ d_3 & b_3 & c_3 \end{vmatrix},$$

so that

$$x \begin{vmatrix} a_1 & b_1 & c_1 \\ a_2 & b_2 & c_2 \\ a_3 & b_3 & c_3 \end{vmatrix} + t \begin{vmatrix} d_1 & b_1 & c_1 \\ d_2 & b_2 & c_2 \\ d_3 & b_3 & c_3 \end{vmatrix} = 0.$$

If we multiply the equations by the cofactors B_1, B_2, and B_3 respectively, we obtain

$$y \begin{vmatrix} a_1 & b_1 & c_1 \\ a_2 & b_2 & c_2 \\ a_3 & b_3 & c_3 \end{vmatrix} + t \begin{vmatrix} a_1 & d_1 & c_1 \\ a_2 & d_2 & c_2 \\ a_3 & d_3 & c_3 \end{vmatrix} = 0.$$

Finally, if we multiply the equations by the cofactors C_1, C_2, and C_3 respectively, we find that

$$z \begin{vmatrix} a_1 & b_1 & c_1 \\ a_2 & b_2 & c_2 \\ a_3 & b_3 & c_3 \end{vmatrix} + t \begin{vmatrix} a_1 & b_1 & d_1 \\ a_2 & b_2 & d_2 \\ a_3 & b_3 & d_3 \end{vmatrix} = 0,$$

thus proving that our forecast made earlier in this section was correct.

If we have a set of *non*-homogeneous equations written in the form

$$\left.\begin{aligned} xa_1 + yb_1 + zc_1 &= d_1, \\ xa_2 + yb_2 + zc_2 &= d_2, \\ xa_3 + yb_3 + zc_3 &= d_3, \end{aligned}\right\} \tag{58}$$

and

$$\Delta = \begin{vmatrix} a_1 & b_1 & c_1 \\ a_2 & b_2 & c_2 \\ a_3 & b_3 & c_3 \end{vmatrix} \neq 0,$$

the application of the methods discussed shows that

$$x\Delta = \begin{vmatrix} d_1 & b_1 & c_1 \\ d_2 & b_2 & c_2 \\ d_3 & b_3 & c_3 \end{vmatrix},$$

$$y\Delta = \begin{vmatrix} a_1 & d_1 & c_1 \\ a_2 & d_2 & c_2 \\ a_3 & d_3 & c_3 \end{vmatrix}, \tag{59}$$

and

$$z\Delta = \begin{vmatrix} a_1 & b_1 & d_1 \\ a_2 & b_2 & d_2 \\ a_3 & b_3 & d_3 \end{vmatrix}.$$

These formulas are often referred to as *Cramer's rule*, and show that if $\Delta \neq 0$, the solution of the equations (58), if there is one, is unique. (See Exercises 17.3, No. 4)

Example 3

Using determinants, solve the equations

$$2x + 4y + z = 5,$$
$$x + y + z = 6,$$
$$2x + 3y + z = 6,$$

We first calculate the determinant

$$\Delta = \begin{vmatrix} 2 & 4 & 1 \\ 1 & 1 & 1 \\ 2 & 3 & 1 \end{vmatrix} = 2(1-3) - 4(1-2) + 1(3-2) = -4 + 4 + 1 = 1$$

and then the three determinants

$$\Delta_1 = \begin{vmatrix} 5 & 4 & 1 \\ 6 & 1 & 1 \\ 6 & 3 & 1 \end{vmatrix} = 5(1-3) - 4(6-6) + 1(18-6) = -10 + 0 + 12 = 2,$$

$$\Delta_2 = \begin{vmatrix} 2 & 5 & 1 \\ 1 & 6 & 1 \\ 2 & 6 & 1 \end{vmatrix} = 2(6-6) - 5(1-2) + 1(6-12) = 0 + 5 - 6 = -1,$$

and

$$\Delta_3 = \begin{vmatrix} 2 & 4 & 5 \\ 1 & 1 & 6 \\ 2 & 3 & 6 \end{vmatrix} \begin{aligned} &= 2(6 - 18) - 4(6 - 12) + 5(3 - 2) \\ &= -24 + 24 + 5 \\ &= 5, \end{aligned}$$

and $x = \Delta_1/\Delta = 2$, $y = \Delta_2/\Delta = -1$, $z = \Delta_3/\Delta = 5$.

EXERCISES 17.3

1. Use Cramer's rule to solve the equations

$$x + y + z = 6,$$
$$2x + 3y + z = 12,$$
$$-x + y - z = 0.$$

2. By writing the given determinant as the sum of eight determinants, each of which is zero, show that

$$\begin{vmatrix} al + a'l' & bl + b'l' & cl + c'l' \\ am + a'm' & bm + b'm' & cm + c'm' \\ an + a'n' & bn + b'n' & cn + c'n' \end{vmatrix} = 0.$$

3. By subtracting column 1 from columns 2 and 3, show that

$$\begin{vmatrix} 1 & 1 & 1 \\ a & b & c \\ a^2 & b^2 & c^2 \end{vmatrix} = \begin{vmatrix} 1 & 0 & 0 \\ a & b - a & c - a \\ a^2 & b^2 - a^2 & c^2 - a^2 \end{vmatrix}$$
$$= (b - a)(c^2 - a^2) - (c - a)(b^2 - a^2)$$
$$= (b - a)(c - a)(c - b).$$

4. By substitution in the original equations, show that the values of x, y, and z given by Cramer's rule, equations (59), do satisfy the original equations (58).

5. Show that

$$\Delta = \begin{vmatrix} a & b & c \\ b & c & a \\ c & a & b \end{vmatrix} = -a^3 - b^3 - c^3 + 3abc.$$

By adding ω (row 2) + ω^2 (row 3) to row 1, where ω is a complex cube root of unity ($\omega^3 = 1$, $\omega \neq 1$), show that $a + \omega b + \omega^2 c$ is a factor of Δ.

Taking $\omega = 1$, show that $a + b + c$ is a factor of Δ. Deduce that

$$-a^3 - b^3 - c^3 + 3abc$$
$$= k(a + b + c)(a + \omega b + \omega^2 c)(a + \omega^2 b + \omega c),$$

where $k = -1$.

18. Vanishing Determinants

The reader will undoubtedly have noticed that in our discussion of the solutions of equations (54) we tacitly assumed that not all the determinants of order 3 which arise in the determination of $x:t$, $y:t$, and $z:t$ are zero. We shall return to this soon, but in the meantime we show that *the vanishing determinant* is an important mathematical tool. We now prove Theorem 7.

Theorem 7. *A necessary and sufficient condition for the homogeneous equations*

$$xa_1 + yb_1 + zc_1 = xa_2 + yb_2 + zc_2 = xa_3 + yb_3 + zc_3 = 0$$

to have a common solution other than $x = y = z = 0$ *is*

$$\Delta = \begin{vmatrix} a_1 & b_1 & c_1 \\ a_2 & b_2 & c_2 \\ a_3 & b_3 & c_3 \end{vmatrix} = 0.$$

Proof. Any common solution also satisfies the equation

$$A_1(xa_1 + yb_1 + zc_1) + A_2(xa_2 + yb_2 + zc_2) + A_3(xa_3 + yb_3 + zc_3) = 0,$$

where A_1, A_2, A_3 are cofactors of a_1, a_2, a_3 respectively in Δ. Since $A_1a_1 + A_2a_2 + A_3a_3 = \Delta$,

but
$$A_1b_1 + A_2b_2 + A_3b_3 = A_1c_1 + A_2c_2 + A_3c_3 = 0,$$

we find that

$$\Delta x = 0.$$

Similarly, any common solution also satisfies

$$\Delta y = \Delta z = 0.$$

If $\Delta \neq 0$, we must have $x = y = z = 0$, so that the equations cannot have a non-trivial solution unless $\Delta = 0$. If the equations *do* have a non-trivial solution, we must have $\Delta = 0$. This condition is therefore *necessary*.

To show that the condition is *sufficient*, we must prove that if $\Delta = 0$, the equations do have a non-trivial solution, other than $x = y = z = 0$.

We know that in this case, since $\Delta = 0$,

$$A_1a_1 + B_1b_1 + C_1c_1 = \Delta = 0,$$

and $$A_1a_2 + B_1b_2 + C_1c_2 = 0 = A_1a_3 + B_1b_3 + C_1c_3,$$

so that (A_1, B_1, C_1) are solutions for (x, y, z), as are (A_2, B_2, C_2) and (A_3, B_3, C_3).

If at least one of $(A_i, B_i, C_i)\,(i = 1, 2, 3)$ is not $(0, 0, 0)$ we have a non-trivial solution.

If $A_1 = B_1 = C_1 = 0$, it follows that

$$b_2c_3 - b_3c_2 = a_2c_3 - a_3c_2 = a_2b_3 - a_3b_2 = 0,$$

so that $$\frac{a_2}{a_3} = \frac{b_2}{b_3} = \frac{c_2}{c_3},$$

and from $$A_2 = B_2 = C_2 = 0$$

we find that $$\frac{a_1}{a_3} = \frac{b_1}{b_3} = \frac{c_1}{c_3}.$$

Hence the equations are identical to each other, except for a multiplicative constant, (cf. the discussion on p. 18) so that we merely have to solve

$$xa_1 + yb_1 + zc_1 = 0$$

to find a common solution for all three equations.

If say, $a_1 \neq 0$, we take $y = \theta$, $z = \varphi$, and $x = -a_1^{-1}(b_1\theta + c_1\varphi)$, and we then have an infinity of solutions and certainly one non-trivial solution. If $a_1 = b_1 = c_1 = 0$, then any (x, y, z) satisfies the equations. This concludes the proof.

In applications, which are numerous, it is the necessity of the condition $\Delta = 0$ which is invoked most frequently.

We find the equation of the plane which passes through the three points (a_1, a_2, a_3), (b_1, b_2, b_3), and (c_1, c_2, c_3).

Let the equation, which we know to be linear in X_1, X_2, X_3 (§ 13) be:

$$p(X_1 - a_1) + q(X_2 - a_2) + r(X_3 - a_3) = 0.$$

Then $$p(b_1 - a_1) + q(b_2 - a_2) + r(b_3 - a_3) = 0,$$

and $$p(c_1 - a_1) + q(c_2 - a_2) + r(c_3 - a_3) = 0.$$

We now have three homogeneous equations in $p{:}q{:}r$, and since a plane does pass through three given points, for a given (X_1, X_2, X_3) in the plane there certainly exists a non-trivial solution. Hence, by the theorem just proved, we must have:

$$\begin{vmatrix} X_1 - a_1 & X_2 - a_2 & X_3 - a_3 \\ b_1 - a_1 & b_2 - a_2 & b_3 - a_3 \\ c_1 - a_1 & c_2 - a_2 & c_3 - a_3 \end{vmatrix} = 0, \tag{60}$$

and this, being a linear relation between X_1, X_2, and X_3, is the equation of the plane through the three points.

Again, let us find the equation to the plane which passes through the point (a_1, a_2, a_3) and contains lines which have direction-ratios $l_1:l_2:l_3$ and $m_1:m_2:m_3$ respectively.

Taking the equation of the plane once again as

$$p(X_1 - a_1) + q(X_2 - a_2) + r(X_3 - a_3) = 0,$$

we know that the direction-ratios of the normal to this plane are $p:q:r$ [§ 13, (41)]. We therefore have two relations which express that this normal is orthogonal to the two given lines, and these are

$$pl_1 + ql_2 + rl_3 = 0,$$

and $$pm_1 + qm_2 + rm_3 = 0.$$

Once again, we have three homogeneous equations in $p:q:r$ with a non-trivial solution, and therefore

$$\begin{vmatrix} X_1 - a_1 & X_2 - a_2 & X_3 - a_3 \\ l_1 & l_2 & l_3 \\ m_1 & m_2 & m_3 \end{vmatrix} = 0 \tag{61}$$

gives the equation of the plane.

EXERCISES 18

1. Show that the equation of the plane through the points $(a_1, 0, 0)$, $(0, a_2, 0)$, and $(0, 0, a_3)$ is

$$\begin{vmatrix} X_1 - a_1 & X_2 & X_3 \\ -a_1 & a_2 & 0 \\ -a_1 & 0 & a_3 \end{vmatrix} = 0,$$

that is: $X_1a_2a_3 + X_2a_1a_3 + X_3a_2a_1 - a_1a_2a_3 = 0.$

2. Show that the equation of the plane which contains the two parallel lines

$$\frac{X_1 - 3}{1} = \frac{X_2 - 2}{-4} = \frac{X_3 - 1}{5}; \quad \frac{X_1 - 2}{1} = \frac{X_2 + 3}{-4} = \frac{X_3 + 1}{5}$$

is

$$\begin{vmatrix} X_1 - 3 & X_2 - 2 & X_3 - 1 \\ 2 - 3 & -3 - 2 & -1 - 1 \\ 1 & -4 & 5 \end{vmatrix} = 0,$$

that is $$11X_1 - X_2 - 3X_3 - 28 = 0.$$

3. Show that the equation of the plane which passes through the line

$$\frac{X_1 - h_1}{l_1} = \frac{X_2 - h_2}{l_2} = \frac{X_3 - h_3}{l_3}$$

and the point (k_1, k_2, k_3) is

$$\begin{vmatrix} X_1 - h_1 & X_2 - h_2 & X_3 - h_3 \\ k_1 - h_1 & k_2 - h_2 & k_3 - h_3 \\ l_1 & l_2 & l_3 \end{vmatrix} = 0.$$

4. Show that the equations of the line through the point $(-6, -4, -6)$ which cuts each of the lines

$$\frac{X_1}{2} = \frac{X_2}{1} = \frac{X_3}{3}; \quad \frac{X_1 + 2}{-1} = \frac{X_2 - 1}{2} = \frac{X_3 + 1}{-1}$$

are

$$\begin{vmatrix} X_1 & X_2 & X_3 \\ 6 & 4 & 6 \\ 2 & 1 & 3 \end{vmatrix} = 0 = \begin{vmatrix} X_1 + 2 & X_2 - 1 & X_3 + 1 \\ -4 & -5 & -5 \\ -1 & 2 & -1 \end{vmatrix}$$

19. The Inner Product of Two Vectors

This concept, introduced for vectors in two dimensions (Chapter 1, § 8), generalizes immediately to vectors in three dimensions.

If $\mathbf{A} = [a_1, a_2, a_3]$ and $\mathbf{B} = [b_1, b_2, b_3]$ are two vectors in three dimensions, and θ is the angle between them, then since the direction-cosines of $\overrightarrow{OA}$ are

$$\frac{a_1}{|OA|}, \quad \frac{a_2}{|OA|}, \quad \frac{a_3}{|OA|},$$

and of $\overrightarrow{OB}$ are

$$\frac{b_1}{|OB|}, \quad \frac{b_2}{|OB|}, \quad \frac{b_3}{|OB|},$$

the cosine-formula of § 10, equation (34) gives us

$$\cos\theta = \frac{a_1b_1 + a_2b_2 + a_3b_3}{|OA|\,|OB|}.$$

We may also write this in the form

$$|\mathbf{A}|\,|\mathbf{B}|\cos\theta = a_1b_1 + a_2b_2 + a_3b_3. \tag{62}$$

We define the *inner-* (or *dot*) *product* of **A** and **B** by the symbol (**A**, **B**), where

$$(\mathbf{A}, \mathbf{B}) = |\mathbf{A}|\,|\mathbf{B}|\cos\theta = a_1b_1 + a_2b_2 + a_3b_3. \tag{63}$$

When **A** = **B**, this leads to

$$(\mathbf{A}, \mathbf{A}) = \|\mathbf{A}\|^2 = a_1^2 + a_2^2 + a_3^2, \tag{64}$$

so that we can write the *modulus*, or *length*, of a vector **A** in terms of an inner product,

$$\|\mathbf{A}\| = (\mathbf{A}, \mathbf{A})^{1/2}.$$

From the definition, we have the following properties:

(i) $(\mathbf{A}, \mathbf{B}) = (\mathbf{B}, \mathbf{A})$,

(ii) $k(\mathbf{A}, \mathbf{B}) = (k\mathbf{A}, \mathbf{B})$,

(iii) $(\mathbf{A} + \mathbf{B}, \mathbf{C}) = (\mathbf{A}, \mathbf{C}) + (\mathbf{B}, \mathbf{C})$,

exactly as in two dimensions.

Example I

From $X(X_1, X_2, X_3)$ a perpendicular is drawn to meet, at N, a line through the origin with direction-cosines

$$\cos\theta_1, \cos\theta_2, \cos\theta_3.$$

Show that

$$ON = X_1\cos\theta_1 + X_2\cos\theta_2 + X_3\cos\theta_3.$$

If $\mathbf{e}_1 = [1, 0, 0]$, $\mathbf{e}_2 = [0, 1, 0]$, $\mathbf{e}_3 = [0, 0, 1]$,

then

$$\mathbf{X} = X_1\mathbf{e}_1 + X_2\mathbf{e}_2 + X_3\mathbf{e}_3.$$

The vector

$$\mathbf{Y} = [\cos\theta_1, \cos\theta_2, \cos\theta_3]$$

has unit modulus, and

$$(\mathbf{X}, \mathbf{Y}) = \|\mathbf{X}\|\,\|\mathbf{Y}\|\cos\theta = ON.$$

Hence $$\begin{aligned} ON &= (X_1\mathbf{e}_1 + X_2\mathbf{e}_2 + X_3\mathbf{e}_3, \mathbf{Y}) \\ &= X_1(\mathbf{e}_1, \mathbf{Y}) + X_2(\mathbf{e}_2, \mathbf{Y}) + X_3(\mathbf{e}_3, \mathbf{Y}) \\ &= X_1 \cos \theta_1 + X_2 \cos \theta_2 + X_3 \cos \theta_3, \end{aligned}$$

by the definition of direction-cosines.

Example 2

Two edges, AB, CD of a tetrahedron $ABCD$ are perpendicular. Prove that the distance between the midpoints of AC and BD is equal to the distance between the midpoints of AD and BC.*

If the vertices are given by the vectors **A**, **B**, **C**, and **D** respectively, we are told that

$$(\mathbf{B} - \mathbf{A}, \mathbf{D} - \mathbf{C}) = 0,$$

since AB is parallel to $\mathbf{B} - \mathbf{A}$, and CD is parallel to $\mathbf{D} - \mathbf{C}$.

The midpoints of AC and BD are, respectively,

$$\tfrac{1}{2}(\mathbf{A} + \mathbf{C}), \qquad \tfrac{1}{2}(\mathbf{B} + \mathbf{D}),$$

and the square of the distance between them is p^2, where

$$p^2 = (\tfrac{1}{2}(\mathbf{A} + \mathbf{C}) - \tfrac{1}{2}(\mathbf{B} + \mathbf{D}), \tfrac{1}{2}(\mathbf{A} + \mathbf{C}) - \tfrac{1}{2}(\mathbf{B} + \mathbf{D})),$$

so that

$$\begin{aligned} 4p^2 &= (\mathbf{A} - \mathbf{B} + \mathbf{C} - \mathbf{D}, \mathbf{C} - \mathbf{D} + \mathbf{A} - \mathbf{B}) \\ &= (\mathbf{A} - \mathbf{B}, \mathbf{A} - \mathbf{B}) + (\mathbf{C} - \mathbf{D}, \mathbf{C} - \mathbf{D}), \end{aligned}$$

since, by the foregoing condition, $(\mathbf{A} - \mathbf{B}, \mathbf{C} - \mathbf{D}) = 0$.

Again, the square of the distance between the midpoints of AD and BC is q^2, where

$$\begin{aligned} 4q^2 &= ((\mathbf{A} + \mathbf{D}) - (\mathbf{B} + \mathbf{C}), (\mathbf{A} + \mathbf{D}) - (\mathbf{B} + \mathbf{C})) \\ &= (\mathbf{A} - \mathbf{B} + \mathbf{D} - \mathbf{C}, \mathbf{A} - \mathbf{B} + \mathbf{D} - \mathbf{C}) \\ &= (\mathbf{A} - \mathbf{B}, \mathbf{A} - \mathbf{B}) + (\mathbf{D} - \mathbf{C}, \mathbf{D} - \mathbf{C}) \\ &= (\mathbf{A} - \mathbf{B}, \mathbf{A} - \mathbf{B}) + (\mathbf{C} - \mathbf{D}, \mathbf{C} - \mathbf{D}), \end{aligned}$$

since once more, $(\mathbf{A} - \mathbf{B}, \mathbf{D} - \mathbf{C}) = 0$, and therefore $p^2 = q^2$.

We may use the inner product to obtain the formula for the perpendicular from a point $H = (h_1, h_2, h_3)$ on to the plane

$$a_1X_1 + a_2X_2 + a_3X_3 + a_4 = 0.$$

The normal to the plane has direction-ratios $a_1{:}a_2{:}a_3$, and we set $\mathbf{A} = [a_1, a_2, a_3]$. Then if N is the foot of the perpendicular from H on to the plane, and $X = (X_1, X_2, X_3)$ is any point in the plane, $\overrightarrow{HX}$ is equal to

* The method given is not the shortest for solving this problem. See Exercise 5, p. 90.

the vector $\mathbf{X} - \mathbf{H}$, and therefore

$$\pm(\mathbf{X} - \mathbf{H}, \mathbf{A}) = |HN| \cdot \|\mathbf{A}\|,$$

so that

$$|HN| = \mp \frac{(\mathbf{X} - \mathbf{H}, \mathbf{A})}{\sqrt{a_1^2 + a_2^2 + a_3^2}}.$$

The numerator of this fraction is

$$\begin{aligned}\pm(\mathbf{X} - \mathbf{H}, \mathbf{A}) &= \pm(\mathbf{X}, \mathbf{A}) \mp (\mathbf{H}, \mathbf{A}) \\ &= \pm\{(X_1 - h_1)a_1 + (X_2 - h_2)a_2 + (X_3 - h_3)a_3\}.\end{aligned}$$

Since (X_1, X_2, X_3) is in the given plane,

$$X_1a_1 + X_2a_2 + X_3a_3 = -a_4,$$

so that finally

$$\text{perpendicular} = |HN| = \mp \frac{(a_1h_1 + a_2h_2 + a_3h_3 + a_4)}{\sqrt{a_1^2 + a_2^2 + a_3^2}}.$$

EXERCISES 19

1. Show that if, in the foregoing proof, $\overrightarrow{HN}$ is in the same direction as the normal $\mathbf{A} = [a_1, a_2, a_3]$ to the plane, then $a_1h_1 + a_2h_2 + a_3h_3 + a_4$ is negative, so that we must accept the minus sign in the formula for $|HN|$.

2. $ABCD$ is a tetrahedron in which AB is perpendicular to CD, and AC is perpendicular to BD. Prove that AD is perpendicular to BC.

3. If AB and CD are two skew (non-intersecting) lines, such as the opposite edges of a tetrahedron $ABCD$, show that there is a unique pair of parallel planes which pass, respectively, through AB and CD, these being parallel to the unique plane through any assigned point O which contains lines parallel to AB and to CD.

4. If $ABCD$ is a tetrahedron, consider Fig. 19 (called a parallelepiped) obtained by drawing the unique pairs of parallel planes through the pairs

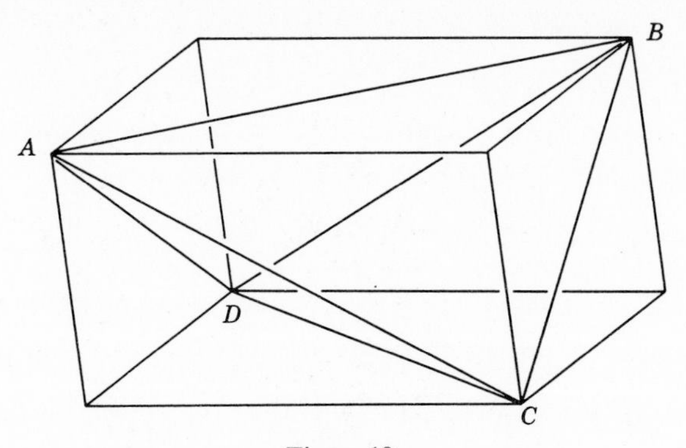

Figure 19

of opposite edges AB and CD, AD and BC, and AC and BD. Show that the pairs of opposite faces of the parallelepiped are parallelograms, with the opposite edges of the tetrahedron as diagonals. If AB is perpendicular to CD, show that one pair of opposite faces are rhombuses.

5. Show in Exercise 4, that a side of such a rhombus is equal to the distance between the midpoints of AC and BD, and also to the distance between the midpoints of AD and BC. Deduce the result of Example 2.

6. If AB is perpendicular to CD and also AC is perpendicular to BD, show that all the edges of the escribed parallelepiped are equal, and deduce the result of Exercise 2, that AD is also perpendicular to BC.

CHAPTER FIVE

Linear Equations With a Unique Solution

We have already seen that the question of the linear dependence of vectors is bound up with the possibility of solving sets of linear equations. In this chapter and the next two we shall consider methods for solving sets of linear equations, and we shall find ourselves considering vectors again, matrices, the manipulation of matrices, and other topics of linear algebra. The geometric preparation of the first three chapters will help us to interpret both methods and results.

20. Regular Systems of Linear Equations

Two planes in three dimensions which are not in a special relation to each other intersect in a line. This line will intersect a third plane in one point if it is not parallel to it and does not lie in it. Thus the common intersection of three planes in three dimensions is a point if the planes are not in a special relation to each other.

Interpreted algebraically, we can say that when they are considered as simultaneous equations, three linear equations in X_1, X_2, X_3 have a unique solution if they are not in a special relation to each other. These are the systems of equations we wish to consider.

We now introduce the double-suffix notation, and write the equations we are considering in the form

$$\left.\begin{aligned} a_{11}X_1 + a_{12}X_2 + a_{13}X_3 &= k_1, \\ a_{21}X_1 + a_{22}X_2 + a_{23}X_3 &= k_2, \\ a_{31}X_1 + a_{32}X_2 + a_{33}X_3 &= k_3. \end{aligned}\right\} \qquad (65)$$

We may write these equations in vector notation if we write $\mathbf{a}_1 = [a_{11}, a_{21}, a_{31}]$, $\mathbf{a}_2 = [a_{12}, a_{22}, a_{32}]$, $\mathbf{a}_3 = [a_{13}, a_{23}, a_{33}]$, and $\mathbf{k} = [k_1, k_2, k_3]$.

Then the three equations are simply (writing the scalar multiples X_1, X_2, and X_3 on the *right*)

$$\mathbf{a}_1 X_1 + \mathbf{a}_2 X_2 + \mathbf{a}_3 X_3 = \mathbf{k}, \tag{66}$$

but since it will be important later to distinguish between a set of numbers such as $[a_{11}, a_{12}, a_{13}]$, which we call a *row* vector, and a set such as

$$\begin{bmatrix} a_{11} \\ a_{21} \\ a_{31} \end{bmatrix},$$

which we call a *column* vector, we take the $\mathbf{a}_1$, $\mathbf{a}_2$, $\mathbf{a}_3$, and $\mathbf{k}$ defined previously as column vectors and write

$$\mathbf{a}_1 = [a_{11}, a_{21}, a_{31}]^T,\ \mathbf{a}_2 = [a_{12}, a_{22}, a_{32}]^T,\ \mathbf{a}_3 = [a_{13}, a_{23}, a_{33}]^T,$$
$$\mathbf{k} = [k_1, k_2, k_3]^T,$$

where the index T, standing for "transpose," indicates that the row vector is to be regarded as a column vector.

If we consider the equation

$$\mathbf{a}_1 X_1 + \mathbf{a}_2 X_2 + \mathbf{a}_3 X_3 = \mathbf{0},$$

this is equivalent to the three equations obtained from (65) by putting $k_1 = k_2 = k_3 = 0$. These equations are the equations of planes through the origin parallel to the respective planes given by equations (65). These three planes through the origin may determine, by the kind of mutual intersection they have, what kind of intersection the three original planes have. This is intuitive geometrically, and motivates the algebraic treatment. We express this algebraically in a precise way by saying that if the three homogeneous equations derived from (65) by writing $k_1 = k_2 = k_3 = 0$ have only the trivial solution $X_1 = X_2 = X_3 = 0$, the three equations given by (65) have a unique solution.

Example I

The equations

$$[2, 1, 2]^T X_1 + [4, 1, 3]^T X_2 + [1, 1, 1]^T X_3 = [5, 6, 6]^T$$

have the unique solution $(2, -1, 5)$, as we found by using determinants in § 17. The determinant

$$\begin{vmatrix} 2 & 4 & 1 \\ 1 & 1 & 1 \\ 2 & 3 & 1 \end{vmatrix}$$

is not zero, and the homogeneous equations derived from the foregoing equation have only the trivial solution, as Theorem 7, § 18 indicates.

But we shall not be using determinants in developing this theory. We prefer to note that the *columns* of the determinant just considered, regarded as vectors, *are linearly independent*. This is equivalent to the statement that the equation

$$[2, 1, 2]^T X_1 + [4, 1, 3]^T X_2 + [1, 1, 1]^T X_3 = \mathbf{0}$$

has only the trivial solution $X_1 = X_2 = X_3 = 0$.

We solve the given equations

$$\left.\begin{aligned} u_1 &\equiv 2X_1 + 4X_2 + X_3 - 5 = 0,\\ u_2 &\equiv X_1 + X_2 + X_3 - 6 = 0,\\ u_3 &\equiv 2X_1 + 3X_2 + X_3 - 6 = 0,\end{aligned}\right\}$$

this time by applying a succession of so-called "elementary" operations to them (cf. § 7, Theorem 2, p. 31) which modifies the set of equations without affecting the solutions, and finally we are able to read off the solutions. These operations are as follows:

I. Writing the equations in a different order.
II. Multiplying an equation by a non-zero scalar.
III. Adding a multiple of one equation to another equation of the system.

The proof that these operations do not affect the solutions has already been indicated (§ 7, Theorem 2, third proof), and it will be given after this example has been worked.

Interchange u_1 and u_2, subtract $2u_2$ from u_1, and then subtract $2u_2$ from u_3. This gives us

$$\left.\begin{aligned} u_2 &\equiv X_1 + X_2 + X_3 - 6 = 0,\\ u_1 - 2u_2 &\equiv \phantom{X_1 + {}} 2X_2 - X_3 + 7 = 0,\\ u_3 - 2u_2 &\equiv \phantom{X_1 + {}} X_2 - X_3 + 6 = 0.\end{aligned}\right\}$$

Now interchange the second and third equation, and then subtract 2 (new second equation) from the new third equation. We now have

$$\left.\begin{aligned} u_2 &\equiv X_1 + X_2 + X_3 - 6 = 0,\\ u_3 - 2u_2 &\equiv \phantom{X_1 + {}} X_2 - X_3 + 6 = 0,\\ u_1 - 2u_2 - 2(u_3 - 2u_2) &= \phantom{X_1 + X_2 - {}} X_3 - 5 = 0,\end{aligned}\right\}$$

and we have finished, because, reading from the bottom upward we have $X_3 = 5$, and substituting in the second equation gives $X_2 = X_3 - 6 = -1$, and substitution in the first equation gives $X_1 = -X_2 - X_3 + 6 = 2$, so that our solution is $(2, -1, 5)$.

We see that only the *coefficients* in these equations are significant in finding a solution, and we could have worked equally well with the array, or *matrix*

$$\left[\begin{array}{ccc|c} 2 & 4 & 1 & 5 \\ 1 & 1 & 1 & 6 \\ 2 & 3 & 1 & 6 \end{array}\right],$$

the vertical dividing line indicating where the sign of equality occurs. The successive operations would then look like this:

$$\left[\begin{array}{ccc|c} 2 & 4 & 1 & +5 \\ 1 & 1 & 1 & +6 \\ 2 & 3 & 1 & +6 \end{array}\right] \to \left[\begin{array}{ccc|c} 1 & 1 & 1 & +6 \\ 2 & 4 & 1 & +5 \\ 2 & 3 & 1 & +6 \end{array}\right] \to \left[\begin{array}{ccc|c} 1 & 1 & 1 & +6 \\ 0 & 2 & -1 & -7 \\ 0 & 1 & -1 & -6 \end{array}\right]$$

$$\to \left[\begin{array}{ccc|c} 1 & 1 & 1 & +6 \\ 0 & 1 & -1 & -6 \\ 0 & 2 & -1 & -7 \end{array}\right] \to \left[\begin{array}{ccc|c} 1 & 1 & 1 & +6 \\ 0 & 1 & -1 & -6 \\ 0 & 0 & 1 & +5 \end{array}\right].$$

We shall see that this final form of the matrix of coefficients, with 1's along the diagonal going downward from the upper left-hand corner to the bottom right-hand corner (called the *principal* diagonal), and zeros everywhere below this diagonal, is characteristic of the equations we are investigating—those with a unique solution. This form of a square matrix is called a *triangular form*.

Before proceeding to the general theory, let us look at a set of equations which do *not* have a unique solution.

Example 2

We consider the set

$$\left.\begin{aligned} 2X_1 + 4X_2 + X_3 &= 1, \\ 3X_1 + 5X_2 \qquad &= 1, \\ 5X_1 + 13X_2 + 7X_3 &= 4 \end{aligned}\right\}$$

which we write

$$\left[\begin{array}{ccc|c} 2 & 4 & 1 & 1 \\ 3 & 5 & 0 & 1 \\ 5 & 13 & 7 & 4 \end{array}\right] \begin{array}{l} = \mathbf{R}_1 \\ = \mathbf{R}_2 \\ = \mathbf{R}_3 \end{array}$$

with $\mathbf{R}_1$, $\mathbf{R}_2$, $\mathbf{R}_3$ expressing the array of numbers in the respective rows. Then

$$\left[\begin{array}{ccc|c} 1 & 2 & \frac{1}{2} & \frac{1}{2} \\ 3 & 5 & 0 & 1 \\ 5 & 13 & 7 & 4 \end{array}\right] \begin{array}{l} = \dfrac{\mathbf{R}_1}{2} \\ = \mathbf{R}_2 \\ = \mathbf{R}_3 \end{array}$$

$$\to \left[\begin{array}{ccc|c} 1 & 2 & \frac{1}{2} & \frac{1}{2} \\ 0 & -1 & -\frac{3}{2} & -\frac{1}{2} \\ 0 & 3 & \frac{9}{2} & \frac{3}{2} \end{array}\right] \begin{array}{l} = \dfrac{\mathbf{R}_1}{2} \\ = \mathbf{R}_2 - \dfrac{3\mathbf{R}_1}{2} \\ = \mathbf{R}_3 - \dfrac{5\mathbf{R}_1}{2} \end{array}$$

$$\to \left[\begin{array}{ccc|c} 1 & 2 & \frac{1}{2} & \frac{1}{2} \\ 0 & 1 & \frac{3}{2} & \frac{1}{2} \\ 0 & 3 & \frac{9}{2} & \frac{3}{2} \end{array}\right] \begin{array}{l} = \dfrac{\mathbf{R}_1}{2} \\ = -\mathbf{R}_2 + \dfrac{3\mathbf{R}_1}{2} \\ = \mathbf{R}_3 - \dfrac{5\mathbf{R}_1}{2} \end{array}$$

$$\to \left[\begin{array}{ccc|c} 1 & 2 & \frac{1}{2} & \frac{1}{2} \\ 0 & 1 & \frac{3}{2} & \frac{1}{2} \\ 0 & 0 & 0 & 0 \end{array}\right] \begin{array}{l} = \dfrac{\mathbf{R}_1}{2} \\ = -\mathbf{R}_2 + \dfrac{3\mathbf{R}_1}{2} \\ = \mathbf{R}_3 - \dfrac{5\mathbf{R}_1}{2} - 3\left(-\mathbf{R}_2 + \dfrac{3\mathbf{R}_1}{2}\right). \end{array}$$

If we try to solve this final set of equations, one is missing, and the solution is reduced to that of two equations and is not unique, since X_3 is not uniquely determined as it was in the previous example. We may put $X_3 = \theta$ (a variable parameter), and then $X_2 = (-3X_2 + 1)/2 = (-3\theta + 1)/2$, and $X_1 = -2X_2 - (X_3 - 1)/2$ gives X_1 in terms of θ also.

In fact we are finding a variable point on the line of intersection of two planes, and this point is $((5\theta - 1)/2, (-3\theta + 1)/2, \theta)$.

The line of zeros in the third row of the final matrix shows that

$$\mathbf{R}_3 - \frac{5\mathbf{R}_1}{2} - 3\left(-\mathbf{R}_2 + \frac{3\mathbf{R}_1}{2}\right) = \mathbf{0},$$

so that

$$\mathbf{R}_3 = 7\mathbf{R}_1 - 3\mathbf{R}_2,$$

which is verified immediately, since

$$5X_1 + 13X_2 + 7X_3 - 4 \equiv 7(2X_1 + 4X_2 + X_3 - 1) - 3(3X_1 + 5X_2 - 1).$$

Hence, in the matrix we were considering, *the third row, considered as a vector*, is *linearly dependent* on the other two, and in this case the equations do *not* have a unique solution.

Example 3

There are sets of equations which have no solution. Consider the set

$$\begin{aligned} u_1 &\equiv 2X_1 + 4X_2 + X_3 \quad - 1 = 0, \\ u_2 &\equiv 3X_1 + 5X_2 \qquad\quad - 1 = 0, \\ u_3 &\equiv 5X_1 + 13X_2 + 7X_3 - 5 = 0, \end{aligned}$$

obtained from those considered in Example 2 by a slight modification. If we carry out the reduction to triangular form performed in the last example we have:

$$\left[\begin{array}{ccc|c} 2 & 4 & 1 & 1 \\ 3 & 5 & 0 & 1 \\ 5 & 13 & 7 & 5 \end{array}\right] \to \left[\begin{array}{ccc|c} 1 & 2 & 1/2 & 1/2 \\ 3 & 5 & 0 & 1 \\ 5 & 13 & 7 & 5 \end{array}\right] \to \left[\begin{array}{ccc|c} 1 & 2 & 1/2 & 1/2 \\ 0 & -1 & -3/2 & -1/2 \\ 0 & 3 & 9/2 & 5/2 \end{array}\right]$$

$$\to \left[\begin{array}{ccc|c} 1 & 2 & 1/2 & 1/2 \\ 0 & 1 & 3/2 & 1/2 \\ 0 & 0 & 0 & 1 \end{array}\right]$$

and the last row of the last matrix gives us the equation

$$0 \cdot X_1 + 0 \cdot X_2 + 0 \cdot X_3 = 1.$$

This is the same kind of paradox as the one discovered when we considered the intersection of two lines in the plane (§ 5, p. 18), and is based on the erroneous assumption that the three equations considered do have a

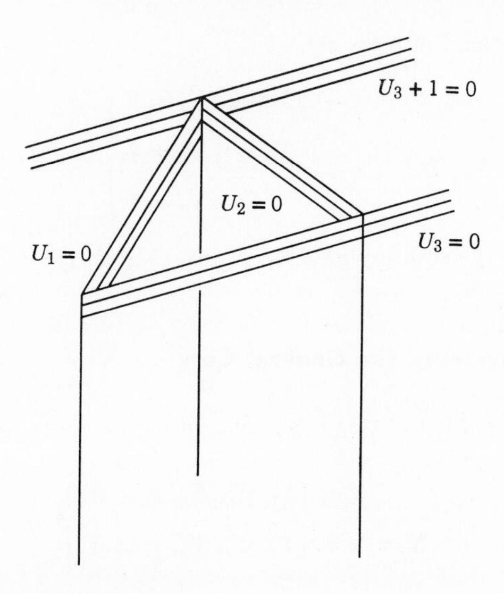

solution. We see, in fact, that

$$5X_1 + 13X_2 + 7X_3 - 5 \equiv 7(2X_1 + 4X_2 + X_3 - 1) - 3(3X_1 + 5X_2 - 1) - 1,$$

which may be written as

$$u_3 + 1 \equiv 7u_1 - 3u_2.$$

Interpreted geometrically, the right-hand side of this identity represents, when equated to zero, a plane through the line of intersection of the two planes $u_1 = 0$ and $u_2 = 0$, whereas the left-hand side of the identity represents, when equated to zero, a plane *parallel* to that given by $u_3 = 0$. The three planes $u_1 = 0$, $u_2 = 0$, and $u_3 = 0$ therefore represent the faces of a *triangular prism*. The planes, taken in pairs, intersect in lines which are parallel, but do not all lie in one plane, and the three planes have no common finite point of intersection.

We are now prepared for the general case of regular linear systems of equations, which we consider in the next section.

EXERCISE 20

1. Show that the set of equations

$$\left.\begin{aligned} X_1 + 5X_2 + 2X_3 &= 9, \\ X_1 + X_2 + 7X_3 &= 6, \\ -3X_2 + 4X_3 &= -2, \end{aligned}\right\}$$

can be transformed into the set

$$\left.\begin{aligned} X_1 + 5X_2 + 2X_3 &= 9, \\ X_2 - \tfrac{5}{4}X_3 &= \tfrac{3}{4}, \\ \tfrac{1}{4}X_3 &= \tfrac{1}{4}, \end{aligned}\right\}$$

which leads to the solution $(X_1, X_2, X_3) = (-3, 2, 1)$.

21. Regular Systems, the General Case

We are now ready to extend the concept of vectors to an ordered set of n numbers:

$$\mathbf{X} = [X_1, X_2, X_3, \ldots, X_n],$$

where

$$\mathbf{X} = \mathbf{Y} = [Y_1, Y_2, Y_3, \ldots, Y_n]$$

if and only if

$$X_i = Y_i \qquad (i = 1, 2, \ldots, n).$$

The operations on these *n-dimensional vectors* (as we may call them) follow the pattern set by those in two and three dimensions. We define

$$\mathbf{X} + \mathbf{Y} = [X_1 + Y_1, X_2 + Y_2, \ldots, X_n + Y_n],$$

and

$$k\mathbf{X} = [kX_1, kX_2, \ldots, kX_n].$$

These n-dimensional vectors obey the laws

(i) $$\mathbf{X} + \mathbf{Y} = \mathbf{Y} + \mathbf{X},$$

(ii) $$(\mathbf{X} + \mathbf{Y}) + \mathbf{Z} = \mathbf{X} + (\mathbf{Y} + \mathbf{Z}),$$

(iii) $$(st)\mathbf{X} = s(t\mathbf{X}),$$

(iv) $$(s + t)\mathbf{X} = s\mathbf{X} + t\mathbf{X},$$

(v) $$s(\mathbf{X} + \mathbf{Y}) = s\mathbf{X} + s\mathbf{Y},$$

(vi) $$1 \cdot \mathbf{X} = \mathbf{X},$$

as in the two and three-dimensional case, and the verification is as simple.

A set of n-dimensional vectors $\mathbf{X}_1, \mathbf{X}_2, \ldots, \mathbf{X}_m$ is said to be *linearly dependent* if numbers $a_1, a_2, \ldots, a_m$, not all zero, exist such that

$$a_1\mathbf{X}_1 + a_2\mathbf{X}_2 + \cdots + a_m\mathbf{X}_m = \mathbf{0},$$

where $\mathbf{0}$ is the zero vector $[0, 0, \ldots, 0]$.

We note once more that any set of vectors containing the zero vector is necessarily linearly dependent, since

$$0 \cdot \mathbf{X}_1 + 0 \cdot \mathbf{X}_2 + \cdots + 0 \cdot \mathbf{X}_m + 1 \cdot \mathbf{0} = \mathbf{0}.$$

If $\mathbf{X}_1, \mathbf{X}_2, \ldots, \mathbf{X}_m$ are not dependent, they are said to be *linearly independent.*

We apply these generalized concepts to the study of the solutions of n linear equations in n unknowns. Let the equations be

$$\left.\begin{aligned} a_{11}X_1 + a_{12}X_2 + \cdots + a_{1n}X_n &= k_1, \\ a_{21}X_1 + a_{22}X_2 + \cdots + a_{2n}X_n &= k_2, \\ \cdot \qquad \cdot \qquad \cdots \qquad \cdot \quad &\quad \cdot \\ a_{n1}X_1 + a_{n2}X_2 + \cdots + a_{nn}X_n &= k_n. \end{aligned}\right\} \tag{67}$$

Once again, we introduce column-vectors

$$\mathbf{a}_j = \begin{bmatrix} a_{1j} \\ a_{2j} \\ \cdot \\ \cdot \\ \cdot \\ a_{nj} \end{bmatrix} = [a_{1j}, a_{2j}, \ldots, a_{nj}]^T,$$

$$\mathbf{k} = [k_1, k_2, \ldots, k_n]^T,$$

using the notation for the transpose of a row-vector, and the equations may be written

$$[a_{11}, a_{21}, \ldots, a_{n1}]^T X_1 + [a_{12}, a_{22}, \ldots, a_{n2}]^T X_2 + \cdots [a_{1n}, a_{2n}, \ldots, a_{nn}]^T X_n = \mathbf{k},$$

that is, in the simple form

$$\mathbf{a}_1 X_1 + \mathbf{a}_2 X_2 + \cdots + \mathbf{a}_n X_n = \mathbf{k}. \tag{68}$$

To solve the equations (68) for $(X_1, X_2, \ldots, X_n)$ is to determine the possible ways of expressing $\mathbf{k}$ as a linear combination of the vectors $\mathbf{a}_1, \mathbf{a}_2, \ldots, \mathbf{a}_n$. We are interested, in this section, in an important special case, when the vectors $\mathbf{a}_1, \mathbf{a}_2, \ldots, \mathbf{a}_n$ are *linearly independent.* The system of n equations in n unknowns given by (68) is then called a *regular system of order n.* We wish to prove Theorem 8.

Theorem 8. *A regular system of equations has exactly one solution.*

The definition of regularity just given involves only the coefficients a_{ij} on the left-hand side of equations (67), and not the numbers $k_1, k_2, \ldots, k_n$ on the right-hand side. Again, to say that $\mathbf{a}_1, \mathbf{a}_2, \ldots, \mathbf{a}_n$ are linearly independent means that there is no non-trivial linear relation between them. This means that the equations

$$\mathbf{a}_1 X_1 + \mathbf{a}_2 X_2 + \cdots + \mathbf{a}_n X_n = \mathbf{0}$$

have only the trivial solution $(0, 0, \ldots, 0)$. We may therefore state Theorem 8 in another form:

Theorem 8*. *If* $\mathbf{a}_1, \mathbf{a}_2, \ldots, \mathbf{a}_n$ *are any n vectors (of dimension n) such that*

$$\mathbf{a}_1 X_1 + \mathbf{a}_2 X_2 + \cdots + \mathbf{a}_n X_n = \mathbf{0}$$

has only the trivial solution $(X_1, X_2, \ldots, X_n) = (0, 0, \ldots, 0)$, *then the system*

$$\mathbf{a}_1 X_1 + \mathbf{a}_2 X_2 + \cdots + \mathbf{a}_n X_2 = \mathbf{k}$$

has, for any vector $\mathbf{k}$, *just one solution* $(X_1, X_2, \ldots, X_n)$.

The proof of this theorem follows a pattern which, by now, should be familiar to the reader. We show that the traditional process of eliminating the variables one by one can be carried out. This process consists in adding multiples of one equation to another. We must show that this modification of the system of equations does not affect the solutions.

We modify the system of equations by carrying out a succession of the following "elementary" operations:

I. Writing the same equations in a different order.
II. Multiplying an equation by a non-zero scalar.
III. Adding a multiple of one equation to another equation of the system.

We now show that these operations, applied to *any* system of linear equations (not only to a regular system) produces an *equivalent* set of linear equations, in the sense that *both systems contain the same number of equations* and have the same solutions.*

This is clear for the operation I, since it amounts to renumbering the equations. To show that operations II and III produce equivalent systems, we write

$$g_i(X) = a_{i1}X_1 + a_{i2}X_2 + \cdots + a_{in}X_n - k_i \qquad (i = 1, 2, \ldots, n).$$

If X' is a solution of the original equations (67), then

$$g_1(X') = g_2(X') = \cdots = g_n(X') = 0. \tag{69}$$

Now apply operation II, say by multiplying the first equation by $\lambda \neq 0$. Then

$$\lambda g_1(X') = g_2(X') = \cdots = g_n(X') = 0, \tag{70}$$

* One, or more of the equations may be of the form $0 = 0$.

which shows that X' satisfies the new equations. Conversely, if equations (70) hold, then since $\lambda \neq 0$ we may divide the first equation by λ and return to equations (69), so that every solution of the new system also satisfies the original system.

Finally, if equations (69) are valid, and we apply operation III, say, by replacing the left-hand side of the first equation by $g_1(X) + \mu g_2(X)$, then by equations (69) we have,

$$g_1(X') + \mu g_2(X') = g_2(X') = \cdots = g_n(X') = 0, \tag{71}$$

and conversely when equations (71) hold, we can return to equations (69) by subtracting $\mu g_2(X)$ from $g_1(X) + \mu g_2(X)$.

Similar reasoning applies when the operations involve equations other than the first and the second. Since the number of equations remains unchanged, the application of the elementary operations I, II, and III produces an equivalent system of equations.

Since we have not used the fact that the system is one of n equations in n unknowns, we can state the result as Theorem 9.

Theorem 9. *The elementary operations I, II, and III described previously, when applied to any system of m linear equations in n unknowns, produce an equivalent system of m linear equations in n unknowns.*

One final result is needed before we actually start on the elimination of the variables. This we state as Theorem 10.

Theorem 10. *The elementary operations I, II, and III described previously, when applied to any regular system of n linear equations in n unknowns, produce an equivalent regular system of n linear equations in n unknowns.*

The proof is immediate, since to say that the original system is regular is to say that the equations only have the trivial solution when $\mathbf{k} = \mathbf{0}$ in equations (68). But on applying the operations I, II, and III to this system, we again have 0 on the right-hand side of the equations, and since the new system is equivalent to the old, the new system has again only the trivial solution. Applying the operations I, II, and III to the equations (68) therefore produces a regular system of equations.

We now begin on the process of using the elementary operations I, II, and III to transform the system of equations

$$\left.\begin{array}{l} a_{11}X_1 + a_{12}X_2 + \cdots + a_{1n}X_n = k_1, \\ a_{21}X_1 + a_{22}X_2 + \cdots + a_{2n}X_n = k_2, \\ \cdot \quad \cdot \quad \cdots \quad \cdot \quad \cdot \\ a_{n1}X_1 + a_{n2}X_2 + \cdots + a_{nn}X_n = k_n \end{array}\right\} \tag{67}$$

into a triangular form, which will enable us to prove Theorem 8.

Suppose the equations are numbered so that $a_{11} \neq 0$ (using operation I). This is possible provided that the first column of coefficients contains a non-zero element. This is always the case, for if not, the first column-vector would be the zero vector, and the columns of the system would be linearly dependent (any set of vectors which contains the zero vector is linearly dependent [see beginning of this section]). We are assuming, however, that the column-vectors of the system are linearly *independent*.

Hence we may suppose that $a_{11} \neq 0$. We can transform the coefficient of X_1 in the first equation by multiplying that equation by a_{11}^{-1} (operation II). The coefficient of X_1 in the first equation is now 1.

If we now subtract a_{i1} (first equation) from the ith equation, for $i = 2, 3, \ldots, n$ (operation III), we obtain a system of equations in which X_1 occurs with the coefficient 1 in the first equation and with the coefficient 0 in the remaining ones. Thus the new and equivalent system looks like this:

$$\left.\begin{aligned} X_1 + b_{12}X_2 + \cdots + b_{1n}X_n &= l_1, \\ b_{22}X_2 + \cdots + b_{2n}X_n &= l_2, \\ \cdot \quad \cdots \quad \cdot \quad &\quad \cdot \\ b_{n2}X_2 + \cdots + b_{nn}X_n &= l_n, \end{aligned}\right\} \tag{72}$$

where the b_{ij} and the l_i are easily determined if necessary. But we are interested in the fact that X_1 has been eliminated from all equations except the first, that the new system is equivalent to the original system, since only operations I, II, and III have been used, and the new system is still regular, by Theorems 9 and 10.

We now look at the equations

$$\left.\begin{aligned} b_{22}X_2 + \cdots + b_{2n}X_n &= l_2, \\ b_{32}X_2 + \cdots + b_{3n}X_n &= l_3, \\ \cdot \quad \cdots \quad \cdot \quad &\quad \cdot \\ b_{n2}X_2 + \cdots + b_{nn}X_n &= l_n, \end{aligned}\right\} \tag{73}$$

which constitute the 2nd, 3rd, ..., nth equation of the set given by (72). This is a set of $(n - 1)$ linear equations in $(n - 1)$ unknowns, $X_2, X_3, \ldots, X_n$. We now prove that *this* set is a set of regular equations.

To do this, we must show that when we replace $l_2, l_3, \ldots, l_n$ by 0 in (73), the equations have only the trivial solution. Suppose they were *not* regular, and had the solution

$$X_2 = u_2, X_3 = u_3, \ldots, X_n = u_n,$$

where at least one of $u_2, u_3, \ldots, u_n$ is not zero. Then we can solve the whole set of equations (72) in which $l_1 = 0$ and $l_2 = l_3 = \cdots = l_n = 0$ by taking

$$X_1 = u_1 = -(b_{12}u_2 + b_{13}u_3 + \cdots + b_{1n}u_n),$$

for this solution satisfies the first equation, and the others are already satisfied, by hypothesis. Furthermore, this solution

$$X_1 = u_1,\ X_2 = u_2, \ldots, X_n = u_n$$

is non-trivial because at least one of $u_2, u_3, \ldots, u_n$ is not zero. We now have a contradiction, because the system given by (72) is regular and has only the trivial solution if we replace $l_1, l_2, \ldots, l_n$ by 0 on the right-hand side.

The set of $(n - 1)$ equations in $(n - 1)$ unknowns given by (73) has been shown to be regular. With this set of equations, we repeat the procedure described above, noting that the operations I, II, and III applied to the equations of the set (73) can be regarded as applying to the set (72), *with no change in the first equation of this set*. Hence at the second stage of the reduction we have a set of equations

$$\left.\begin{aligned} X_1 + b_{12}X_2 + b_{13}X_3 + \cdots + b_{1n}X_n &= l_1, \\ X_2 + c_{23}X_3 + \cdots + c_{2n}X_n &= m_2, \\ c_{33}X_3 + \cdots + c_{3n}X_n &= m_3, \\ \cdot \quad \cdots \quad \cdot \quad &\quad \cdot \\ c_{n3}X_3 + \cdots + c_{nn}X_n &= m_n, \end{aligned}\right\} \qquad (74)$$

where the whole set (74) is equivalent to the original set (67), and the set given by

$$\left.\begin{aligned} c_{33}X_3 + \cdots + c_{3n}X_n &= m_3, \\ \cdot \quad \cdots \quad \cdot \quad &\quad \cdot \\ c_{n3}X_3 + \cdots + c_{nn}X_n &= m_n, \end{aligned}\right\} \qquad (75)$$

is still regular.

Continuing in this way, we eventually end up with the set of equations

$$\left.\begin{aligned} X_1 + b_{12}X_2 + b_{13}X_3 + \cdots + b_{1,n-1}X_{n-1} + b_{1n}X_n &= l_1, \\ X_2 + c_{23}X_3 + \cdots + c_{2,n-1}X_{n-1} + c_{2n}X_n &= m_2, \\ X_3 + \cdots + d_{3,n-1}X_{n-1} + d_{3n}X_n &= p_3, \\ \cdot \quad \cdots \quad \cdot \quad \cdot \quad &\quad \cdot \\ X_{n-1} + d_{n-1,n}X_n &= p_{n-1}, \\ X_n &= p_n, \end{aligned}\right\} \qquad (76)$$

and these have the same solutions as the original equations (67).

Equations (76) can easily be solved, however, and the solution is unique. We begin at the bottom, and find that $X_n = p_n$. Substituting in the equation just above, we have

$$X_{n-1} = -d_{n-1,n}p_n + p_{n-1},$$

and moving upward, we find $X_{n-2}, X_{n-3}, \ldots, X_2$, and finally X_1. This completes the proof of Theorem 8 and also gives us a speedy method for solving linear equations which are regular. We shall confirm this statement by working another example.

Example I

Solve the equations

$$\begin{aligned} X_1 - 2X_2 - 3X_3 + X_4 &= 7, \\ -X_1 + 3X_2 + 5X_3 - X_4 &= -9, \\ 2X_1 + X_2 - X_3 + 3X_4 &= 18, \\ 3X_1 - X_2 + X_3 + 4X_4 &= 15. \end{aligned}$$

We operate with the matrix

$$\left[\begin{array}{cccc|c} 1 & -2 & -3 & 1 & 7 \\ -1 & 3 & 5 & -1 & -9 \\ 2 & 1 & -1 & 3 & 18 \\ 3 & -1 & 1 & 4 & 15 \end{array}\right]$$

the vertical line between columns 4 and 5 indicating where the = sign comes in. We already have the a_{11} term = 1 (coefficient of X_1 in the first equation), so that we can proceed to eliminate the remaining terms in the first column. We have

$$\left[\begin{array}{cccc|c} 1 & -2 & -3 & 1 & 7 \\ -1 & 3 & 5 & -1 & -9 \\ 2 & 1 & -1 & 3 & 18 \\ 3 & -1 & 1 & 4 & 15 \end{array}\right] \to \left[\begin{array}{cccc|c} 1 & -2 & -3 & 1 & 7 \\ 0 & 1 & 2 & 0 & -2 \\ 0 & 5 & 5 & 1 & 4 \\ 0 & 5 & 10 & 1 & -6 \end{array}\right] \begin{array}{l} \mathbf{R}_1 \\ \mathbf{R}_2 + \mathbf{R}_1 \\ \mathbf{R}_3 - 2\mathbf{R}_1 \\ \mathbf{R}_4 - 3\mathbf{R}_1 \end{array}$$

We now begin again with this second matrix and call the rows, beginning with the second, $\mathbf{R}_2{}^*$, $\mathbf{R}_3{}^*$, and $\mathbf{R}_4{}^*$, Then $\mathbf{R}_2{}^*$ is ready for action, with unity as the coefficient of X_2. We therefore eliminate X_2 from the third and fourth equations:

$$\begin{bmatrix} 1 & -2 & -3 & 1 & \vert & 7 \\ 0 & 1 & 2 & 0 & \vert & -2 \\ 0 & 5 & 5 & 1 & \vert & 4 \\ 0 & 5 & 10 & 1 & \vert & -6 \end{bmatrix} \rightarrow \begin{bmatrix} 1 & 2 & -3 & 1 & \vert & 7 \\ 0 & 1 & 2 & 0 & \vert & -2 \\ 0 & 0 & -5 & 1 & \vert & 14 \\ 0 & 0 & 0 & 1 & \vert & 4 \end{bmatrix} \begin{matrix} \\ \\ \mathbf{R}_3{}^* - 5\mathbf{R}_2{}^* \\ \mathbf{R}_4{}^* - 5\mathbf{R}_2{}^* \end{matrix}$$

and we have finished, the final matrix being in triangular form in one less operation than we expected. Starting from the bottom $X_4 = 4$, then moving up, $-5X_3 + X_4 = 14$, (there was no point in dividing this row by 5). Hence $X_3 = -2$, and $X_2 + 2X_3 = -2$, so that $X_2 = 2$, and finally $X_1 + 2X_2 - 3X_3 + X_4 = 7$ gives us $X_1 = 1$, and the unique solution of these equations is $(1, 2, -2, 4)$.

EXERCISES 21

1. Find the unique solution of the equations

$$\begin{aligned} 2X_1 + X_2 + 2X_3 - X_4 &= 0, \\ 6X_1 + 8X_2 + 12X_3 - 13X_4 &= -21, \\ 10X_1 + 2X_2 + 2X_3 + 3X_4 &= 21, \\ -4X_1 + X_3 - 3X_4 &= -13. \end{aligned}$$

2. Show that the triangular system of equations

$$\begin{aligned} a_{11}X_1 + a_{12}X_2 + a_{13}X_3 + \cdots + a_{1n}X_n &= k_1, \\ a_{22}X_2 + a_{23}X_3 + \cdots + a_{2n}X_n &= k_2, \\ a_{33}X_3 + \cdots + a_{3n}X_n &= k_3, \\ \cdot \quad \cdot \quad \cdot \quad \cdots \quad \cdot \quad & \cdot \\ a_{nn}X_n &= k_n, \end{aligned}$$

is regular if, and only if, all the diagonal coefficients $a_{11}, a_{22}, a_{33}, \ldots, a_{nn}$ are different from zero.

22. Deductions from the Theorems on Regular Systems

The worked Example 2 of § 20 indicates that there may be a connection between the independence or dependence of the rows of a matrix, considered as vectors, and the independence or dependence of the columns, considered as vectors. This connection will be discussed very fully in a later chapter (Chapter 7, § 31). Here we observe that if one *row*, say the last row, of the matrix of coefficients of n linear equations in n unknowns consists of zeros, the system cannot be regular, which means that the *columns* cannot be linearly independent. To be specific, let the system be once more

$$\left.\begin{aligned} a_{11}X_1 + a_{12}X_2 + \cdots + a_{1n}X_n &= k_1, \\ a_{21}X_1 + a_{22}X_2 + \cdots + a_{2n}X_n &= k_2, \\ \cdot \qquad \cdot \qquad \cdots \qquad \cdot \quad &\quad \cdot \\ a_{n1}X_1 + a_{n2}X_2 + \cdots + a_{nn}X_n &= k_n, \end{aligned}\right\} \tag{67}$$

and suppose that

$$a_{n1} = a_{n2} = \cdots = a_{nn} = 0.$$

Then the *row*-vectors of the matrix of coefficients, that is,

$$\mathbf{R}_i = [a_{i1}, a_{i2}, \ldots, a_{in}] \qquad (i = 1, \ldots, n)$$

are dependent, since $\mathbf{R}_n$ is the zero-vector. We show that in this case the *column*-vectors

$$\mathbf{a}_i = [a_{1i}, a_{2i}, \ldots, a_{ni}]^T \qquad (i = 1, \ldots, n)$$

are also linearly dependent.

This follows from the fact that a regular system, in which the columns are independent, has a unique solution for *any* values of $k_1, k_2, \ldots, k_n$, the constants on the right of equations (67). But if $a_{n1} = a_{n2} = \cdots = a_{nn} = 0$, the equations (67) have no solution unless $k_n = 0$ also.

Hence the n vectors

$$\mathbf{a}_1 = [a_{11}, a_{21}, \ldots, a_{n-1,1}, 0]^T, \ldots, \mathbf{a}_n = [a_{1n}, a_{2n}, \ldots, a_{n-1,n}, 0]^T$$

cannot be linearly independent, and therefore are dependent. We formulate this as Theorem 11.

Theorem 11. *If n vectors of dimension n have their last component equal to zero, they are linearly dependent.*

We can now deduce the important Theorem 12.

Theorem 12. *Any $n + 1$ vectors of dimension n are linearly dependent.*

We had intimations of this theorem in Theorems 2 and 6 of § 7 and § 16 respectively.

Proof. Let $\mathbf{u}_i = [u_{i1}, u_{i2}, \ldots, u_{in}] \qquad (i = 1, \ldots, n + 1)$ be the $n + 1$ vectors of dimension n. We extend the dimension of each vector and write

$$\mathbf{u}_i^* = [u_{i1}, u_{i2}, \ldots, u_{in}, 0] \qquad (i = 1, \ldots, n + 1).$$

We now have $n + 1$ vectors of dimension $n + 1$, and the last component of each is 0, so by Theorem 11 (with $n + 1$ substituted for n), the $\mathbf{u}_i^*$ are *dependent*; that is, constants $\lambda_1, \lambda_2, \ldots, \lambda_{n+1}$, not all zero, exist such that

$$\lambda_1\mathbf{u}_1^* + \lambda_2\mathbf{u}_2^* + \cdots + \lambda_{n+1}\mathbf{u}_{n+1}^* = \mathbf{0}.$$

If we restrict our consideration to the first n entries in each vector $\mathbf{u}_i^*$, this leads us to

$$\lambda_1 u_{1i} + \lambda_2 u_{2i} + \cdots + \lambda_{n+1} u_{n+1,i} = 0 \qquad (i = 1, \ldots, n),$$

which is equivalent to

$$\lambda_1\mathbf{u}_1 + \lambda_2\mathbf{u}_2 + \cdots + \lambda_{n+1}\mathbf{u}_{n+1} = \mathbf{0},$$

so that the $n + 1$ original vectors of dimension n are linearly dependent.

Theorem 12, Corollary. *A set of n homogeneous equations in n + 1 unknowns always has a non-trivial solution.*

Proof. Let the equations be

$$\begin{aligned} a_{11}X_1 + a_{12}X_2 + \cdots + a_{1,n+1}X_{n+1} &= 0, \\ a_{21}X_1 + a_{22}X_2 + \cdots + a_{2,n+1}X_{n+1} &= 0, \\ \cdot \qquad \cdot \qquad \cdots \qquad \cdot \qquad & \quad \cdot \\ a_{n1}X_1 + a_{n2}X_2 + \cdots + a_{n,n+1}X_{n+1} &= 0. \end{aligned}$$

Then these equations have a non-trivial solution if the equation

$$\mathbf{a}_1X_1 + \mathbf{a}_2X_2 + \cdots + \mathbf{a}_{n+1}X_{n+1} = \mathbf{0}$$

is satisfied by values of $X_1, X_2, \ldots, X_{n+1}$ not all zero, where $\mathbf{a}_1, \mathbf{a}_2, \ldots, \mathbf{a}_{n+1}$ are the column-vectors given by the matrix of coefficients of the equations. But the fact that such values of $X_1, X_2, \ldots, X_{n+1}$ exist is precisely the content of Theorem 12.

We introduced vectors

$$\mathbf{e}_1 = [1, 0, 0], \qquad \mathbf{e}_2 = [0, 1, 0], \qquad \mathbf{e}_3 = [0, 0, 1]$$

into space of three dimensions, noted that these vectors are linearly independent, and that any vector $\mathbf{X} = [X_1, X_2, X_3]$ is expressible as a sum of linear multiples of these vectors:

$$\mathbf{X} = X_1\mathbf{e}_1 + X_2\mathbf{e}_2 + X_3\mathbf{e}_3.$$

This notion generalizes immediately to the space of n-dimensional vectors, since we may write

$$\mathbf{e}_1 = [1, 0, \ldots, 0], \qquad \mathbf{e}_2 = [0, 1, \ldots, 0], \cdots, \mathbf{e}_n = [0, 0, \ldots, 1],$$

where it is clear that we can only have

$$\lambda_1\mathbf{e}_1 + \lambda_2\mathbf{e}_2 + \cdots + \lambda_n\mathbf{e}_n = \mathbf{0}$$

if $\lambda_1 = \lambda_2 = \cdots = \lambda_n = 0$, so that $\mathbf{e}_1, \mathbf{e}_2, \ldots, \mathbf{e}_n$ are linearly independent, and $\mathbf{X} = [X_1, X_2, \ldots, X_n]$ can be written in the form

$$\mathbf{X} = X_1\mathbf{e}_1 + X_2\mathbf{e}_2 + \cdots + X_n\mathbf{e}_n.$$

We say that $\mathbf{X}$ is *linearly dependent* on the set $\mathbf{e}_1, \ldots, \mathbf{e}_n$. Of course, since the foregoing equation can be written in the form

$$-\mathbf{X} + X_1\mathbf{e}_1 + X_2\mathbf{e}_2 + \cdots + X_n\mathbf{e}_n = \mathbf{0},$$

the set consisting of $\mathbf{X}$ and $\mathbf{e}_1, \mathbf{e}_2, \ldots, \mathbf{e}_n$ is a dependent set; but we are able to express $\mathbf{X}$ linearly in terms of $\mathbf{e}_1, \mathbf{e}_2, \ldots, \mathbf{e}_n$ because the scalar multiplying $\mathbf{X}$ is not zero. If $\mathbf{X}, \mathbf{X}_1, \ldots, \mathbf{X}_m$ is a set of linearly dependent vectors, so that

$$\lambda\mathbf{X} + \lambda_1\mathbf{X}_1 + \cdots + \lambda_m\mathbf{X}_m = \mathbf{0},$$

we can only assert that $\mathbf{X}$ can be expressed as a sum of linear multiples of $\mathbf{X}_1, \ldots, \mathbf{X}_m$ if $\lambda \neq 0$. Hence the statement that $\mathbf{X}$ is linearly dependent on $\mathbf{e}_1, \ldots, \mathbf{e}_n$ is a stronger statement than "the set consisting of $\mathbf{X}$ and $\mathbf{e}_1, \ldots, \mathbf{e}_n$ is a dependent set." We now give a definition.

Definition. *If $\mathbf{Y}_1, \mathbf{Y}_2, \ldots, \mathbf{Y}_m$ are linearly independent n-dimensional vectors such that any n-dimensional vector $\mathbf{X}$ is linearly dependent on $\mathbf{Y}_1, \mathbf{Y}_2, \ldots, \mathbf{Y}_m$, then the set $\mathbf{Y}_1, \mathbf{Y}_2, \ldots, \mathbf{Y}_m$ is said to form a* BASIS *for n-dimensional vectors.*

We can now prove Theorem 13.

Theorem 13. *Any n linearly independent n-dimensional vectors form a basis for all n-dimensional vectors.*

Proof. Let $\mathbf{Y}_1, \mathbf{Y}_2, \ldots, \mathbf{Y}_n$ be any given set of linearly independent n-dimensional vectors, and let $\mathbf{X}$ be any n-dimensional vector. By Theorem 12, the set of $n + 1$ vectors $\mathbf{Y}_1, \mathbf{Y}_2, \ldots, \mathbf{Y}_n, \mathbf{X}$ is a linearly dependent set, and there is therefore a relation

$$\lambda\mathbf{X} + \lambda_1\mathbf{Y}_1 + \lambda_2\mathbf{Y}_2 + \cdots + \lambda_n\mathbf{Y}_n = \mathbf{0}$$

in which not all of the coefficients $\lambda, \lambda_1, \lambda_2, \ldots, \lambda_n$ are zero. Now, we cannot have $\lambda = 0$, since then not all of $\lambda_1, \lambda_2, \ldots, \lambda_n$ are zero, and the vectors $\mathbf{Y}_1, \mathbf{Y}_2, \ldots, \mathbf{Y}_n$ would be linearly *dependent*, contrary to hypothesis. Hence $\lambda \neq 0$, and we can write

$$\mathbf{X} = \mu_1\mathbf{Y}_1 + \mu_2\mathbf{Y}_2 + \cdots + \mu_n\mathbf{Y}_n,$$

where $\mu_i = -\lambda_i\lambda^{-1}$ $(i = 1, \ldots, n)$. This proves the theorem.

Example I

We show that for three-dimensional vectors the vectors $\mathbf{Y}_1 = [1, 1, 1]$ $\mathbf{Y}_2 = [1, 2, 0]$, and $\mathbf{Y}_3 = [1, 1, -1]$ form a basis.

First, we check the linear independence of the three vectors. If they were dependent, we should be able to find λ, μ, ν, not all zero, such that

$$\lambda \mathbf{Y}_1 + \mu \mathbf{Y}_2 + \nu \mathbf{Y}_3 = \mathbf{0}.$$

This equation involves the three equations

$$\begin{aligned} \lambda + \mu + \nu &= 0, \\ \lambda + 2\mu + \nu &= 0, \\ \lambda \qquad - \nu &= 0, \end{aligned}$$

and these have only the trivial solution, since the determinant

$$\begin{vmatrix} 1 & 1 & 1 \\ 1 & 2 & 1 \\ 1 & 0 & -1 \end{vmatrix} = -2 \neq 0,$$

(Theorem 7, § 18, p. 83).

To show the linear dependence of any vector $\mathbf{X} = [X_1, X_2, X_3]$ on $\mathbf{Y}_1$, $\mathbf{Y}_2$, $\mathbf{Y}_3$, we wish to find λ_1, λ_2, λ_3 such that

$$\mathbf{X} = \lambda_1 \mathbf{Y}_1 + \lambda_2 \mathbf{Y}_2 + \lambda_3 \mathbf{Y}_3,$$

which involves the three-equations

$$\begin{aligned} X_1 &= \lambda_1 + \lambda_2 + \lambda_3, \\ X_2 &= \lambda_1 + 2\lambda_2 + \lambda_3, \\ X_3 &= \lambda_1 \qquad - \lambda_3, \end{aligned}$$

and we can solve these equations by Cramer's rule, or by reduction to diagonal form, which gives us

$$\begin{aligned} \lambda_1 + \lambda_2 + \lambda_3 &= X_1, \\ \lambda_2 \qquad &= X_2 - X_1, \\ -\lambda_2 - 2\lambda_3 &= X_3 - X_1, \end{aligned}$$

at the first stage. This is sufficient, and we do not need to complete the process, since we see that:

$$\lambda_2 = X_2 - X_1, \qquad \lambda_3 = \tfrac{1}{2}(X_1 - X_3 - \lambda_2) = \tfrac{1}{2}(2X_1 - X_2 - X_3),$$

$$\lambda_1 = X_1 - \lambda_2 - \lambda_3 = \tfrac{1}{2}(2X_1 - X_2 + X_3),$$

so that

$$\mathbf{X} = \tfrac{1}{2}(2X_1 - X_2 + X_3)\mathbf{Y}_1 + (X_2 - X_1)\mathbf{Y}_2 + \tfrac{1}{2}(2X_1 - X_2 - X_3)\mathbf{Y}_3.$$

EXERCISES 22

1. Determine a value of k that makes the following three vectors linearly dependent:

$$\mathbf{Y}_1 = [1, 2, k], \qquad \mathbf{Y}_2 = [0, 1, k-1], \qquad \mathbf{Y}_3 = [3, 4, 3].$$

When $k = 2$, show that the vectors are independent, and express the vector $\mathbf{X} = [7, 13, 11]$ in terms of them.

2. Determine whether or not the following vectors are linearly independent. If not, express $\mathbf{Y}_3$ as a linear combination of $\mathbf{Y}_1$ and $\mathbf{Y}_2$.

$$\mathbf{Y}_1 = [1, 2, -1], \qquad \mathbf{Y}_2 = [2, 1, 4], \qquad \mathbf{Y}_3 = [-1, 7, -17].$$

23. The Notion of a Basis

Our generalization of the concept of a vector in space of two and three dimensions has led to the definition of a vector as $\mathbf{X} = [X_1, X_2, \ldots, X_n]$, a mathematical entity defined by an ordered set of n numbers, or components, with certain rules for identification, addition, and scalar multiplication But we have not talked, except vaguely, of the *space* of these vectors.

We shall be more precise in the next section and extend the notion of vector, but here we continue to think of vectors as being merely ordered sets of n numbers. Suppose that we have a set of vectors, all of the same dimension, and we know that there exists a basis $\mathbf{Y}_1, \mathbf{Y}_2, \ldots, \mathbf{Y}_n$ in this set for the whole collection of vectors. Then any vector $\mathbf{X}$ of the set can be expressed linearly in terms of the basis, say, as

$$\mathbf{X} = a_1\mathbf{Y}_1 + a_2\mathbf{Y}_2 + \cdots + a_n\mathbf{Y}_n.$$

We have the simple, but important theorem 14.

Theorem 14. *The expression of a vector in terms of a given basis is unique.*

Proof. If $\mathbf{X} = a_1\mathbf{Y}_1 + a_2\mathbf{Y}_2 + \cdots + a_n\mathbf{Y}_n,$

and $\mathbf{X} = b_1\mathbf{Y}_1 + b_2\mathbf{Y}_2 + \cdots + b_n\mathbf{Y}_n$

are two expressions for $\mathbf{X}$ in terms of the basis, then

$$\mathbf{X} = a_1\mathbf{Y}_1 + a_2\mathbf{Y}_2 + \cdots + a_n\mathbf{Y}_n = b_1\mathbf{Y}_1 + b_2\mathbf{Y}_2 + \cdots + b_n\mathbf{Y}_n.$$

Hence

$$(a_1 - b_1)\mathbf{Y}_1 + (a_2 - b_2)\mathbf{Y}_2 + \cdots + (a_n - b_n)\mathbf{Y}_n = \mathbf{0},$$

and since the $\mathbf{Y}_i$ are linearly independent, we have

$$a_i = b_i \qquad (i = 1, 2, \ldots, n).$$

The expression for $\mathbf{X}$ in terms of the given basis is therefore unique.

We can therefore regard a basis as determining a *coordinate system* for the vectors of the set we are considering. Any vector $\mathbf{X}$ determines the ordered set of numbers $[a_1, a_2, \ldots, a_n]$, given by

$$\mathbf{X} = a_1\mathbf{Y}_1 + a_2\mathbf{Y}_2 + \cdots + a_n\mathbf{Y}_n,$$

in a unique manner. If

$$\mathbf{Z} = c_1\mathbf{Y}_1 + c_2\mathbf{Y}_2 + \cdots + c_n\mathbf{Y}_n$$

is any other vector of the set, and we suppose that the set contains both $k\mathbf{X}$ and $\mathbf{X} + \mathbf{Z}$, then since

$$k\mathbf{X} = (ka_1)\mathbf{Y}_1 + (ka_2)\mathbf{Y}_2 + \cdots + (ka_n)\mathbf{Y}_n,$$

and

$$\mathbf{X} + \mathbf{Z} = (a_1 + c_1)\mathbf{Y}_1 + (a_2 + c_2)\mathbf{Y}_2 + \cdots + (a_n + c_n)\mathbf{Y}_n,$$

we see that our collection of vectors behaves exactly like the vectors defined as

$$\mathbf{X}^* = [a_1, a_2, \ldots, a_n],$$

with $\quad k\mathbf{X}^* = [ka_1, ka_2, \ldots, ka_n],$

where if $\quad \mathbf{Z}^* = [c_1, c_2, \ldots, c_n],$

we define $\quad \mathbf{X}^* + \mathbf{Z}^* = [a_1 + c_1, a_2 + c_2, \ldots, a_n + c_n].$

If the set also contains the zero vector $\mathbf{0}$ (this is included in the previous hypothesis by taking $\mathbf{Z} = -\mathbf{X}$), we note that the expression for $\mathbf{0}$ in terms of the basis is

$$\mathbf{0} = 0 \cdot \mathbf{Y}_1 + 0 \cdot \mathbf{Y}_2 + \cdots + 0 \cdot \mathbf{Y}_n,$$

and this is again unique, since the $\mathbf{Y}_1, \mathbf{Y}_2, \ldots, \mathbf{Y}_n$ are linearly independent. Hence the zero vector behaves in its set in the same way that the vector

$$\mathbf{0}^* = [0, 0, \ldots, 0]$$

behaves in the set of vectors

$$\mathbf{X}^* = [a_1, a_2, \ldots, a_n].$$

Every vector

$$\mathbf{X} = a_1\mathbf{Y}_1 + a_2\mathbf{Y}_2 + \cdots + a_n\mathbf{Y}_n$$

determines the vector

$$\mathbf{X}^* = [a_1, a_2, \ldots, a_n]$$

uniquely, and conversely every vector $\mathbf{X}^*$ determines the vector $\mathbf{X}$ uniquely. Such a correspondence, or mapping, is called a *one-to-one* correspondence. With the laws of operation for vectors under which we operate, the vectors of the set containing $\mathbf{X}$ behave exactly like the vectors $\mathbf{X}^*$ defined by n ordered entries, that is, like n-dimensional vectors.

We say that two sets of vectors are *isomorphic* when their algebraic structure is identical (a more precise definition will be given later in § 24, p. 117], and we have proved Theorem 15.

Theorem 15. *A collection (set) of vectors which contains a basis consisting of n vectors and also contains, together with any vectors* $\mathbf{X}$ *and* $\mathbf{Z}$, *the vectors* $k\mathbf{X}$ ($k = 0$ *is included) and* $\mathbf{X} + \mathbf{Z}$, *is isomorphic to the set of all n-dimensional vectors.*

We note in particular that linear dependence in one set implies linear dependence in the other. Therefore if $\mathbf{X}_1^*, \mathbf{X}_2^*, \ldots, \mathbf{X}_r^*$ are linearly dependent, which implies a relation

$$\lambda_1\mathbf{X}_1^* + \lambda_2\mathbf{X}_2^* + \cdots + \lambda_r\mathbf{X}_r^* = \mathbf{0},^*$$

with not all the $\lambda_i = 0$, we also have the relation

$$\lambda_1\mathbf{X}_1 + \lambda_2\mathbf{X}_2 + \cdots + \lambda_r\mathbf{X}_r = \mathbf{0}$$

in the original set of vectors.

We now want to prove that if our given set of vectors has another basis, consisting of the vectors $\mathbf{U}_1, \mathbf{U}_2, \ldots, \mathbf{U}_m$, then we must have $m = n$.

By the theorem we have just proved, the vectors in our set behave like n-dimensional vectors. Hence, by Theorem 12, § 22, p. 106 any $n + 1$ of them are linearly dependent. Therefore, if $m > n$, the vectors $\mathbf{U}_1, \mathbf{U}_2, \ldots, \mathbf{U}_{n+1}$ are linearly dependent, which is impossible, since this means that there exist $\lambda_1, \lambda_2, \ldots, \lambda_{n+1}$, not all zero, such that

$$\lambda_1\mathbf{U}_1 + \lambda_2\mathbf{U}_2 + \cdots + \lambda_{n+1}\mathbf{U}_{n+1} = \mathbf{0},$$

and we can write this as

$$\lambda_1\mathbf{U}_1 + \lambda_2\mathbf{U}_2 + \cdots + \lambda_{n+1}\mathbf{U}_{n+1} + 0 \cdot \mathbf{U}_{n+2} + \cdots + 0 \cdot \mathbf{U}_m = \mathbf{0},$$

which implies that the set $\mathbf{U}_1, \ldots, \mathbf{U}_m$ is dependent, contrary to hypothesis.

Hence $m \leqslant n$. Interchanging the roles played by m and n, we can prove in an exactly similar manner that $n \leqslant m$, and therefore $m = n$, and we have proved Theorem 16.

Theorem 16. *The number of elements in a basis is uniquely determined.*

We know that

$$\mathbf{e}_1 = [1, 0, \ldots, 0], \quad \mathbf{e}_2 = [0, 1, \ldots, 0], \ldots, \mathbf{e}_n = [0, 0, \ldots, 1]$$

is a basis for the set of vectors $\mathbf{X} = [X_1, X_2, \ldots, X_n]$, and since we would like to talk of the *dimension* of a set of vectors as *the unique number of elements in a basis for the set*, it is comforting that we can associate the dimension n with the vectors we have been calling n-dimensional vectors.

CHAPTER SIX

Vector Spaces

24. Vectors and Vector Spaces

We now become slightly more formal, and talk of *vector spaces*. These are merely sets of vectors for which certain rules of combination are applicable. It is useful to have a symbol which is shorthand for the phrase "is an element of", and we use the symbol $\in$ for this purpose, so that

$$\mathbf{X} \in V$$

is read:

$$\mathbf{X} \textit{ is an element of the set } V.$$

Suppose now that $\mathbf{X}, \mathbf{Y}, \ldots$ are elements of a set V, that for any two elements in the set an operation of addition is defined, denoted by $+$, and that a scalar multiplication of elements of V by elements of the field of real numbers (which we call R) is defined, and denoted by $r\mathbf{X}$, where $r \in R$, $\mathbf{X} \in V$.

Definition. *The set V is called a* VECTOR SPACE OVER THE FIELD R OF REAL NUMBERS, *or a* REAL VECTOR SPACE, *if the following conditions are satisfied* (there are two sets):

1. If $\mathbf{X}, \mathbf{Y} \in V$, then $\mathbf{X} + \mathbf{Y} \in V$.
2. If $\mathbf{X}, \mathbf{Y}, \mathbf{Z} \in V$, then

$$(\mathbf{X} + \mathbf{Y}) + \mathbf{Z} = \mathbf{X} + (\mathbf{Y} + \mathbf{Z}).$$

3. There is a vector $\mathbf{0} \in V$ such that

$$\mathbf{0} + \mathbf{X} = \mathbf{X} + \mathbf{0} = \mathbf{X}, \quad \text{for all} \quad \mathbf{X} \in V.$$

4. For every $\mathbf{X} \in V$ there is a vector $-\mathbf{X} \in V$ such that

$$\mathbf{X} + (-\mathbf{X}) = (-\mathbf{X}) + (\mathbf{X}) = \mathbf{0}.$$

5. For vectors $\mathbf{X}, \mathbf{Y} \in V$,

$$\mathbf{X} + \mathbf{Y} = \mathbf{Y} + \mathbf{X}.$$

These conditions may be summarized by the statement: *the vectors* $\mathbf{X} \in V$ *form an Abelian group under the operation of addition.*

The second set of conditions involve the operation of scalar multiplication.

1* If $\mathbf{X} \in V$, and $r \in R$ (the field of real numbers), then

$$r\mathbf{X} \in V.$$

2* If $\mathbf{X} \in V$, $r, s, \in R$, then

$$(rs)\mathbf{X} = r(s\mathbf{X}).$$

3* If $\mathbf{X} \in V$, $r, s \in R$, then

$$(r + s)\mathbf{X} = r\mathbf{X} + s\mathbf{X}.$$

4* If $\mathbf{X}, \mathbf{Y} \in V$, $r \in R$, then

$$r(\mathbf{X} + \mathbf{Y}) = r\mathbf{X} + r\mathbf{Y}.$$

5* For all $\mathbf{X} \in V$, $\quad 1 \cdot \mathbf{X} = \mathbf{X}$.

These operations should be very familiar to the reader by now, and they show that, by this definition, the vectors

$$\mathbf{X} = [X_1, X_2, \ldots, X_n]$$

consisting of ordered n-tuples of real numbers, where addition is defined by

$$\mathbf{X} + \mathbf{Y} = [X_1 + Y_1, X_2 + Y_2, \ldots, X_n + Y_n],$$

and scalar multiplication by

$$r\mathbf{X} = [rX_1, rX_2, \ldots, rX_n],$$

form a vector space over R. We shall give this vector space a name and call it $V_n(R)$

There are other vector spaces over R, however, which is the reason for setting out the conditions to be fulfilled in a formal manner.

Example I

Consider the set of all polynomials in x:

$$\mathbf{X} = p_0 + p_1x + p_2x^2 + \cdots + p_{n-1}x^{n-1}$$

with real coefficients, of degree $\leqslant n - 1$. If

$$\mathbf{Y} = q_0 + q_1x + q_2x^2 + \cdots + q_{n-1}x^{n-1},$$

we define addition in the usual way:

$$\mathbf{X} + \mathbf{Y} = (p_0 + q_0) + (p_1 + q_1)x + \cdots + (p_{n-1} + q_{n-1})x^{n-1},$$

and scalar multiplication as

$$r\mathbf{X} = rp_0 + rp_1x + \cdots + rp_{n-1}x^{n-1}.$$

The zero polynomial is

$$\mathbf{0} = 0 + 0 \cdot x + \cdots + 0 \cdot x^{n-1},$$

and
$$-\mathbf{X} = -p_0 - p_1x - p_2x^2 - \cdots - p_{n-1}x^{n-1}.$$

It is clear that all the conditions for a vector space given earlier are satisfied. In fact, the powers of x in the polynomial merely serve the purpose of *ordering* the coefficients $p_0, p_1, \ldots, p_{n-1}$, and the vector space of polynomials is isomorphic to the space of vectors

$$\mathbf{X}^* = [p_0, p_1, p_2, \ldots, p_{n-1}],$$

with the usual rules for addition and scalar multiplication.

Not all vector spaces are finite-dimensional, however.

Example 2

Consider the set V of all real-valued functions defined on the interval $0 \leqslant x \leqslant 1$. If $\mathbf{X}$ is an element of the set, let $\mathbf{X}(x) = y$, and if $\mathbf{Y}$ is another element of the set, let $\mathbf{Y}(x) = z$. Then we define

$$\mathbf{X} + \mathbf{Y}$$

to be the real-valued function which is such that

$$(\mathbf{X} + \mathbf{Y})(x) = y + z,$$

and we define $r\mathbf{X}$ to be the real-valued function which is such that

$$r\mathbf{X}(x) = ry.$$

The zero of the set is the function $\mathbf{0}$ which is zero at all points of the interval.

The conditions for a vector space are satisfied here also, but there is no finite basis for vectors in this space.

Subsets of a vector space can also be vector spaces. Let $\mathbf{X}_1, \mathbf{X}_2, \ldots, \mathbf{X}_r$ be vectors in $V_n(R)$. Then the set V of all vectors of the form

$$a_1\mathbf{X}_1 + a_2\mathbf{X}_2 + \cdots + a_r\mathbf{X}_r,$$

where the a_i are real numbers, is a vector space over R. This is verified immediately, and we can also say that the space V just defined is the *smallest* vector space that contains $\mathbf{X}_1, \mathbf{X}_2, \ldots, \mathbf{X}_r$, in the sense that any vector space W which contains $\mathbf{X}_1, \mathbf{X}_2, \ldots, \mathbf{X}_r$ must contain $a_1\mathbf{X}_1, a_2\mathbf{X}_2, \ldots, a_r\mathbf{X}_r$, and consequently $a_1\mathbf{X}_1 + a_2\mathbf{X}_2 + \cdots + a_r\mathbf{X}_r$, by the definition of a vector space.

Definition. *A non-empty subset W of a real vector space V is a* SUBSPACE *of V if for every pair of vectors $\mathbf{X}$ and $\mathbf{Y}$ of W, the vectors $\mathbf{X} + \mathbf{Y}$ and $r\mathbf{X}$ (for any $r \in R$) are also contained in W.*

This definition is naturally framed so that a subspace of a vector space is also a vector space. The reason for being rather careful here is that a subset of a vector space V is not necessarily a vector subspace, since, for example, it need not contain the zero vector, which lies in every vector space.

EXERCISES 24.1

1. Let V be the vector space defined in Example 2, p. 116, given by the set of all real-valued functions defined on the interval $0 \leqslant x \leqslant 1$. Show that the following subsets of V are subspaces of V:

(*a*) The set of all functions $\mathbf{X}$ for which $\mathbf{X}(1) = 0$.

(*b*) The set of all functions $\mathbf{X}$ for which $\mathbf{X}(0) = \mathbf{X}(1)$.

Show that the set of all functions $\mathbf{X}$ for which $\mathbf{X}(x) \geqslant 0$ do not form a subspace.

2. Prove that a subspace of $V_n(R)$ is a vector space over R.

3. Prove that if $\mathbf{X}_1, \mathbf{X}_2, \ldots, \mathbf{X}_r$ are vectors in $V_n(R)$, the set of all vectors of the form

$$a_1\mathbf{X}_1 + a_2\mathbf{X}_2 + \cdots + a_r\mathbf{X}_r \quad (a_i \in R)$$

forms a vector space over R.

We conclude this section by giving the definition of *isomorphic vector spaces*. Let V and V^* be two vector spaces defined over the same field R, and suppose that there is a one-to-one correspondence between the vectors $\mathbf{X}$ of V and the vectors $\mathbf{X}^*$ of V^*. Then if in this correspondence

$$\mathbf{X} \to \mathbf{X}^*, \qquad \mathbf{Y} \to \mathbf{Y}^*,$$

and we find that

$$\mathbf{X} + \mathbf{Y} \to \mathbf{X}^* + \mathbf{Y}^*,$$

and also

$$r\mathbf{X} \to r\mathbf{X}^* \qquad (r \in R),$$

then we say that *the two vector spaces are isomorphic.*

EXERCISES 24.2

1. Prove that if V and V^* are isomorphic vector spaces, the zero vector in V is mapped on the zero vector in V^*.

2. Prove also that if V has a finite basis consisting of n independent vectors, so has V^*.

25. Linear Dependence and Generators

We have restricted ourselves in this book to the consideration of vector spaces over the field of real numbers, but the definition can be extended to vector spaces over any field, for example to vector spaces over the field of complex numbers, or restricted to vector spaces over the field of rational numbers. In the case of complex numbers, for example, n-tuples of complex numbers

$$\mathbf{X} = [c_1, c_2, \ldots, c_n],$$

with

$$r\mathbf{X} = [rc_1, rc_2, \ldots, rc_n],$$

where r is a complex number, form a vector space $V_n(C)$, where C is the field of complex numbers.

Our vectors, as we saw in Examples 1 and 2 of § 24, need not be n-tuples of numbers, but since we shall deal with vector spaces with a finite basis [and these are isomorphic to $V_n(R)$, since we shall only deal with real numbers (Theorem 15, § 23)], more general types of vector will not appear in our work.

We saw that the set of vectors given by

$$a_1\mathbf{X}_1 + a_2\mathbf{X}_2 + \cdots + a_r\mathbf{X}_r \qquad (a_i \in R)$$

where the $\mathbf{X}_i$ lie in a given vector space V also forms a vector space. We denote this space by

$$V^* = L\{\mathbf{X}_1, \mathbf{X}_2, \ldots, \mathbf{X}_r\},$$

and say that the vectors $\mathbf{X}_1, \mathbf{X}_2, \ldots, \mathbf{X}_r$ are *a set of generators for* V^*, or that V^* is *generated* (or *spanned*) by the vectors $\mathbf{X}_1, \mathbf{X}_2, \ldots, \mathbf{X}_r$.

The notation is chosen to bring out the fact that every vector of V^* is a linear combination of the vectors $\mathbf{X}_1, \mathbf{X}_2, \ldots, \mathbf{X}_r$.

We defined *basis* in § 22, p. 108. We can now say that if

$$V^* = L\{\mathbf{X}_1, \mathbf{X}_2, \ldots, \mathbf{X}_r\},$$

$\mathbf{X}_1, \mathbf{X}_2, \ldots, \mathbf{X}_r$ form a basis for the vectors in V^*, if $\mathbf{X}_1, \mathbf{X}_2, \ldots, \mathbf{X}_r$ are linearly independent.

A basis for $V_n(R)$ is given by the n vectors (§ 22):

$$\mathbf{e}_1 = [1, 0, 0, \ldots, 0],\ \mathbf{e}_2 = [0, 1, 0, \ldots, 0], \ldots, \mathbf{e}_n = [0, 0, \ldots, 0, 1],$$

so that we can write

$$V_n = L\{\mathbf{e}_1, \mathbf{e}_2, \ldots, \mathbf{e}_n\}.$$

We also saw, in Theorem 13, § 22, that if $\mathbf{X}_1, \mathbf{X}_2, \ldots, \mathbf{X}_n$ is *any* linearly independent set of vectors in $V_n(R)$, then

$$V_n(R) = L\{\mathbf{X}_1, \mathbf{X}_2, \ldots, \mathbf{X}_n\}.$$

Example 1

We saw in the Example, § 22, that the vectors $\mathbf{Y}_1 = [1, 1, 1]$, $\mathbf{Y}_2 = [1, 2, 0]$, and $\mathbf{Y}_3 = [1, 1, -1]$ form a basis for $V_3(R)$. Hence we can write

$$V_3(R) = L\{\mathbf{Y}_1, \mathbf{Y}_2, \mathbf{Y}_3\}.$$

We now prove some more theorems about bases for vector spaces. Our first one is helpful in removing unwanted members from a set of generators. We assume now that all the vectors we are considering lie in some definite vector space V.

Theorem 17. *The non-zero vectors $\mathbf{X}_1, \mathbf{X}_2, \ldots, \mathbf{X}_r$ are linearly dependent if, and only if, some $\mathbf{X}_k$, with $k \geqslant 2$, is a linear combination of the preceding $\mathbf{X}_i$, that is of $\mathbf{X}_1, \mathbf{X}_2, \ldots, \mathbf{X}_{k-1}$.*

Proof. If

$$\mathbf{X}_k = a_1\mathbf{X}_1 + a_2\mathbf{X}_2 + \cdots + a_{k-1}\mathbf{X}_{k-1} \qquad (a_i \in R),$$

then

$$a_1\mathbf{X}_1 + a_2\mathbf{X}_2 + \cdots + a_{k-1}\mathbf{X}_{k-1} - \mathbf{X}_k = \mathbf{0},$$

so that the vectors $\mathbf{X}_1, \mathbf{X}_2, \ldots, \mathbf{X}_{k-1}, \mathbf{X}_k$ are linearly dependent, and since we can write this as

$$a_1\mathbf{X}_1 + a_2\mathbf{X}_2 + \cdots + a_{k-1}\mathbf{X}_{k-1} - \mathbf{X}_k + 0 \cdot \mathbf{X}_{k+1} + \cdots + 0 \cdot \mathbf{X}_r = \mathbf{0},$$

the set $\mathbf{X}_1, \mathbf{X}_2, \ldots, \mathbf{X}_k, \ldots, \mathbf{X}_r$ is linearly dependent. This proves the "if" part of the theorem.

To prove the "only if" part, suppose that the non-zero vectors $\mathbf{X}_1, \ldots, \mathbf{X}_r$ are linearly dependent. Then

$$a_1\mathbf{X}_1 + a_2\mathbf{X}_2 + \cdots + a_k\mathbf{X}_k + \cdots + a_r\mathbf{X}_r = \mathbf{0} \qquad (a_i \in R),$$

and not all the a_i are zero. Moving from the right to the left, we look at the coefficients $a_r, a_{r-1}, \ldots, a_2, a_1$ in order, and stop at the first coefficient a_k which is *not* zero. Our equation therefore looks like this:

$$a_1\mathbf{X}_1 + a_2\mathbf{X}_2 + \cdots + a_k\mathbf{X}_k = \mathbf{0}, \qquad (a_k \neq 0).$$

Now we cannot have $k = 1$, which would give us

$$a_1\mathbf{X}_1 = \mathbf{0} \qquad (a_1 \neq 0),$$

since $\mathbf{X}_1 \neq \mathbf{0}$. Hence $k \geqslant 2$, and since we can write

$$\mathbf{X}_k = -a_1a_k^{-1}\mathbf{X}_1 - a_2a_k^{-1}\mathbf{X}_2 - \cdots - a_{k-1}a_k^{-1}\mathbf{X}_{k-1},$$

we have proved the theorem.

We now want to show that we can get rid of the dependent vectors in a system of generators for a vector space V^*.

Theorem 18. *If* $V^* = L\{\mathbf{X}_1, \mathbf{X}_2, \ldots, \mathbf{X}_r\}$, *then there is a linearly independent subset of* $\mathbf{X}_1, \mathbf{X}_2, \ldots, \mathbf{X}_r$ *which also generates* V^*.

Proof. If $\mathbf{X}_1, \mathbf{X}_2, \ldots, \mathbf{X}_r$ are already independent, we have finished, taking "*subset*" = "*set* $\{\mathbf{X}_1, \mathbf{X}_2, \ldots, \mathbf{X}_r\}$."

We suppose then that the vectors $\mathbf{X}_1, \mathbf{X}_2, \ldots, \mathbf{X}_r$ are linearly dependent, and by Theorem 17 we find the first vector in the set

$$\mathbf{X}_1, \mathbf{X}_2, \ldots, \mathbf{X}_r,$$

moving from left to right, which is dependent on the preceding vectors. We can assume $\mathbf{X}_1 \neq \mathbf{0}$, for if it were zero, we should remove it. Hence if $\mathbf{X}_k$ is the vector just specified, $k \geqslant 2$, and $\mathbf{X}_k$ is linearly dependent on $\mathbf{X}_1, \mathbf{X}_2, \ldots, \mathbf{X}_{k-1}$.

The vectors $\mathbf{X}_1, \mathbf{X}_2, \ldots, \mathbf{X}_{k-1}$ are themselves linearly *independent*. For if they were dependent, Theorem 17 shows that $\mathbf{X}_k$ would not be the *first* vector dependent on the preceding set of vectors. Now consider the vector space:

$$V^{**} = L\{\mathbf{X}_1, \mathbf{X}_2, \ldots, \mathbf{X}_{k-1}, \mathbf{X}_{k+1}, \ldots, \mathbf{X}_r\}.$$

We assert that $V^{**} = V^*$. In other words, $\mathbf{X}_k$ can be dropped from the generating system without its absence being noticed.

To prove this, we note that the set of vectors V^{**} is *contained in* (or is equal to) the set of vectors V^*, since

$$a_1\mathbf{X}_1 + \cdots + a_{k-1}\mathbf{X}_{k-1} + a_{k+1}\mathbf{X}_{k+1} + \cdots + a_r\mathbf{X}_r$$

$$= a_1\mathbf{X}_1 + \cdots + a_{k-1}\mathbf{X}_{k-1} + 0 \cdot \mathbf{X}_k + a_{k+1}\mathbf{X}_{k+1} + \cdots + a_r\mathbf{X}_r.$$

We write this

$$V^{**} \subseteq V^*.$$

On the other hand,

$$V^* \subseteq V^{**},$$

for if $\mathbf{X} = a_1\mathbf{X}_1 + a_2\mathbf{X}_2 + \cdots + a_{k-1}\mathbf{X}_{k-1} + a_k\mathbf{X}_k + \cdots + a_r\mathbf{X}_r$ is any vector of V^*, and $a_k = 0$, then $\mathbf{X} \in V^{**}$. If $a_k \neq 0$, we know that

$$\mathbf{X}_k = b_1\mathbf{X}_1 + b_2\mathbf{X}_2 + \cdots + b_{k-1}\mathbf{X}_{k-1},$$

since $\mathbf{X}_k$ is linearly dependent on $\mathbf{X}_1, \mathbf{X}_2, \ldots, \mathbf{X}_{k-1}$. Hence

$$\mathbf{X} = (a_1 + a_kb_1)\mathbf{X}_1 + (a_2 + a_kb_2)\mathbf{X}_2 + \cdots + (a_{k-1} + a_kb_{k-1})\mathbf{X}_{k-1} + a_{k+1}\mathbf{X}_{k+1} + \cdots + a_r\mathbf{X}_r,$$

so that $X \in V^{**}$. Since from $X \in V^*$ we have proved that $X \in V^{**}$, it follows that

$$V^* \subseteq V^{**},$$

and since also

$$V^{**} \subseteq V^*,$$

we deduce that $V^* = V^{**}$. Hence

$$L\{\mathbf{X}_1, \mathbf{X}_2, \ldots, \mathbf{X}_{k-1}, \mathbf{X}_k, \mathbf{X}_{k+1}, \ldots, \mathbf{X}_r\} = L\{\mathbf{X}_1, \mathbf{X}_2, \ldots, \mathbf{X}_{k-1}, \mathbf{X}_{k+1}, \ldots, \mathbf{X}_r\},$$

where we now know that $\mathbf{X}_1, \mathbf{X}_2, \ldots, \mathbf{X}_{k-1}$ are independent.

If the whole set of generators on the right is not an independent set, we repeat the process, dropping out at the next stage the first vector $\mathbf{X}_i$ $(i \geqslant k + 1)$ which is dependent on the preceding vectors. After a finite number of steps we end up with a linearly independent subset of $\mathbf{X}_1, \mathbf{X}_2, \ldots, \mathbf{X}_r$ which generates $L\{\mathbf{X}_1, \mathbf{X}_2, \ldots, \mathbf{X}_r\}$. This concludes the proof.

Having shown how to *contract* a set of generators, let us see how to *expand* a set of generators. We know that in $V_n(R)$ any basis contains n linearly independent vectors. If we are given r $(<n)$ linearly independent vectors $\mathbf{X}_1, \ldots, \mathbf{X}_r$, can we add vectors $\mathbf{X}_{r+1}, \ldots, \mathbf{X}_n$ so that the total set $\mathbf{X}_1, \mathbf{X}_2, \ldots, \mathbf{X}_r, \mathbf{X}_{r+1}, \ldots, \mathbf{X}_n$ is a basis for V_n? This is possible, and we state the possibility as Theorem 19.

Theorem 19. *The linearly independent set of vectors* $\mathbf{X}_1, \mathbf{X}_2, \ldots, \mathbf{X}_r$ $(r < n)$ *in* $V_n(R)$ *can always be extended to a basis* $\mathbf{X}_1, \mathbf{X}_2, \ldots, \mathbf{X}_r, \mathbf{X}_{r+1}, \ldots, \mathbf{X}_n$ *for* $V_n(R)$.

Proof. Since $r < n$, Theorem 16 assures us that the vector space

$$V_r = L\{\mathbf{X}_1, \mathbf{X}_2, \ldots, \mathbf{X}_r\}$$

cannot contain all the vectors of $V_n(R)$. Hence there is at least one vector $\mathbf{X}_{r+1} \in V_n$ which is not contained in V_r. Since $\mathbf{X}_{r+1}$ is not in V_r, the set $\mathbf{X}_1, \mathbf{X}_2, \ldots, \mathbf{X}_r, \mathbf{X}_{r+1}$ consists once more of linearly independent vectors. If $r + 1 < n$,

$$V_{r+1} = L\{\mathbf{X}_1, \ldots, \mathbf{X}_r, \mathbf{X}_{r+1}\}$$

does not coincide with V_n, and we may continue the process, until finally we have

$$V_n = L\{\mathbf{X}_1, \ldots, \mathbf{X}_r, \mathbf{X}_{r+1}, \ldots, \mathbf{X}_n\},$$

and we have extended the given set to one which generates $V_n(R)$.

We note that we may begin with $r = 0$, in which case $\mathbf{X}_1$ is any vector $\neq \mathbf{0}$, $\mathbf{X}_2$ is any vector not contained in $L\{\mathbf{X}_1\}$, and so on.

Example 2

The four vectors [1, 3, 4], [0, −1, −2], [3, 7, 8], and [1, 1, 5] in V_3 cannot be linearly independent, by Theorem 12, § 22. The second is not a multiple of the first, so it is not linearly dependent on it. To test whether the first three vectors are dependent, we note that the determinant

$$\begin{vmatrix} 1 & 3 & 4 \\ 0 & -1 & -2 \\ 3 & 7 & 8 \end{vmatrix} = 0,$$

and the cofactors of the elements in the first column are 6, 4, and −2 respectively, indicating that

$$6[1, 3, 4] + 4[0, -1, -2] - 2[3, 7, 8] = [0, 0, 0].$$

Hence we can omit [3, 7, 8] as a generator of V_3, and since [1, 1, 5] is *not* dependent on the first two vectors, because the determinant

$$\begin{vmatrix} 1 & 3 & 4 \\ 0 & -1 & -2 \\ 1 & 1 & 5 \end{vmatrix} \neq 0,$$

we have

$$V_3 = L\{[1, 3, 4], [0, -1, -2], [1, 1, 5]\}.$$

Example 3

Let us find a basis for V_3, beginning with the vector $\mathbf{E}_1 = [5, 6, 7]$. We choose any vector $\mathbf{E}_2$ not in $L\{\mathbf{E}_1\}$, and since $\mathbf{E}_2 = [5, 6, 9]$ is not a multiple of $\mathbf{E}_1$, we are certain it is independent of $\mathbf{E}_1$.

We finally have to choose a vector $\mathbf{E}_3$ which is not in the vector space $L\{\mathbf{E}_1, \mathbf{E}_2\}$. If $\mathbf{E}_3 = [p, q, r]$, we want the determinant

$$\begin{vmatrix} p & q & r \\ 5 & 6 & 7 \\ 5 & 6 & 9 \end{vmatrix}$$

to be unequal to zero. We can therefore take $\mathbf{E}_3 = [p, 0, 0]$ for any $p \neq 0$, and

$$V_3 = \{[5, 6, 7], [5, 6, 9], [p, 0, 0]\},$$

for any $p \neq 0$.

EXERCISES 25

1. Given that $V_3 = L\{\mathbf{E}_1, \mathbf{E}_2, \mathbf{E}_3\}$, where

$$\mathbf{E}_1 = [5, 6, 7], \qquad \mathbf{E}_2 = [5, 6, 9], \qquad \mathbf{E}_3 = [2, 0, 0],$$

replace $\mathbf{E}_2$ and $\mathbf{E}_3$ by vectors $\mathbf{E}_2^*$, $\mathbf{E}_3^*$ respectively such that:

(*a*) $\mathbf{E}_2^*$ is in $L\{\mathbf{E}_1, \mathbf{E}_2\}$ and $(\mathbf{E}_1, \mathbf{E}_2^*) = 0$, so that $\mathbf{E}_1$ and $\mathbf{E}_2^*$ are orthogonal, and

(*b*) $(\mathbf{E}_1, \mathbf{E}_3^*) = (\mathbf{E}_2^*, \mathbf{E}_3^*) = 0$, so that $\mathbf{E}_3^*$ is orthogonal to $\mathbf{E}_1$ and to $\mathbf{E}_2^*$.

2. If $\mathbf{E}_1$, $\mathbf{E}_2$, $\mathbf{E}_3$ are three mutually orthogonal non-zero vectors in V_3, prove that they are necessarily linearly independent.

3. Delete, from the sequence of five vectors in V_3,

$$[4, 0, 2], [0, 3, 6], [8, -9, -14], [0, 0, 1], [8, 9, 10]$$

those which are linearly dependent on the preceding vectors. Do the remaining vectors generate V_3?

26. The Echelon Form

Examples of vector dependence or independence in V_3 are easily solved by the use of determinants, but we can deal with vectors of higher dimension without the help of determinants. To test whether n given vectors

$$\mathbf{a}_1 = [a_{11}, a_{21}, \ldots, a_{n1}]^T, \qquad \mathbf{a}_2 = [a_{12}, a_{22}, \ldots, a_{n2}]^T, \ldots$$
$$\mathbf{a}_n = [a_{1n}, a_{2n}, \ldots, a_{nn}]^T$$

are linearly dependent or not, we have to consider whether the equations

$$\mathbf{a}_1 X_1 + \mathbf{a}_2 X_2 + \cdots + \mathbf{a}_n X_n = \mathbf{0}$$

have a non-trivial solution. We solve the n resulting equations

$$\left.\begin{aligned} a_{11}X_1 + a_{12}X_2 + \cdots + a_{1n}X_n &= 0, \\ a_{21}X_1 + a_{22}X_2 + \cdots + a_{2n}X_n &= 0, \\ \cdot \qquad \cdot \qquad \cdots \qquad \cdot \quad &\quad \cdot \\ a_{n1}X_1 + a_{n2}X_2 + \cdots + a_{nn}X_n &= 0 \end{aligned}\right\}$$

by reduction to triangular form, as in the proof of Theorem 8, § 21. If we do obtain a triangular form:

$$\begin{bmatrix} b_{11} & b_{12} & \cdot & \cdot & b_{1n} \\ 0 & b_{22} & \cdot & \cdot & b_{2n} \\ \cdot & \cdot & \cdot & \cdot & \cdot \\ \cdot & \cdot & \cdot & \cdot & \cdot \\ 0 & 0 & \cdot & 0 & b_{nn} \end{bmatrix}$$

with all $b_{ii} \neq 0$, then we find that $X_1 = X_2 = \cdots = X_n = 0$, and the vectors $\mathbf{a}_1, \mathbf{a}_2, \ldots, \mathbf{a}_n$ are independent. But if the n vectors $\mathbf{a}_1, \mathbf{a}_2, \ldots, \mathbf{a}_n$ are linearly dependent, we do *not* obtain a triangular form with all $b_{ii} \neq 0$.

To see more clearly what happens, we consider m vectors in $V_n (m \leqslant n)$:

$$\mathbf{a}_1 = [a_{11}, a_{21}, \ldots, a_{n1}]^T, \ldots, \mathbf{a}_m = [a_{1m}, a_{2m}, \ldots, a_{nm}]^T,$$

and consider whether the equations

$$\mathbf{a}_1 X_1 + \mathbf{a}_2 X_2 + \cdots + \mathbf{a}_m X_m = \mathbf{0}$$

have a non-trivial solution. We have to solve the n equations in m unknowns, $(m \leqslant n)$:

$$\left.\begin{aligned} a_{11}X_1 + a_{12}X_2 + \cdots + a_{1m}X_m &= 0, \\ a_{21}X_1 + a_{22}X_2 + \cdots + a_{2m}X_m &= 0, \\ \cdot \quad \cdot \quad \cdots \quad \cdot \quad & \;\cdot \\ a_{n1}X_1 + a_{n2}X_2 + \cdots + a_{nm}X_m &= 0. \end{aligned}\right\} \tag{77}$$

We have taken $m \leqslant n$ because we know that any $n + 1$ vectors in V_n (and therefore any number $> n + 1$) are linearly dependent (Theorem 12 § 22). Given $m \leqslant n$ vectors, they may be independent or dependent. If independent, the foregoing equations have only the trivial solution. If dependent, there will be non-trivial solutions.

To determine the solutions, we use the elementary transformations I, II, and III of § 21 to obtain an equivalent set of n equations in m unknowns, that is, a set with the same solutions as the given set. But now we cannot say in advance that no column in the matrix

$$\begin{bmatrix} a_{11} & a_{12} & \cdots & a_{1m} \\ a_{21} & a_{22} & \cdots & a_{2m} \\ \cdot & \cdot & \cdots & \cdot \\ a_{n1} & a_{n2} & \cdots & a_{nm} \end{bmatrix} \tag{77*}$$

will consist of zeros. The first column may well consist of zeros, but not all the columns will consist of zeros. As soon as we reach a column with a non-zero entry, we apply operation I to get it into the first row, and then apply operations II and III as in the proof of Theorem 8, § 21, p. 102 to wipe out the other non-zero coefficients in that column.

The matrix then looks like this (the columns of zeros need not be present):

$$\begin{bmatrix} 0 & \cdot & \cdot & 1 & b_{1s} & \cdot & \cdot & b_{1m} \\ 0 & \cdot & \cdot & 0 & b_{2s} & \cdot & \cdot & b_{2m} \\ \cdot & \cdot & \cdot & \cdot & \cdot & \cdot & \cdot & \cdot \\ \cdot & \cdot & \cdot & \cdot & \cdot & \cdot & \cdot & \cdot \\ \cdot & \cdot & \cdot & \cdot & \cdot & \cdot & \cdot & \cdot \\ 0 & \cdot & \cdot & 0 & b_{ns} & \cdot & \cdot & b_{nm} \end{bmatrix} \tag{78}$$

We now leave the first row alone, and work on the submatrix

$$\begin{bmatrix} b_{2s} & \cdots & b_{2m} \\ \cdot & \cdots & \cdot \\ b_{ns} & \cdots & b_{nm} \end{bmatrix}$$

in the same way, noting that operations I, II, and III applied to the rows of this matrix may be regarded as similar operations on the rows of the matrix (78) which leave the first row unchanged. Proceeding thus we obtain a matrix in *echelon form*.

Definition. *A matrix is said to be in echelon form when, as we scan the rows from left to right, beginning at the top and moving down, the number of zeros encountered in a row before we meet a non-zero entry steadily increases, until all subsequent rows consist of zeros.*

For example, the matrix

$$\begin{bmatrix} 0 & 1 & a & b \\ 0 & 0 & 1 & c \\ 0 & 0 & 0 & 1 \\ 0 & 0 & 0 & 0 \\ 0 & 0 & 0 & 0 \end{bmatrix} \tag{79}$$

is in echelon form.

With each step down we move at least one step to the right before we meet a non-zero entry, when a matrix is in echelon form, and our matrix has n rows and m columns. If $m < n$, some rows of this matrix consist entirely of zeros, and these are the rows at the bottom of the matrix. Let us see what this means in terms of the original matrix (77)* obtained from the equations (77) on p. 124.

We are manipulating the *rows* of the matrix (77)* so let us denote the row-vectors by

$$\mathbf{R}_1 = [a_{11}, a_{12}, \ldots, a_{1m}], \qquad \mathbf{R}_2 = [a_{21}, a_{22}, \ldots, a_{2m}], \ldots,$$
$$\mathbf{R}_n = [a_{n1}, a_{n2}, \ldots, a_{nm}].$$

Then it is clear that any operation I, II or III applied to $\mathbf{R}_1, \mathbf{R}_2, \ldots, \mathbf{R}_n$ produces a vector of the vector space

$$V_r = L\{\mathbf{R}_1, \mathbf{R}_2, \ldots, \mathbf{R}_n\}.$$

We call this vector space the *row-space* of the matrix (77)*.

Not all the vectors $\mathbf{R}_1, \mathbf{R}_2, \ldots, \mathbf{R}_n$ are the zero vector. We choose one of them which is not zero by the procedure described previously and put it in the first row, and then put other non-zero vectors of V_r in the second, third, . . . rows so that we have a matrix in echelon form, and the final rows of the echelon matrix contain zero vectors.

Now, *the non-zero rows of the final matrix in echelon form represent linearly independent vectors of* V_r (see Exercises 26, 1, 2.) Also, if we keep a check on the row-vectors of the original matrix (77)*, we see that the appearance of a row of zeros in the final echelon matrix indicates that one of the row-vectors in the matrix (77)* is linearly dependent on the others. This was illustrated in Example 2, § 20, p. 94 and will be further illustrated in Example 1 below.

It appears, therefore, that if we transform the matrix (77)* into echelon form, we are presented with a basis for the row-space $V_r = L\{\mathbf{R}_1, \mathbf{R}_2, \ldots, \mathbf{R}_n\}$, and also told which of the original row-vectors $\mathbf{R}_1, \mathbf{R}_2, \ldots, \mathbf{R}_n$ is linearly dependent on the other row-vectors. This will be investigated in more detail when we consider the rank of a matrix (p. 176).

Example 1

Find a basis for

$$L\{[1, -1, 2, 3], [1, 0, 1, 0], [3, 4, 5, 6]\}$$

which includes the vector [5, 3, 8, 9].

We consider the matrix

$$\begin{bmatrix} 5 & 3 & 8 & 9 \\ 1 & -1 & 2 & 3 \\ 1 & 0 & 1 & 0 \\ 3 & 4 & 5 & 6 \end{bmatrix},$$

where we have put the vector [5, 3, 8, 9] firmly in the first row. Transforming this to echelon form,

$$\begin{bmatrix} 5 & 3 & 8 & 9 \\ 1 & -1 & 2 & 3 \\ 1 & 0 & 1 & 0 \\ 3 & 4 & 5 & 6 \end{bmatrix} \begin{matrix} \mathbf{R}_1 \\ \mathbf{R}_2 \\ \mathbf{R}_3 \\ \mathbf{R}_4 \end{matrix} \rightarrow \begin{bmatrix} 1 & \frac{3}{5} & \frac{8}{5} & \frac{9}{5} \\ 1 & -1 & 2 & 3 \\ 1 & 0 & 1 & 0 \\ 3 & 4 & 5 & 6 \end{bmatrix} \begin{matrix} \frac{\mathbf{R}_1}{5} \\ \mathbf{R}_2 \\ \mathbf{R}_3 \\ \mathbf{R}_4 \end{matrix}$$

$$\rightarrow \begin{bmatrix} 1 & \frac{3}{5} & \frac{8}{5} & \frac{9}{5} \\ 0 & \frac{-8}{5} & \frac{2}{5} & \frac{6}{5} \\ 0 & \frac{-3}{5} & \frac{-3}{5} & \frac{-9}{5} \\ 0 & \frac{11}{5} & \frac{1}{5} & \frac{3}{5} \end{bmatrix} \begin{matrix} \frac{\mathbf{R}_1}{5} \\ \mathbf{R}_2 - \frac{\mathbf{R}_1}{5} \\ \mathbf{R}_3 - \frac{\mathbf{R}_1}{5} \\ \mathbf{R}_4 - \frac{3\mathbf{R}_1}{5} \end{matrix} \rightarrow \begin{bmatrix} 1 & \frac{3}{5} & \frac{8}{5} & \frac{9}{5} \\ 0 & 1 & \frac{-1}{4} & \frac{-3}{4} \\ 0 & 1 & 1 & 3 \\ 0 & 11 & 1 & 3 \end{bmatrix} \begin{matrix} \frac{\mathbf{R}_1}{5} \\ \frac{-5\mathbf{R}_2}{8} + \frac{\mathbf{R}_1}{8} \\ \frac{-5\mathbf{R}_3}{3} + \frac{\mathbf{R}_1}{3} \\ 5\mathbf{R}_4 - 3\mathbf{R}_1 \end{matrix}$$

$$\rightarrow \begin{bmatrix} 1 & \frac{3}{5} & \frac{8}{5} & \frac{9}{5} \\ 0 & 1 & \frac{-1}{4} & \frac{-3}{4} \\ 0 & 0 & \frac{5}{4} & \frac{15}{4} \\ 0 & 0 & \frac{15}{4} & \frac{45}{4} \end{bmatrix} \begin{matrix} \frac{\mathbf{R}_1}{5} \\ \frac{\mathbf{R}_1 - 5\mathbf{R}_2}{8} \\ \frac{\mathbf{R}_1 - 5\mathbf{R}_3}{3} - \frac{\mathbf{R}_1 - 5\mathbf{R}_2}{8} \\ 5\mathbf{R}_4 - 3\mathbf{R}_1 - 11\frac{\mathbf{R}_1 - 5\mathbf{R}_2}{8}. \end{matrix}$$

We now see that the fourth row is a multiple of the third row, and the final echelon form of the matrix is

$$\begin{bmatrix} 1 & \frac{3}{5} & \frac{8}{5} & \frac{9}{5} \\ 0 & 1 & \frac{-1}{4} & \frac{-3}{4} \\ 0 & 0 & 1 & 3 \\ 0 & 0 & 0 & 0 \end{bmatrix}.$$

A basis for the space consists of the three vectors

$$[5, 3, 8, 9], [5, 3, 8, 9] - 5[1, -1, 2, 3],$$

and

$$5[5, 3, 8, 9] + 15[1, -1, 2, 3] - 40[1, 0, 1, 0],$$

in terms of the original vectors. The relation between the fourth row-vector and the others is

$$5\mathbf{R}_4 - 3\mathbf{R}_1 - 11\frac{\mathbf{R}_1 - 5\mathbf{R}_2}{8} = 3\frac{\mathbf{R}_1 - 5\mathbf{R}_3}{3} - 3\frac{\mathbf{R}_1 - 5\mathbf{R}_2}{8},$$

or

$$40\mathbf{R}_4 - 24\mathbf{R}_1 - 11(\mathbf{R}_1 - 5\mathbf{R}_2) = 8(\mathbf{R}_1 - 5\mathbf{R}_3) - 3(\mathbf{R}_1 - 5\mathbf{R}_2),$$

that is,

$$40\mathbf{R}_4 = 40\mathbf{R}_1 - 40\mathbf{R}_2 - 40\mathbf{R}_3,$$

$$\mathbf{R}_4 = \mathbf{R}_1 - \mathbf{R}_2 - \mathbf{R}_3,$$

and this is easily verified to be correct.

EXERCISES 26

1. Show that the first three rows of the echelon matrix

$$\begin{bmatrix} 0 & 1 & a & b & c & d \\ 0 & 0 & 0 & 1 & e & f \\ 0 & 0 & 0 & 0 & 1 & g \\ 0 & 0 & 0 & 0 & 0 & 0 \end{bmatrix}$$

are linearly independent. Show also that the three columns containing the leading unity elements of these rows, namely the second, fourth, and fifth columns, are linearly independent.

2. If the first k rows of a matrix in echelon form are non-zero, and denoted by $\mathbf{R}_1, \mathbf{R}_2, \ldots, \mathbf{R}_k$, prove that $\lambda_1\mathbf{R}_1 + \lambda_2\mathbf{R}_2 + \cdots + \lambda_k\mathbf{R}_k = \mathbf{0}$ necessarily implies $\lambda_1 = \lambda_2 = \cdots = \lambda_k = 0$, so that these rows are linearly independent.

If the remaining rows of the matrix are rows of zeros, show that the k columns, each of which contains the leading unity element of a row, are independent.

3. Prove that the $n - r$ vectors exhibited below are always independent, whatever the values of the c_{ij} which appear:

$$\begin{aligned} \mathbf{Y}_{r+1} &= [c_{1,r+1}, c_{2,r+1}, \ldots, c_{r,r+1}, 1, 0, 0, \ldots, 0] \\ \mathbf{Y}_{r+2} &= [c_{1,r+2}, c_{2,r+2}, \ldots, c_{r,r+2}, 0, 1, 0, \ldots, 0] \\ &\cdot \quad \cdot \quad \cdot \quad \cdots \quad \cdot \quad \cdot \quad \cdot \quad \cdot \quad \cdots \quad \cdot \\ \mathbf{Y}_n &= [c_{1,n}, c_{2,n}, \ldots, c_{r,n}, 0, 0, 0, \ldots, 1]. \end{aligned}$$

We now return to the considerations which led to the discussion of the echelon form, namely the solution of n homogeneous equations in m unknowns ($n \geqslant m$):

$$\left.\begin{array}{l} a_{11}X_1 + a_{12}X_2 + \cdots + a_{1m}X_m = 0, \\ a_{21}X_1 + a_{22}X_2 + \cdots + a_{2m}X_m = 0, \\ \quad \cdot \qquad \cdot \qquad \cdots \qquad \cdot \qquad \cdot \\ a_{n1}X_1 + a_{n2}X_2 + \cdots + a_{nm}X_m = 0. \end{array}\right\} \tag{80}$$

The echelon form of equations is derived by application of the elementary transformations I, II, and III of § 21 to the equations (80), and we can therefore say that the non-zero rows of the echelon matrix represent a set of equations equivalent to the set (80), while the zero rows represent equations linearly dependent on the equations represented by the non-zero rows, and these can therefore be ignored.

The echelon matrix has at least $n - m$ rows of zeros, and the equations (80) have the trivial solution only when the echelon matrix has the form

$$\begin{bmatrix} 1 & & & \\ 0 & 1 & & \\ \cdot & \cdot & \cdot & \cdot & \cdot \\ 0 & & \cdot & \cdot & 1 \\ 0 & 0 & \cdot & \cdot & 0 \\ \cdot & \cdot & \cdot & \cdot & \cdot \\ 0 & 0 & \cdot & \cdot & 0 \end{bmatrix} \begin{array}{l} \left.\begin{array}{l} \\ \\ \\ \\ \end{array}\right\} m, \\ \\ \\ \\ \end{array}$$

there being exactly $n - m$ rows of zeros. The set of equations equivalent to (80) are then of the form

$$\left.\begin{array}{r} X_1 + c_{12}X_2 + \cdots + c_{1m}X_m = 0, \\ X_2 + \cdots + c_{2m}X_m = 0, \\ \cdot \qquad \cdots \qquad \cdot \qquad \cdot \\ X_m = 0, \end{array}\right\} \tag{81}$$

and solving from the last equation upward, we see that

$$X_m = X_{m-1} = \cdots = X_2 = X_1 = 0.$$

Here a basis for the row-space

$$V_r = L\{\mathbf{R}_1, \mathbf{R}_2, \ldots, \mathbf{R}_n\}$$

contains just m independent vectors, represented by the first m rows of the echelon matrix. This implies that there are m amongst the n row-vectors $\mathbf{R}_1, \mathbf{R}_2, \ldots, \mathbf{R}_n$ which are linearly independent, since the number of vectors in a basis for a given vector space is independent of the basis (Theorem 16, § 23, p. 113).

Returning to the original subject of our enquiry, the possible dependence of m vectors in V_n $(m \leqslant n)$:

$$\mathbf{a}_1 = [a_{11}, a_{21}, \ldots, a_{n1}]^T, \ldots, \mathbf{a}_m = [a_{1m}, a_{2m}, \ldots; a_{nm}]^T,$$

which led to equations (80), we conclude that these m *column*-vectors are linearly independent if m of the *row-vectors* of the matrix (77)* are independent. Again, this subject will be considered more fully in § 31, Chapter 8.

The *one step down, one step to the right pattern* of an echelon matrix shows that there are *at least* $n - m$ rows of zeros, so there *cannot be more than* m independent row-vectors amongst $\mathbf{R}_1, \mathbf{R}_2, \ldots, \mathbf{R}_n$, and m is, of course, the number of columns in the matrix (77)*. Once again, the full impact of this remark will be felt later (Theorem 36, § 31, Chapter 8).

If there are fewer than m independent vectors amongst the row-vectors $\mathbf{R}_1, \mathbf{R}_2, \ldots, \mathbf{R}_n$, the echelon matrix will have more than $n - m$ rows of zeros. We are therefore reduced to solving m' equations in m unknowns, where $m' < m$, and these always have a non-trivial solution (Theorem 12, Corollary p. 107). Hence the m vectors

$$\mathbf{a}_1 = [a_{11}, a_{21}, \ldots, a_{n1}]^T, \ldots, \mathbf{a}_m = [a_{1m}, a_{2m}, \ldots, a_{nm}]^T$$

are always linearly dependent if there are fewer than m independent vectors amongst the n row-vectors

$$\mathbf{R}_1 = [a_{11}, a_{12}, \ldots, a_{1m}], \ldots, \mathbf{R}_n = [a_{n1}, a_{n2}, \ldots, a_{nm}].$$

We now have all the apparatus necessary for the evaluation of the dependence of vectors.

Example 2

Determine a basis for the set of all vectors V of $V_4(R)$ which satisfy the equation

$$X_1 + X_2 + X_3 + X_4 = 0.$$

To solve this equation we can put $X_4 = \theta$, $X_3 = \varphi$ and $X_2 = \psi$, and then $X_1 = -(\theta + \varphi + \psi)$, and

$$X_1 = -(\theta + \varphi + \psi), \quad X_2 = \psi, \quad X_3 = \varphi, \quad X_4 = \theta$$

is a general solution. This may be written

$$\mathbf{X} = [X_1, X_2, X_3, X_4] = \theta[-1, 0, 0, 1] + \varphi[-1, 0, 1, 0] + \psi[-1, 1, 0, 0],$$

which shows that the solution vectors are linearly dependent on the three vectors

$$[-1, 0, 0, 1], \qquad [-1, 0, 1, 0], \qquad [-1, 1, 0, 0].$$

If we interchange the second and third vectors, the matrix of row vectors transforms into the following echelon matrix:

$$\begin{bmatrix} -1 & 0 & 0 & 1 \\ -1 & 1 & 0 & 0 \\ -1 & 0 & 1 & 0 \end{bmatrix} \to \begin{bmatrix} 1 & 0 & 0 & -1 \\ 0 & 1 & 0 & -1 \\ 0 & 0 & 1 & -1 \end{bmatrix}.$$

This echelon form shows that these row vectors are linearly independent, and therefore form a basis for the solution vectors. The basis cannot contain more than three members, since four independent vectors would generate V_4 itself.

Example 3

Determine a basis for the subspace of $V_5(R)$ for which $X_1 = X_2 = -X_3$.

We have to solve the two equations

$$\left.\begin{aligned} X_1 - X_2 &= 0, \\ X_2 + X_3 &= 0, \end{aligned}\right\}$$

and the matrix of coefficients is already in echelon form. We can take $X_5 = \theta$, $X_4 = \varphi$, $X_3 = \psi$, and then $X_2 = -\psi$, and $X_1 = -\psi$, so that a solution vector is of the form:

$$\mathbf{X} = [-\psi, -\psi, \psi, \varphi, \theta],$$

so that

$$\mathbf{X} = \theta[0, 0, 0, 0, 1] + \varphi[0, 0, 0, 1, 0] + \psi[-1, -1, 1, 0, 0],$$

and a basis consists of the (evidently) independent vectors:

$$[0, 0, 0, 0, 1], \qquad [0, 0, 0, 1, 0], \qquad [-1, -1, 1, 0, 0].$$

By now we expect a single equation to diminish the number of basis elements by 1, and two equations which are independent to diminish the number by 2. This question is investigated in the next section.

27. Intersections and Joins of Subspaces

We return to the subject of subspaces of a vector space, and give again the definition of § 24.

Definition. *A non-empty subset W of a real vector space V is a vector subspace of V if, for every pair of vectors $\mathbf{X}$ and $\mathbf{Y}$ of W, the vectors $\mathbf{X} + \mathbf{Y}$ and $r\mathbf{X}$* (for any $r \in R$) *are also contained in W.*

Associated with any two subspaces U and W of a real vector space V there are two important subspaces, their *intersection* and their *join.*

Definition. *The* INTERSECTION *of U and W, denoted by the symbol $U \cap W$, is defined to consist of the set of all vectors which lie both in U and in W.*

Theorem 20. *The intersection of U and W, any two subspaces of a real vector space V, is itself a subspace of V.*

Proof. If $\mathbf{X}$ and $\mathbf{Y}$ are any two vectors in the intersection, then $\mathbf{X} + \mathbf{Y}$ lies in the intersection, since $\mathbf{X} + \mathbf{Y}$ lies both in U and in W, and $r\mathbf{X}$ $(r \in R)$ lies both in U and in W, and is therefore in $U \cap W$. Hence the intersection is itself a vector space.

Clearly $U \cap W \subseteq U$, and $U \cap W \subseteq W$.

Definition. *The* JOIN *of U and W consists of the set of all vectors*

$$\mathbf{X} + \mathbf{Y} \qquad (\mathbf{X} \in U, \mathbf{Y} \in W).$$

Theorem 21. *The join of U and W is a vector subspace of V.*

Proof. Let $\mathbf{Z} = \mathbf{X} + \mathbf{Y}$ and $\mathbf{Z}' = \mathbf{X}' + \mathbf{Y}'$ be two vectors of the join. Then $\mathbf{Z} + \mathbf{Z}' = \mathbf{X} + \mathbf{Y} + \mathbf{X}' + \mathbf{Y}' = (\mathbf{X} + \mathbf{X}') + (\mathbf{Y} + \mathbf{Y}')$, and $\mathbf{X} + \mathbf{X}' \in U$, $\mathbf{Y} + \mathbf{Y}' \in W$, so that $\mathbf{Z} + \mathbf{Z}'$ also lies in the join.

Again, $r\mathbf{Z} = r(\mathbf{X} + \mathbf{Y}) = r\mathbf{X} + r\mathbf{Y}$, and $r\mathbf{X} \in U$ and $r\mathbf{Y} \in W$, so that $r\mathbf{Z}$ also lies in the join. Hence the join of the vector subspaces U and W, denoted by $U + W$, is a vector subspace of V.

If we take $\mathbf{Y} = 0$, we see that $U + W$ *contains* U, and if we take $\mathbf{X} = \mathbf{0}$, we see that $U + W$ *contains* V. We may write:

$$U \subseteq U + W, \qquad W \subseteq U + W.$$

Example 1

Let U be the subspace of $V_3(R)$ which consists of all vectors of the form $[X_1, X_2, 0]$, and W the subspace spanned by the vectors $[1, 1, 1]$ and $[3, 4, 5]$. Determine the subspaces $U \cap W$ and $U + W$.

Subspace W consists of all vectors of the form

$$p[1, 1, 1] + q[3, 4, 5],$$

and for this vector to lie in U, we want the third coordinate to be zero.

Hence $p + 5q = 0$, so that all vectors of the form

$$-5k[1, 1, 1] + k[3, 4, 5]$$

lie both in U and in W. Hence

$$U \cap W = k[3, 4, 5] - 5k[1, 1, 1] = k[-2, -1, 0].$$

$U + W$ consists of all vectors of the form

$$\begin{aligned} &p[1, 1, 1] + q[3, 4, 5] + [X_1, X_2, 0] \\ &\qquad = p[1, 1, 1] + q[3, 4, 5] + X_1[1, 0, 0] + X_2[0, 1, 0]. \end{aligned}$$

If three of the four vectors

$$[1, 1, 1], \qquad [3, 4, 5], \qquad [1, 0, 0], \qquad [0, 1, 0]$$

are independent, then $U + W = V_3(R)$. We check for independence by reducing the matrix:

$$\begin{bmatrix} 1 & 1 & 1 \\ 3 & 4 & 5 \\ 1 & 0 & 0 \\ 0 & 1 & 0 \end{bmatrix} \rightarrow \begin{bmatrix} 1 & 1 & 1 \\ 0 & 1 & 2 \\ 0 & -1 & -1 \\ 0 & 1 & 0 \end{bmatrix} \rightarrow \begin{bmatrix} 1 & 1 & 1 \\ 0 & 1 & 2 \\ 0 & 0 & 1 \\ 0 & 0 & -2 \end{bmatrix} \rightarrow \begin{bmatrix} 1 & 1 & 1 \\ 0 & 1 & 2 \\ 0 & 0 & 1 \\ 0 & 0 & 0 \end{bmatrix},$$

which shows that the first three vectors written down are linearly independent.

EXERCISES 27.1

1. Show that the following subsets of $V_n(R)$ constitute subspaces (here $\mathbf{X} = [X_1, X_2, \ldots, X_n]$).
   (*a*) All $\mathbf{X}$ with $X_2 = 0$.
   (*b*) All $\mathbf{X}$ such that $3X_1 - 2X_2 = 0$.
2. Show that the following subsets of $V_n(R)$ do not constitute subspaces:
   (*a*) All $\mathbf{X}$ such that either $X_1 = 0$ *or* $X_2 = 0$.
   (*b*) All $\mathbf{X}$ such that $X_1 + X_2 = 1$.
3. If U is spanned by $\mathbf{X}_1, \mathbf{X}_2, \ldots, \mathbf{X}_p$, and W is spanned by $\mathbf{Y}_1, \mathbf{Y}_2, \ldots, \mathbf{Y}_q$, show that $U + W$ is spanned by $\mathbf{X}_1, \mathbf{X}_2, \ldots, \mathbf{X}_p, \mathbf{Y}_1, \mathbf{Y}_2, \ldots, \mathbf{Y}_q$.
4. Prove that the set of all solutions $(X_1, X_2, \ldots, X_n)$ of the two homogeneous equations

$$a_{11}X_1 + a_{12}X_2 + \cdots + a_{1n}X_n = 0,$$

$$a_{21}X_1 + a_{22}X_2 + \cdots + a_{2n}X_n = 0$$

form a subspace of $V_n(R)$. Does this result extend to m homogeneous equations in n unknowns?

We now have the means at our disposal to prove Theorem 22.

Theorem 22. *If U and W are any two subspaces of a vector space V, then their dimensions satisfy*

$$d[U] + d[W] = d[U \cap W] + d[U + W].$$

The dimension of a vector space is the number of elements in a basis for that space, and we know that this number is independent of the particular basis chosen (Theorem 16, § 23). We also know that if we are given a number of independent vectors in a space, we can augment them so as to obtain a basis for the space (Theorem 19, § 25).

Proof. Let $d[U] = p$, and $d[W] = q$, and suppose that $d[U \cap W] = r$. Choose any basis $\mathbf{X}_1, \mathbf{X}_2, \ldots, \mathbf{X}_r$ in $U \cap W$. Since $U \cap W \subseteq U$, we can augment this basis in U by vectors $\mathbf{X}_{r+1}, \ldots, \mathbf{X}_p$, so that $\mathbf{X}_1, \ldots, \mathbf{X}_r, \mathbf{X}_{r+1}, \ldots, \mathbf{X}_p$ is a basis for U, and since $U \cap W \subseteq W$, we can augment the basis $\mathbf{X}_1, \ldots, \mathbf{X}_r$ to a basis $\mathbf{X}_1, \ldots, \mathbf{X}_r, \mathbf{Y}_{r+1}, \ldots, \mathbf{Y}_q$, in W.

Now the vectors $\mathbf{X}_1, \ldots, \mathbf{X}_r, \mathbf{X}_{r+1}, \ldots, \mathbf{X}_p, \mathbf{Y}_{r+1}, \ldots, \mathbf{Y}_q$ clearly span $U + W$, since if $\mathbf{X} \in U$ and $\mathbf{Y} \in W$, and

$$\mathbf{X} = a_1\mathbf{X}_1 + \cdots + a_r\mathbf{X}_r + a_{r+1}\mathbf{X}_{r+1} + \cdots + a_p\mathbf{X}_p,$$

and
$$\mathbf{Y} = b_1\mathbf{X}_1 + \cdots + b_r\mathbf{X}_r + b_{r+1}\mathbf{Y}_{r+1} + \cdots + b_q\mathbf{Y}_q,$$

then

$$\begin{aligned}\mathbf{X} + \mathbf{Y} = (a_1 + b_1)\mathbf{X}_1 + \cdots + (a_r + b_r)\mathbf{X}_r \\ + a_{r+1}\mathbf{X}_{r+1} + \cdots + a_p\mathbf{X}_p + b_{r+1}\mathbf{Y}_{r+1} + \cdots + b_q\mathbf{Y}_q \\ \in L\{\mathbf{X}_1, \ldots, \mathbf{X}_r, \mathbf{X}_{r+1}, \ldots, \mathbf{X}_p, \mathbf{Y}_{r+1}, \ldots, \mathbf{Y}_q\}.\end{aligned}$$

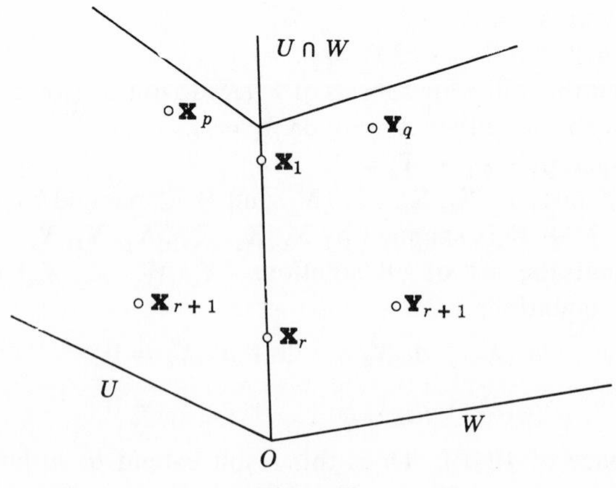

Figure 20

Conversely any vector

$$\mathbf{Z} \in L\{\mathbf{X}_1, \ldots, \mathbf{X}_r, \mathbf{X}_{r+1}, \ldots, \mathbf{X}_p, \mathbf{Y}_{r+1}, \ldots, \mathbf{Y}_q\}$$

can be written as $\mathbf{Z} = \mathbf{X} + \mathbf{Y}$, where $\mathbf{X} \in U$, $\mathbf{Y} \in W$.

We show that the vectors

$$\mathbf{X}_1, \ldots, \mathbf{X}_r, \mathbf{X}_{r+1}, \ldots, \mathbf{X}_p, \mathbf{Y}_{r+1}, \ldots, \mathbf{Y}_q$$

are linearly independent. If there were a non-trivial relation:

$$a_1\mathbf{X}_1 + \cdots + a_r\mathbf{X}_r + a_{r+1}\mathbf{X}_{r+1} + \cdots + a_p\mathbf{X}_p + b_{r+1}\mathbf{Y}_{r+1} + \cdots + b_q\mathbf{Y}_q = \mathbf{0},$$

it would imply that the vector

$$a_{r+1}\mathbf{X}_{r+1} + \cdots + a_p\mathbf{X}_p = -(a_1\mathbf{X}_1 + \cdots + a_r\mathbf{X}_r + b_{r+1}\mathbf{Y}_{r+1} + \cdots + b_q\mathbf{Y}_q)$$

is in W. But the vector on the left-hand side lies in U. We should therefore have $a_{r+1}\mathbf{X}_{r+1} + \cdots + a_p\mathbf{X}_p$ in $U \cap W$, so that

$$a_{r+1}\mathbf{X}_{r+1} + \cdots + a_p\mathbf{X}_p = d_1\mathbf{X}_1 + \cdots + d_r\mathbf{X}_r.$$

Since, however, the vectors $\mathbf{X}_1, \ldots, \mathbf{X}_r, \mathbf{X}_{r+1}, \ldots, \mathbf{X}_p$ form a basis for U, we must have

$$a_{r+1} = \cdots = a_p = 0.$$

Similarly, interchanging the rôles of U and W,

$$b_{r+1} = \cdots = b_q = 0,$$

which leaves us with

$$a_1\mathbf{X}_1 + \cdots + a_r\mathbf{X}_r = \mathbf{0},$$

and therefore $$a_1 = a_2 = \cdots = a_r = 0.$$

Hence the vectors

$$\mathbf{X}_1, \ldots, \mathbf{X}_r, \mathbf{X}_{r+1}, \ldots, \mathbf{X}_p, \mathbf{Y}_{r+1}, \ldots, \mathbf{Y}_q$$

are independent, so that, on counting their number,

$$d[U + W] = p + q - r,$$

and since $$p + q = r + (p + q - r),$$

we have $$d[U] + d[W] = d[U \cap W] + d[U + W], \tag{82}$$

which proves the theorem.

To apply this theorem when $U \cap W = \mathbf{0}$, we must define the dimension of the space which consists of the zero vector only to be 0, so that $d[\mathbf{0}] = 0$.

In geometrical applications we must not forget that vector spaces always contain the zero vector, so that the geometry of, for example, vector subspaces of $V_3(R)$ is the geometry of the lines and planes which pass through the origin (0, 0, 0). If $\mathbf{A} = [a_1, a_2, a_3]$ is any fixed non-zero vector, the vector space $L\{\mathbf{A}\}$ consists of all vectors which lie on a fixed line through the origin. The dimension of this space is 1. A plane through the origin is

$$L\{\mathbf{A}, \mathbf{B}\},$$

where **A**, **B** are two independent vectors, and this has dimension 2.

If two planes through the origin are distinct, intersecting in a line, the foregoing formula shows that their join is the whole of V_3, since it has dimension 3.

A plane and a line which does not lie in it but intersects it at the origin determine a join of dimension 3, since $d[U \cap W] = 0$.

In general, we call two vector subspaces U and W *complementary* if U and W are such that

$$d[U \cap W] = 0, \qquad d[U + W] = n.$$

We then have

$$d[U] + d[W] = n.$$

Given U and $d[U] = p$, it is not difficult to determine a complementary subspace W such that $d[W] = n - p$. We suppose that

$$U = L\{\mathbf{Y}_1, \mathbf{Y}_2, \ldots, \mathbf{Y}_p\},$$

and augment the basis which generates U to a basis for the whole space V_n, by adding the vectors $\mathbf{Y}_{p+1}, \mathbf{Y}_{p+2}, \ldots, \mathbf{Y}_n$. Then choose

$$W = L\{\mathbf{Y}_{p+1}, \mathbf{Y}_{p+2}, \ldots, \mathbf{Y}_n\},$$

and it is clear that $U \cap W = \mathbf{0}$, and $U + W = V_n$.

EXERCISES 27.2

1. If U and W are variable subspaces in $V_n(R)$ of fixed dimensions p and q respectively, find the greatest possible dimension of $U + W$ and the least possible dimension of $U \cap W$.
2. Prove that for subspaces of V_n the conditions

$$U \cap W = U \cap W', \qquad U + W = U + W', \qquad W \subseteq W'$$

imply $W = W'$.

We can apply the dimension Theorem 22 to find the dimension of the vector space W of solutions of the one equation

$$a_1X_1 + a_2X_2 + \cdots + a_nX_n = 0. \qquad (*)$$

Let $\mathbf{H}$ be any vector which does *not* satisfy this equation, and $\mathbf{Y}$ any vector of V_n. We show that we can write

$$\mathbf{Y} = \lambda\mathbf{H} + \mathbf{X}',$$

where $\mathbf{X}'$ is a suitable solution vector of (*), so that V_n can be represented as the join of $L\{\mathbf{H}\}$ and W:

$$V_n = L\{\mathbf{H}\} + W.$$

To do this we note that the set of vectors

$$\mathbf{X} = t\mathbf{H} + (1 - t)\mathbf{Y} \qquad (**)$$

contains $\mathbf{H}$ for $t = 1$, contains $\mathbf{Y}$ for $t = 0$, and also contains a vector $\mathbf{X}'$ lying in W. To find $\mathbf{X}'$ all that we have to do is to substitute for $\mathbf{X}$ in (*), and we obtain a linear equation for t, which determines t and therefore $\mathbf{X}'$. In fact the equation (**) represents a *line* in $V_n(R)$, and this line intersects the vector subspace determined by (*) in a unique point.

We now have, for a definite value t' of t, ($t' \neq 1$),

$$\mathbf{X}' = t'\mathbf{H} + (1 - t')\mathbf{Y},$$

so that

$$\mathbf{Y} = \lambda\mathbf{H} + \mu\mathbf{X}',$$

where $\mu\mathbf{X}'$, like $\mathbf{X}'$, is a solution of the equation (*). If the line HY joining the endpoints H and Y of the respective vectors $\mathbf{H}$ and $\mathbf{Y}$ is *parallel* to the hyperplane represented by equation (*) p. 136, the method given for determining $\mathbf{X}'$ breaks down, since the coefficient of t in the linear equation

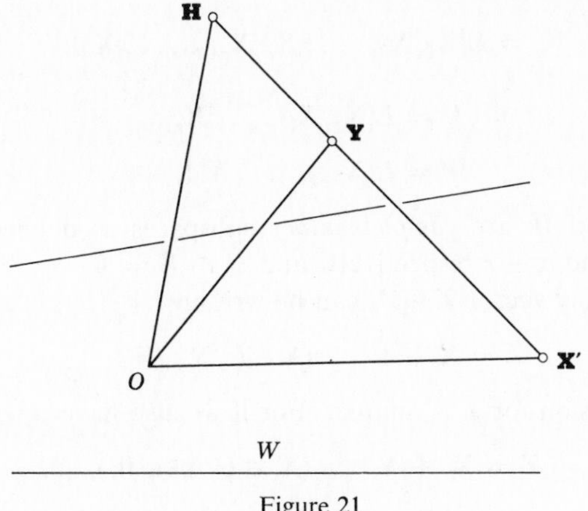

Figure 21

which determines t' is zero. But in this case the line HY is parallel to a vector lying in the hyperplane, so that we have

$$\mathbf{Y} - \mathbf{H} = \mathbf{X}',$$

where $\mathbf{X}'$ is a solution of (*), and therefore

$$\mathbf{Y} = \mathbf{H} + \mathbf{X}'$$

in this case also.

Hence V_n is the join of $L\{\mathbf{H}\}$, of dimension 1, and W, the solution space of equation (*). The formula

$$d[L\{\mathbf{H}\}] + d[W] = d[L\{\mathbf{H}\} + W] + d[L\{\mathbf{H}\} \cap W]$$

becomes

$$1 + d[W] = n + 0,$$

since $L\{\mathbf{H}\}$ and W have only the zero vector in common. Hence

$$d[W] = n - 1,$$

which shows that the dimension of the solution space of a single homogeneous linear equation is $n - 1$.

We shall prove a more general result at the conclusion of § 28, and return to it again in Theorem 32, § 31.

We defined the *join* of subspaces U and W of $V_n(R)$ as the totality of vectors

$$\mathbf{X} + \mathbf{Y} \qquad (\mathbf{X} \in U, \mathbf{Y} \in W),$$

and proved in Theorem 21 that this totality forms a vector space. We may express $V_n(R)$ itself as the join of two subspaces U and W in a variety of ways. In fact, if

$$V_n = L\{\mathbf{X}_1, \mathbf{X}_2, \ldots, \mathbf{X}_r, \mathbf{X}_{r+1}, \ldots, \mathbf{X}_n\},$$

we may take

$$U = L\{\mathbf{X}_1, \mathbf{X}_2, \ldots, \mathbf{X}_r\},$$

$$W = L\{\mathbf{X}_{r+1}, \ldots, \mathbf{X}_n\},$$

and then U and W are *complementary* subspaces as defined above, of dimensions r and $n - r$ respectively, and $U \cap W = \mathbf{0}$.

In this case any vector $\mathbf{Z} \in V_n$ can be written

$$\mathbf{Z} = \mathbf{X} + \mathbf{Y} \qquad (\mathbf{X} \in U, \mathbf{Y} \in W),$$

and this expression for $\mathbf{Z}$ is unique. For if we also have

$$\mathbf{Z} = \mathbf{X}' + \mathbf{Y}' \qquad (\mathbf{X}' \in U, \mathbf{Y}' \in W),$$

then

$$\mathbf{X} - \mathbf{X}' = \mathbf{Y}' - \mathbf{Y},$$

and the left-hand side represents a vector in U, while the right-hand side represents a vector in W, so that each side represents a vector in the intersection of U and W. But since $U \cap W = \mathbf{0}$, we must have $\mathbf{X} = \mathbf{X}'$ and $\mathbf{Y} = \mathbf{Y}'$.

Definition. *If $V = U + W$, where U and W are subspaces of V, and $U \cap W = \mathbf{0}$, we write $V = U \oplus W$, and say that W is the* DIRECT SUM *of the subspaces U and W.*

In this case, where $U \cap W = \mathbf{0}$, we can always write

$$U = L\{\mathbf{X}_1, \mathbf{X}_2, \ldots, \mathbf{X}_r\}, \qquad W = L\{\mathbf{X}_{r+1}, \ldots, \mathbf{X}_n\},$$

where

$$V = L\{\mathbf{X}_1, \ldots, \mathbf{X}_r, \mathbf{X}_{r+1}, \ldots, \mathbf{X}_n\},$$

and the expression for any vector $\mathbf{Z} \in V$ as the sum $\mathbf{X} + \mathbf{Y}$, $\mathbf{X} \in U$ and $\mathbf{Y} \in W$, is unique.

Conversely, if the expression $\mathbf{Z} = \mathbf{X} + \mathbf{Y}$ for any vector $\mathbf{Z} \in V$ is unique, we must have $U \cap W = \mathbf{0}$. For if $\mathbf{K} \in U \cap W$ $(\mathbf{K} \neq \mathbf{0})$, the expression

$$\mathbf{K} = \mathbf{0} + \mathbf{K} = \mathbf{K} + \mathbf{0}$$

is an expression for $\mathbf{K}$ in two distinct ways as a sum of a vector of U and a vector of W.

Example 2

Let $U = L\{[1, 1, 1], [0, -2, 3]\}$. Find a subspace $W \in V_3$ such that $V_3 = U \oplus W$.

Since the vectors generating U are independent, all we have to do is to find a third independent vector $\mathbf{X}_3$, and $W = L\{\mathbf{X}_3\}$.

We can take $\mathbf{X}_3 = [1, -1, 5]$, for example, or $\mathbf{X}_3 = [2, 0, 6]$. There is an infinity of choices, since if $\mathbf{X}_3 = [a, b, c]$, all we need to ensure the independence of $[1, 1, 1]$, $[0, -2, 3]$ and $[a, b, c]$ is the condition:

$$\begin{vmatrix} 1 & 1 & 1 \\ 0 & -2 & 3 \\ a & b & c \end{vmatrix} \neq 0.$$

EXERCISES 27.3

1. If $U = L\{[1, 0, 3], [2, -1, 6]\}$, find two other subspaces W such that $V_3 = U \oplus W$.

2. If $V = U \oplus W$, and $\mathbf{X}$ is a vector of V such that $\mathbf{X} = \mathbf{Y} + \mathbf{Z}$, where $\mathbf{Y} \in U$ and $\mathbf{Z} \in W$, then $\mathbf{Y}$ is called the *projection* of $\mathbf{X}$ on U, and $\mathbf{Z}$ is called the *projection* of $\mathbf{X}$ on W.

If $V_3 = U \oplus W$, where $U = L\{[1, 0, 3], [2, -1, 6]\}$, and $W = L\{[1, 1, 1]\}$, find the projection of $\mathbf{X} = [4, 1, -2]$ on U and on W. Interpret your result geometrically.

3. If $V = U \oplus W$, when is the projection of a vector $\mathbf{X}$ of V on U the zero vector $\mathbf{0}$?

28. The Inner Product of Two Vectors

We conclude this chapter with a brief discussion of the inner product of two vectors $\mathbf{A}$, $\mathbf{B}$ in V_n. If $\mathbf{A} = [a_1, a_2, \ldots, a_n]$, $\mathbf{B} = [b_1, b_2, \ldots, b_n]$, we define the *inner product*, written $(\mathbf{A}, \mathbf{B})$, as:

$$(\mathbf{A}, \mathbf{B}) = a_1b_1 + a_2b_2 + \cdots + a_nb_n. \tag{83}$$

This generalizes the concept for three-dimensional vectors (§ 19), and we have, once more, the properties

$$\left.\begin{array}{ll} \text{(i)} & (\mathbf{A}, \mathbf{B}) = (\mathbf{B}, \mathbf{A}), \\ \text{(ii)} & k(\mathbf{A}, \mathbf{B}) = (k\mathbf{A}, \mathbf{B}) = (\mathbf{A}, k\mathbf{B}), \\ \text{(iii)} & (\mathbf{A} + \mathbf{B}, \mathbf{C}) = (\mathbf{A}, \mathbf{C}) + (\mathbf{B}, \mathbf{C}). \end{array}\right\} \tag{84}$$

These are immediately verifiable.

We are especially interested in the case when $(\mathbf{A}, \mathbf{B}) = 0$, when we say that $\mathbf{A}$ and $\mathbf{B}$ are *orthogonal* vectors. There are a number of theorems concerning orthogonal vectors we wish to prove.

Theorem 23. *If a vector* $\mathbf{X}$ *is orthogonal to each of the vectors* $\mathbf{Y}_1, \mathbf{Y}_2, \ldots, \mathbf{Y}_m$, *then it is orthogonal to every vector in the subspace* $L\{\mathbf{Y}_1, \mathbf{Y}_2, \ldots, \mathbf{Y}_m\}$.

Proof. Any vector in the subspace is

$$\mathbf{Y} = a_1\mathbf{Y}_1 + a_2\mathbf{Y}_2 + \cdots + a_m\mathbf{Y}_m,$$

and

$$\begin{aligned} (\mathbf{X}, \mathbf{Y}) &= (\mathbf{X}, a_1\mathbf{Y}_1 + \cdots + a_m\mathbf{Y}_m) \\ &= (\mathbf{X}, a_1\mathbf{Y}_1) + \cdots + (\mathbf{X}, a_m\mathbf{Y}_m) \\ &= a_1(\mathbf{X}, \mathbf{Y}_1) + \cdots + a_m(\mathbf{X}, \mathbf{Y}_m) \\ &= a_1(0) + \cdots + a_m(0) = 0, \end{aligned}$$

so that $\mathbf{X}$ and $\mathbf{Y}$ are orthogonal.

If in (83) we put $\mathbf{B} = \mathbf{A}$, we have

$$(\mathbf{A}, \mathbf{A}) = a_1^2 + a_2^2 + \cdots + a_n^2,$$

and this is $\|\mathbf{A}\|^2$, the square of the *length*, or *modulus* of the vector $\mathbf{A}$.

Since we are using real numbers for our coordinates,

$$(\mathbf{A}, \mathbf{A}) \geqslant 0,$$

and $\|\mathbf{A}\| = 0$ if and only if

$$a_1 = a_2 = \cdots = a_n = 0,$$

when $\mathbf{A} = \mathbf{0}$.

The "unit vectors" we introduced in § 22, p. 107,

$$\mathbf{e}_1 = [1, 0, \ldots, 0], \ldots, \mathbf{e}_n = [0, 0, \ldots, 0, 1]$$

are mutually orthogonal, and each is of unit length. Such a basis for the vector space $V_n(R)$ is called a *normal orthogonal basis*, or *orthonormal basis.*

Definition. *Vectors* $\mathbf{X}_1, \mathbf{X}_2, \ldots, \mathbf{X}_m$ *are said to form an orthonormal set if*

(i) $\|\mathbf{X}_i\| = 1$, for all i, and

(ii) $(\mathbf{X}_i, \mathbf{X}_j) = 0 \quad (i \neq j)$.

We now prove that orthogonality implies linear independence.

Theorem 24. *If* $\mathbf{X}_1, \mathbf{X}_2, \ldots, \mathbf{X}_m$ *are non-zero mutually orthogonal vectors of* $V_n(R)$, *they are linearly independent.*

Proof. If $\lambda_1\mathbf{X}_1 + \lambda_2\mathbf{X}_2 + \cdots + \lambda_m\mathbf{X}_m = \mathbf{0}$, then

$$\lambda_1(\mathbf{X}_1, \mathbf{X}_i) + \lambda_2(\mathbf{X}_2, \mathbf{X}_i) + \cdots + \lambda_i(\mathbf{X}_i, \mathbf{X}_i) + \cdots + \lambda_m(\mathbf{X}_m, \mathbf{X}_i) = 0,$$

which leaves us with

$$\lambda_i(\mathbf{X}_i, \mathbf{X}_i) = 0,$$

since all the other inner products $= 0$. Because $(\mathbf{X}_i, \mathbf{X}_i) > 0$, the vector $\mathbf{X}_i$ not being zero, we deduce that

$$\lambda_i = 0 \qquad (i = 1, 2, \ldots, m),$$

which proves the theorem.

We deduce that if

$$V = L\{\mathbf{X}_1, \mathbf{X}_2, \ldots, \mathbf{X}_m\},$$

so that $\mathbf{X}_1, \mathbf{X}_2, \ldots, \mathbf{X}_m$ span V, they also form a basis for V, because, being mutually orthogonal, they are independent.

Definition. *Two subspaces* U *and* W *of* $V_n(R)$ *are called orthogonal subspaces of* $V_n(R)$ *if* $(\mathbf{X}, \mathbf{Y}) = 0$ *for all* $\mathbf{X} \in U$ *and* $\mathbf{Y} \in W$.

As a simple example, any vector in $V_3(R)$ which lies in the plane Ox_2x_3 is orthogonal to the vector Ox_1, and if $\mathbf{e}_1$, $\mathbf{e}_2$, and $\mathbf{e}_3$ are the unit vectors, the subspaces

$$L\{\mathbf{e}_1\} \quad \text{and} \quad L\{\mathbf{e}_2, \mathbf{e}_3\}$$

are orthogonal subspaces. We prove Theorem 25.

Theorem 25. *The set of all vectors of $V_n(R)$ orthogonal to a given set $\mathbf{X}_1, \mathbf{X}_2, \ldots, \mathbf{X}_m$ forms a vector subspace W of $V_n(R)$.*

Proof. Let $\mathbf{Y}$ and $\mathbf{Z}$ be any two vectors orthogonal to every vector of the set $\mathbf{X}_1, \ldots, \mathbf{X}_m$. Since

$$(\mathbf{Y} + \mathbf{Z}, \mathbf{X}_i) = (\mathbf{Y}, \mathbf{X}_i) + (\mathbf{Z}, \mathbf{X}_i) = 0 + 0 = 0,$$

the vector $\mathbf{Y} + \mathbf{Z}$ is orthogonal to every $\mathbf{X}_i$. And

$$(k\mathbf{Y}, \mathbf{X}_i) = k(\mathbf{Y}, \mathbf{X}_i) = 0,$$

so that $k\mathbf{Y}$ is orthogonal to every $\mathbf{X}_i$. Hence the set of vectors $\mathbf{Y}, \mathbf{Z}, \ldots$ forms a vector subspace of $V_n(R)$, by the definition on p. 132.

If $\mathbf{Y}_1, \mathbf{Y}_2, \ldots, \mathbf{Y}_q$ form a basis for the vectors orthogonal to $\mathbf{X}_1, \ldots, \mathbf{X}_m$, it is clear that the subspaces $L\{\mathbf{X}_1, \mathbf{X}_2, \ldots, \mathbf{X}_m\}$ and $L\{\mathbf{Y}_1, \mathbf{Y}_2, \ldots, \mathbf{Y}_q\}$ are orthogonal subspaces.

We can now gratify any aesthetic preference we may have for coordinate axes which are mutually orthogonal, and show that any set of vectors which form a basis for a subspace may be replaced by an *orthogonal* set which also form a basis for the subspace. We illustrate the process in a subspace containing three independent vectors. It is called *the Gram-Schmidt process.*

Let $\mathbf{X}_1, \mathbf{X}_2, \mathbf{X}_3$ be three linearly independent vectors in $V_n(R)$. Choose the first vector of the new basis $\mathbf{Y}_1, \mathbf{Y}_2, \mathbf{Y}_3$ to be

$$\mathbf{Y}_1 = \mathbf{X}_1.$$

We want $\mathbf{Y}_2$ to lie in $L\{\mathbf{X}_1, \mathbf{X}_2\}$ and to be orthogonal to $\mathbf{X}_1$. If we take

$$\mathbf{Y}_2 = \mathbf{X}_2 + \lambda\mathbf{Y}_1,$$

we note that $\mathbf{Y}_2 \neq \mathbf{0}$, since if $\mathbf{Y}_2 = \mathbf{0}$, this would involve the linear dependence of $\mathbf{Y}_1 = \mathbf{X}_1$ and $\mathbf{X}_2$. Also

$$\mathbf{Y}_2 \in L\{\mathbf{Y}_1, \mathbf{X}_2\} = L\{\mathbf{X}_1, \mathbf{X}_2\}.$$

We require the condition

$$(\mathbf{X}_1, \mathbf{Y}_2) = (\mathbf{X}_1, \mathbf{X}_2 + \lambda\mathbf{Y}_1) = (\mathbf{X}_1, \mathbf{X}_2) + \lambda(\mathbf{X}_1, \mathbf{Y}_1) = 0.$$

Since the coefficient of $\lambda = (\mathbf{X}_1, \mathbf{Y}_1) = (\mathbf{X}_1, \mathbf{X}_1) \neq 0$, this condition can be satisfied.

Again, since $\mathbf{Y}_2$ is expressed in terms of $\mathbf{X}_2$ and $\mathbf{Y}_1 = \mathbf{X}_1$,

$$L\{\mathbf{Y}_1, \mathbf{Y}_2\} \subseteq L\{\mathbf{X}_1, \mathbf{X}_2\},$$

but since also we can solve the equation

$$\mathbf{Y}_2 = \mathbf{X}_2 + \lambda \mathbf{Y}_1$$

for $\mathbf{X}_2$, and express $\mathbf{X}_2$ in terms of $\mathbf{Y}_1$ and $\mathbf{Y}_2$,

$$L\{\mathbf{X}_1, \mathbf{X}_2\} \subseteq L\{\mathbf{Y}_1, \mathbf{Y}_2\},$$

so that

$$L\{\mathbf{X}_1, \mathbf{X}_2\} = L\{\mathbf{Y}_1, \mathbf{Y}_2\}.$$

Alternatively, we could say that since $\mathbf{Y}_2$ is orthogonal to $\mathbf{Y}_1 = \mathbf{X}_1$, $\mathbf{Y}_1$ and $\mathbf{Y}_2$ are independent, so that the two independent vectors $\mathbf{X}_1, \mathbf{X}_2$ have been replaced by two independent orthogonal vectors:

$$\left.\begin{aligned} \mathbf{Y}_1 &= \mathbf{X}_1, \\ \mathbf{Y}_2 &= \mathbf{X}_2 - \frac{(\mathbf{X}_1, \mathbf{X}_2)}{(\mathbf{X}_1, \mathbf{Y}_1)} \mathbf{Y}_1 \end{aligned}\right\}$$

which we write:

$$\left.\begin{aligned} \mathbf{Y}_1 &= \mathbf{X}_1, \\ \mathbf{Y}_2 &= \mathbf{X}_2 - \frac{(\mathbf{X}_2, \mathbf{Y}_1)}{(\mathbf{Y}_1, \mathbf{Y}_1)} \mathbf{Y}_1. \end{aligned}\right\}$$

We continue this process, and try to find a vector $\mathbf{Y}_3$ orthogonal to $\mathbf{Y}_1$ and to $\mathbf{Y}_2$. We write

$$\mathbf{Y}_3 = \mathbf{X}_3 + \lambda \mathbf{Y}_2 + \mu \mathbf{Y}_1,$$

and note that since $\mathbf{X}_3 \notin L\{\mathbf{Y}_1, \mathbf{Y}_2\} = L\{\mathbf{X}_1, \mathbf{X}_2\}$, we cannot have $\mathbf{Y}_3 = \mathbf{0}$, which would imply the linear dependence of $\mathbf{X}_3$, $\mathbf{Y}_2$, and $\mathbf{Y}_1$. Again, the expression for $\mathbf{Y}_3$ in terms of $\mathbf{X}_3$, $\mathbf{Y}_2$, and $\mathbf{Y}_1$ shows that

$$L\{\mathbf{Y}_1, \mathbf{Y}_2, \mathbf{Y}_3\} \subseteq L\{\mathbf{X}_1, \mathbf{X}_2, \mathbf{X}_3\},$$

since $L\{\mathbf{Y}_1, \mathbf{Y}_2\} = L\{\mathbf{X}_1, \mathbf{X}_2\}$. Conversely, since we can solve for $\mathbf{X}_3$ in terms of $\mathbf{Y}_3$, $\mathbf{Y}_2$, and $\mathbf{Y}_1$,

$$L\{\mathbf{X}_1, \mathbf{X}_2, \mathbf{X}_3\} \subseteq L\{\mathbf{Y}_1, \mathbf{Y}_2, \mathbf{Y}_3\},$$

so that

$$L\{\mathbf{Y}_1, \mathbf{Y}_2, \mathbf{Y}_3\} = L\{\mathbf{X}_1, \mathbf{X}_2, \mathbf{X}_3\}.$$

We now choose λ, μ to satisfy

$$(\mathbf{Y}_3, \mathbf{Y}_1) = (\mathbf{X}_3, \mathbf{Y}_1) + \lambda(\mathbf{Y}_2, \mathbf{Y}_1) + \mu(\mathbf{Y}_1, \mathbf{Y}_1) = 0.$$

Since $(\mathbf{Y}_2, \mathbf{Y}_1) = 0$, and $(\mathbf{Y}_1, \mathbf{Y}_1) \neq 0$, this gives

$$\mu = -\frac{(\mathbf{X}_3, \mathbf{Y}_1)}{(\mathbf{Y}_1, \mathbf{Y}_1)}.$$

We also want

$$(\mathbf{Y}_3, \mathbf{Y}_2) = (\mathbf{X}_3, \mathbf{Y}_2) + \lambda(\mathbf{Y}_2, \mathbf{Y}_2) + \mu(\mathbf{Y}_1, \mathbf{Y}_2) = 0,$$

which gives

$$\lambda = -\frac{(\mathbf{X}_3, \mathbf{Y}_2)}{(\mathbf{Y}_2, \mathbf{Y}_2)},$$

so that

$$\left.\begin{aligned} \mathbf{Y}_3 &= \mathbf{X}_3 - \frac{(\mathbf{X}_3, \mathbf{Y}_2)}{(\mathbf{Y}_2, \mathbf{Y}_2)}\mathbf{Y}_2 - \frac{(\mathbf{X}_3, \mathbf{Y}_1)}{(\mathbf{Y}_1, \mathbf{Y}_1)}\mathbf{Y}_1 \\ \mathbf{Y}_2 &= \mathbf{X}_2 - \frac{(\mathbf{X}_2, \mathbf{Y}_1)}{(\mathbf{Y}_1, \mathbf{Y}_1)}\mathbf{Y}_1, \\ \mathbf{Y}_1 &= \mathbf{X}_1 \end{aligned}\right\}$$

replaces the set of independent vectors $\mathbf{X}_1, \mathbf{X}_2, \mathbf{X}_3$ by a set $\mathbf{Y}_1, \mathbf{Y}_2, \mathbf{Y}_3$ of mutually orthogonal vectors.

We have given the process in detail because the extension to m independent vectors $\mathbf{X}_1, \mathbf{X}_2, \ldots, \mathbf{X}_m$ is immediate. We can show that

$$\left.\begin{aligned} \mathbf{Y}_1 &= \mathbf{X}_1, \\ \mathbf{Y}_i &= \mathbf{X}_i - \frac{(\mathbf{X}_i, \mathbf{Y}_{i-1})}{(\mathbf{Y}_{i-1}, \mathbf{Y}_{i-1})}\mathbf{Y}_{i-1} - \cdots - \frac{(\mathbf{X}_i, \mathbf{Y}_1)}{(\mathbf{Y}_1, \mathbf{Y}_1)}\mathbf{Y}_1 \end{aligned}\right\} \tag{85}$$

for $i = 2, 3, \ldots, m$ gives us a set $\mathbf{Y}_1, \mathbf{Y}_2, \ldots, \mathbf{Y}_m$ of mutually orthogonal vectors which are such that

$$L\{\mathbf{Y}_1, \mathbf{Y}_2, \ldots, \mathbf{Y}_m\} = L\{\mathbf{X}_1, \mathbf{X}_2, \ldots, \mathbf{X}_m\}.$$

Since any non-zero vector can be made into a unit vector by multiplication by a suitable scalar, and this will not affect its orthogonality properties, any basis can be replaced by a basis of orthogonal vectors of unit length. Such a basis has already been called an orthonormal basis. We express this as Theorem 26.

Theorem 26. *An orthonormal basis can be found for any vector subspace of V_n.*

Example 1

Find an orthogonal basis for the three-dimensional subspace of V_4:

$$L\{[1, 1, 1, 1], [2, 0, -1, 3], [3, 1, 2, 5]\}.$$

We set

$$\mathbf{Y}_1 = [1, 1, 1, 1],$$

then, using the formula (85):

$$\mathbf{Y}_2 = [2, 0, -1, 3] - \frac{([2, 0, -1, 3], [1, 1, 1, 1])}{([1, 1, 1, 1], [1, 1, 1, 1])}[1, 1, 1, 1]$$

$$= [2, 0, -1, 3] - [1, 1, 1, 1] = [1, -1, -2, 2],$$

and we see that $\mathbf{Y}_1$ and $\mathbf{Y}_2$ are orthogonal. We also have

$$\mathbf{Y}_3 = [3, 1, 2, 5] + \lambda[1, -1, -2, 2] + \mu[1, 1, 1, 1],$$

where

$$\lambda = -\frac{([3, 1, 2, 5], [1, -1, -2, 2])}{([1, -1, -2, 2], [1, -1, -2, 2])} = \frac{-(8)}{10} = \frac{-4}{5},$$

and

$$\mu = -\frac{([3, 1, 2, 5], [1, 1, 1, 1])}{([1, 1, 1, 1], [1, 1, 1, 1])} = \frac{-11}{4},$$

so that

$$\mathbf{Y}_3 = [3, 1, 2, 5] - \frac{4}{5}[1, -1, -2, 2] - \frac{11}{4}[1, 1, 1, 1]$$

$$= \frac{[-11, -19, +17, 13]}{20},$$

and this is orthogonal to $\mathbf{Y}_1 = [1, 1, 1, 1]$ and to $\mathbf{Y}_2 = [1, -1, -2, 2]$.

The three vectors [1, 1, 1, 1], [2, 0, −1, 3], [3, 1, 2, 5] have now been replaced by the orthogonal vectors

$$[1, 1, 1, 1], [1, -1, -2, 2], \frac{[-11, -19, 17, 13]}{20},$$

and each set of three vectors generates the same linear subspace of $V_4(R)$.

We have discussed *complementary* subspaces of V_n earlier on in this section. We also defined the *direct sum* of two subspaces. We now prove Theorem 27.

Theorem 27. *If U is a subspace of $V_n(R)$, there exists a unique subspace W of $V_n(R)$ orthogonal to U such that $V_n = U \oplus W$.*

Proof. Let a basis for U be the set of vectors $\mathbf{X}_1, \mathbf{X}_2, \ldots, \mathbf{X}_p$. We can *extend* this set to a basis $\mathbf{X}_1, \mathbf{X}_2, \ldots, \mathbf{X}_p, \mathbf{X}_{p+1}, \ldots, \mathbf{X}_n$ of V_n, so that

$$V_n = L\{\mathbf{X}_1, \ldots, \mathbf{X}_p, \mathbf{X}_{p+1}, \ldots, \mathbf{X}_n\}.$$

Apply the Gram-Schmidt process to this basis to obtain an orthogonal basis for V_n, say,

$$V_n = L\{\mathbf{Y}_1, \ldots, \mathbf{Y}_p, \mathbf{Y}_{p+1}, \ldots, \mathbf{Y}_n\}.$$

We know from the method for determining this basis that

$$L\{\mathbf{X}_1, \ldots, \mathbf{X}_p\} = L\{\mathbf{Y}_1, \ldots, \mathbf{Y}_p\}.$$

We choose
$$W = L\{\mathbf{Y}_{p+1}, \ldots, \mathbf{Y}_n\};$$
then
$$U \cap W = \mathbf{0},$$
$$V = U \oplus W,$$
and W is orthogonal to U.

To show that W is unique, we prove that any vector $\mathbf{X}$ orthogonal to all vectors of U must lie in W. We know that $\mathbf{X} = \mathbf{Y} + \mathbf{Z}$, where $\mathbf{Y} \in U$, and $\mathbf{Z} \in W$, and that this expression for $\mathbf{X}$ is unique. But

$$(\mathbf{X}, \mathbf{Y}) = (\mathbf{Y} + \mathbf{Z}, \mathbf{Y}) = (\mathbf{Y}, \mathbf{Y}) + (\mathbf{Z}, \mathbf{Y}) = 0,$$

and $(\mathbf{Z}, \mathbf{Y}) = 0$, so that $(\mathbf{Y}, \mathbf{Y}) = 0$ and therefore $\mathbf{Y} = \mathbf{0}$. Hence $\mathbf{X} \in W$, and W is defined uniquely as the set of vectors orthogonal to all the vectors in U.

We conclude this section with another method of describing subspaces of $V_n(R)$. Let U and W be orthogonal complements in $V_n(R)$, and suppose that U has a basis:

$$\begin{aligned}
\mathbf{Y}_1 &= [a_{11}, a_{12}, \ldots, a_{1n}], \\
\mathbf{Y}_2 &= [a_{21}, a_{22}, \ldots, a_{2n}], \\
&\cdot \quad \cdot \quad \cdot \quad \cdots \quad \cdot \\
\mathbf{Y}_p &= [a_{p1}, a_{p2}, \ldots, a_{pn}].
\end{aligned}$$

Every vector $\mathbf{X} = [X_1, X_2, \ldots, X_n]$ of W satisfies the relations:

$$(\mathbf{X}, \mathbf{Y}_1) = (\mathbf{X}, \mathbf{Y}_2) = \cdots = (\mathbf{X}, \mathbf{Y}_p) = 0,$$

and these give the equations

$$\left.\begin{aligned}
a_{11}X_1 + a_{12}X_2 + \cdots + a_{1n}X_n &= 0, \\
a_{21}X_1 + a_{22}X_2 + \cdots + a_{2n}X_n &= 0, \\
\cdot \qquad \cdot \qquad \cdots \qquad \cdot \quad & \cdot \\
a_{p1}X_1 + a_{p2}X_2 + \cdots + a_{pn}X_n &= 0.
\end{aligned}\right\}$$

We know that no vectors outside W satisfy these equations, and we can therefore describe the *solution space* of these equations as the vector space W, which is of dimension $n - p$, and the orthogonal complement of U in V_n. The p vectors $\mathbf{Y}_1, \ldots, \mathbf{Y}_p$ are independent, so that the p row vectors of the matrix of coefficients of the foregoing equations are independent. We shall pursue the solution of linear equations further in the next chapter.

EXERCISES 28

1. Prove that the intersection $U \cap W$ of two orthogonal spaces U and W consists of the zero vector only.

2. Show that the Gram-Schmidt process applied to the four vectors

$$[1, 0, 1, 0], \qquad [1, 1, 3, 0], \qquad [0, 1, 0, 0], \qquad [0, 0, 0, 1]$$

produces the four mutually orthogonal vectors

$$[1, 0, 1, 0], \qquad [-1, 1, 1, 0], \qquad [1/3, 2/3, -1/3, 0], \qquad [0, 0, 0, 1].$$

3. Find a subspace W of V_4 orthogonal to $U = L\{[1, 0, 1, 0], [1, 1, 3, 0]\}$ and such that $U \oplus W = V_4$.

4. Let $V_n = U \oplus W$, where U and W are orthogonal subspaces. Then for any vector $\mathbf{X} \in V_n$ we have $\mathbf{X} = \mathbf{Y} + \mathbf{Z}$, where $\mathbf{Y} \in U$ and $\mathbf{Z} \in W$. The vector $\mathbf{Y}$ is called the *orthogonal projection* of $\mathbf{X}$ on U, and $\mathbf{Z}$ is the *orthogonal projection* of $\mathbf{X}$ on W. Find the orthogonal projection of $\mathbf{X} = [1, -2, 3, 0]$ on the subspace $L\{[0, 1, -2, 0], [1, 2, 1, 0]\}$, where the vectors all lie in V_4.

CHAPTER SEVEN

Matrices

In this chapter we shall discuss matrices, operations with matrices, and applications to the theory of linear equations and determinants.

29. Definitions

Once more we shall restrict ourselves to the field R of real numbers, so that when we speak of numbers, we are talking about real numbers.

An m by n matrix (written $m \times n$ matrix) is a rectangular array of mn numbers, with m rows and n columns, thus:

$$\mathbf{A} = [a_{ij}] \qquad (i = 1, \ldots, m; j = 1, \ldots, n),$$

that is:

$$\mathbf{A} = \begin{bmatrix} a_{11} & a_{12} & \cdots & a_{1n} \\ a_{21} & a_{22} & \cdots & a_{2n} \\ \cdot & \cdot & \cdots & \cdot \\ a_{m1} & a_{m2} & \cdots & a_{mn} \end{bmatrix}.$$

We have come across such arrays with great frequency in previous chapters, as coefficients in a system of linear equations.

The rows of the matrix

$$[a_{11}, a_{12}, \ldots, a_{1n}], [a_{21}, a_{22}, \ldots, a_{2n}], \ldots, [a_{m1}, a_{m2}, \ldots, a_{mn}]$$

can be considered as vectors, as we have seen when we talked of a *row space* in § 26, p. 126. The columns

$$\begin{bmatrix} a_{11} \\ a_{21} \\ \cdot \\ \cdot \\ \cdot \\ a_{m1} \end{bmatrix}, \begin{bmatrix} a_{12} \\ a_{22} \\ \cdot \\ \cdot \\ \cdot \\ a_{m2} \end{bmatrix}, \ldots, \begin{bmatrix} a_{1n} \\ a_{2n} \\ \cdot \\ \cdot \\ \cdot \\ a_{mn} \end{bmatrix}$$

may also be considered as vectors in $V_m(R)$, and for convenience we write these as row-vectors:

$$[a_{11}, a_{21}, \ldots, a_{m1}]^T, \ldots, [a_{1n}, a_{2n}, \ldots, a_{mn}]^T,$$

the T index (read "transpose") indicating that the row is to be considered as a column.

Two matrices are said to have the same *shape* when each is an $m \times n$ matrix. A matrix is said to be a *square* matrix when it is an $n \times n$ matrix.

We only consider a relation of *equality* between matrices of the same shape. The matrices

$$\mathbf{A} = \begin{bmatrix} a_{11} & \cdots & a_{1n} \\ \cdot & \cdots & \cdot \\ a_{m1} & \cdots & a_{mn} \end{bmatrix}, \quad \mathbf{B} = \begin{bmatrix} b_{11} & \cdots & b_{1n} \\ \cdot & \cdots & \cdot \\ b_{m1} & \cdots & b_{mn} \end{bmatrix}$$

are said to be *equal*, written $\mathbf{A} = \mathbf{B}$, if and only if

$$a_{ij} = b_{ij} \qquad (i = i, \ldots, m;\ j = 1, \ldots n),$$

that is, if and only if the arrays look identical.

We have already introduced the transpose of a row of a matrix. The *transpose* of an $m \times n$ matrix $\mathbf{A} = [a_{ij}]$ is obtained by writing the rows of $\mathbf{A}$, in order, as columns. The transposed matrix is denoted by $\mathbf{A}^T$, and we have

$$\mathbf{A} = \begin{bmatrix} a_{11} & a_{12} & \cdots & a_{1n} \\ a_{21} & a_{22} & \cdots & a_{2n} \\ \cdot & \cdot & \cdots & \cdot \\ a_{m1} & a_{m2} & \cdots & a_{mn} \end{bmatrix}, \quad \mathbf{A}^T = \begin{bmatrix} a_{11} & a_{21} & \cdots & a_{m1} \\ a_{12} & a_{22} & \cdots & a_{m2} \\ \cdot & \cdot & \cdots & \cdot \\ a_{1n} & a_{2n} & \cdots & a_{mn} \end{bmatrix}.$$

If $\mathbf{A}$ is $m \times n$, $\mathbf{A}^T$ is $n \times m$. We see that

$$(\mathbf{A}^T)^T = \mathbf{A},$$

and there can only be a relation of equality between $\mathbf{A}$ and $\mathbf{A}^T$ if $m = n$.

If $m = n$ and $\mathbf{A} = \mathbf{A}^T$, $\mathbf{A}$ is said to be a *symmetric* matrix. For example,

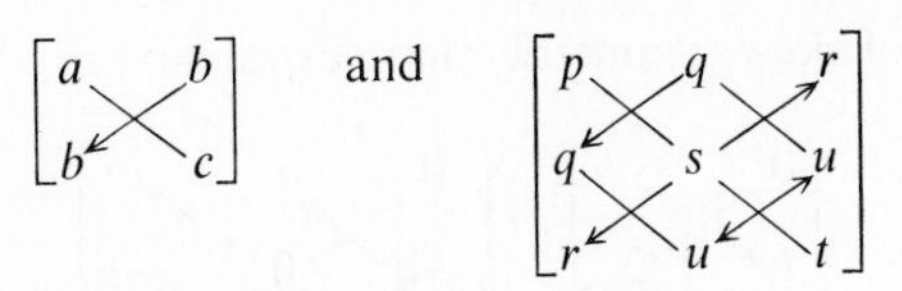

are both symmetric matrices. The condition reads:

$$a_{ij} = a_{ji} \qquad (i, j = 1, 2, \ldots, n),$$

so that elements which are mirror images in *the principal diagonal* (which consists of all the elements a_{ii} ($i = 1, 2, \ldots, n$)) are identical. No condition is imposed on the elements a_{ii} themselves.

We now define certain operations on a matrix.

Multiplication by a Scalar

If $\mathbf{A} = [a_{ij}]$, and $k \in R$, we define

$$k\mathbf{A} = [ka_{ij}], \qquad (i = 1, \ldots, m;\ j = 1, \ldots, n),$$

so that *every* element of the matrix $\mathbf{A}$ is multiplied by k. For example,

$$k\begin{bmatrix} a_{11} & a_{12} & a_{13} \\ a_{21} & a_{22} & a_{23} \end{bmatrix} = \begin{bmatrix} ka_{11} & ka_{12} & ka_{13} \\ ka_{21} & ka_{22} & ka_{23} \end{bmatrix}.$$

We write $-1 \cdot \mathbf{A} = -\mathbf{A}$, and so

$$-\mathbf{A} = [-a_{ij}],$$

and

$$-\begin{bmatrix} a_{11} & a_{12} & a_{13} \\ a_{21} & a_{22} & a_{23} \end{bmatrix} = \begin{bmatrix} -a_{11} & -a_{12} & -a_{13} \\ -a_{21} & -a_{22} & -a_{23} \end{bmatrix}.$$

If $\mathbf{A}$ is an $n \times n$ matrix, we have seen that $\mathbf{A} = \mathbf{A}^T$ is the definition of a *symmetric* matrix. We now define a *skew-symmetric* matrix to be one for which

$$\mathbf{A} = -\mathbf{A}^T.$$

This condition involves the n^2 equations:

$$a_{ij} = -a_{ji} \qquad (i, j = 1, \ldots, n),$$

and when $i = j$, we have the equations

$$a_{ii} = -a_{ii} \qquad (i = 1, \ldots, n),$$

so that

$$a_{ii} = 0 \qquad (i = 1, \ldots, n).$$

As examples of skew-symmetric matrices we have:

$$\begin{bmatrix} 0 & -b \\ b & 0 \end{bmatrix}, \quad \begin{bmatrix} 0 & q & r \\ -q & 0 & -s \\ -r & s & 0 \end{bmatrix}.$$

Reflection in the principal diagonal *changes* the sign of the element.

Addition of Matrices

We only define the addition of matrices of the same shape, and then we add corresponding elements. If

$$\mathbf{A} = \begin{bmatrix} a_{11} & \cdots & a_{1n} \\ \cdot & & \cdot \\ \cdot & \cdots & \cdot \\ \cdot & & \cdot \\ a_{m1} & \cdots & a_{mn} \end{bmatrix}, \quad \mathbf{B} = \begin{bmatrix} b_{11} & \cdots & b_{1n} \\ & & \\ \cdot & \cdots & \cdot \\ & & \\ b_{m1} & \cdots & b_{mn} \end{bmatrix},$$

we define

$$\mathbf{A} + \mathbf{B} = \begin{bmatrix} a_{11} + b_{11} & \cdots & a_{1n} + b_{1n} \\ \cdot & & \cdot \\ \cdot & \cdots & \cdot \\ \cdot & & \cdot \\ a_{m1} + b_{m1} & \cdots & a_{mn} + b_{mn} \end{bmatrix},$$

and evidently

$$\mathbf{A} + \mathbf{B} = \mathbf{B} + \mathbf{A}.$$

If $\mathbf{C} = [c_{ij}]$ is also an $m \times n$ matrix,

$$\mathbf{A} + (\mathbf{B} + \mathbf{C}) = (\mathbf{A} + \mathbf{B}) + \mathbf{C},$$

as is clear from the definition.

We define the $m \times n$ *zero matrix* to be the matrix with zero for every entry, thus

$$\mathbf{0} = \begin{bmatrix} 0 & \cdots & 0 \\ \cdot & \cdots & \cdot \\ 0 & \cdots & 0 \end{bmatrix},$$

and then for any $m \times n$ matrix $\mathbf{A}$,

$$\mathbf{A} + \mathbf{0} = \mathbf{0} + \mathbf{A} = \mathbf{A}.$$

We have defined $-\mathbf{A}$, and now we see that

$$\mathbf{A} - \mathbf{A} = -\mathbf{A} + \mathbf{A} = \mathbf{0}.$$

Multiplication of Matrices

The addition and scalar multiplication of matrices have not introduced any features markedly different from similar definitions for vectors with mn components. But multiplication introduces a new method of composition. This can be given adequate motivation, but we propose to leave this out for the present. (See Chapter 9, § 37, p. 212, for the motivation.)

The matrix product $\mathbf{AB}$ of an $m \times n$ matrix $\mathbf{A}$ and a $p \times q$ matrix $\mathbf{B}$ can only be formed if $\mathbf{B}$ is $n \times q$, that is, if the number of rows in $\mathbf{B}$ is equal to the number of columns in $\mathbf{A}$.

If this condition is satisfied, the element in the ith row and jth column of the product $\mathbf{C} = \mathbf{AB}$ is formed by taking the inner product of the ith *row*-vector of $\mathbf{A}$, and the jth *column*-vector of $\mathbf{B}$; thus:

$$c_{ij} = a_{i1}b_{1j} + a_{i2}b_{2j} + \cdots + a_{in}b_{nj},$$

or, diagrammatically:

$$\mathbf{C} = [c_{ij}] = \begin{bmatrix} a_{11} & \cdots & a_{1n} \\ \cdot & \cdots & \cdot \\ \boxed{a_{i1} \quad \cdots \quad a_{in}} \\ \cdot & \cdots & \cdot \\ a_{m1} & \cdots & a_{mn} \end{bmatrix} \begin{bmatrix} b_{11} & \cdot\cdot & b_{1j} & \cdot\cdot & b_{1q} \\ \cdot & & \cdot & & \cdot \\ \cdot & \cdot\cdot & \cdot & \cdot\cdot & \cdot \\ \cdot & & \cdot & & \cdot \\ b_{n1} & \cdot\cdot & b_{nj} & \cdot\cdot & b_{nq} \end{bmatrix}.$$

We can think of the ith row of $\mathbf{A}$ being picked up, turned clockwise through a right angle, laid along the jth column of $\mathbf{B}$, corresponding elements multiplied together, and the sum entered into the ith row and the jth column space in $\mathbf{C}$.

For example,

$$\begin{bmatrix} a_{11} & a_{12} & a_{13} \\ a_{21} & a_{22} & a_{23} \end{bmatrix} \begin{bmatrix} b_{11} & b_{12} \\ b_{21} & b_{22} \\ b_{31} & b_{32} \end{bmatrix}$$

$$= \begin{bmatrix} a_{11}b_{11} + a_{12}b_{21} + a_{13}b_{31} & a_{11}b_{12} + a_{12}b_{22} + a_{13}b_{32} \\ a_{21}b_{11} + a_{22}b_{21} + a_{23}b_{31} & a_{21}b_{12} + a_{22}b_{22} + a_{23}b_{32} \end{bmatrix}.$$

The product $\mathbf{AB}$ of an $m \times n$ matrix $\mathbf{A}$ and an $n \times p$ matrix $\mathbf{B}$ is an $m \times p$ matrix. We can think of the common n vanishing in the multiplication:

$$(m \times \not{n})(\not{n} \times p) = m \times p,$$

having served its purpose.

We do *not* have, as a rule,

$$\mathbf{AB} = \mathbf{BA}.$$

In fact, if $\mathbf{AB}$ is defined, $\mathbf{BA}$ may not even be defined, since for multiplication of an $n \times p$ matrix $\mathbf{B}$ by an $m \times n$ matrix $\mathbf{A}$, we must have $p = m$. Hence the matrix products

$$\mathbf{AB}, \mathbf{BA}$$

are both defined if and only if $\mathbf{A}$ is $m \times n$ and $\mathbf{B}$ is $n \times m$. Then $\mathbf{AB}$ is $m \times m$, and $\mathbf{BA}$ is $n \times n$, and so the only possibility for $\mathbf{AB} = \mathbf{BA}$ lies in $m = n$. But even here, when $\mathbf{A}$ and $\mathbf{B}$ are both square matrices of the same shape, $\mathbf{AB} \neq \mathbf{BA}$ in general, as a simple example shows. Take

$$\mathbf{A} = \begin{bmatrix} 1 & -1 \\ 2 & 3 \end{bmatrix}, \quad \mathbf{B} = \begin{bmatrix} 0 & 4 \\ 1 & 1 \end{bmatrix},$$

then

$$\mathbf{AB} = \begin{bmatrix} -1 & 3 \\ 3 & 11 \end{bmatrix}, \quad \mathbf{BA} = \begin{bmatrix} 8 & 12 \\ 3 & 2 \end{bmatrix}.$$

With this warning, we proceed with some exercises for the student to test his understanding of the rule for multiplication.

EXERCISES 29.1

1. Show that

$$\begin{bmatrix} 1 & 3 \\ 4 & 5 \\ 6 & 7 \end{bmatrix} \begin{bmatrix} 0 & 4 & 8 \\ 2 & 6 & 10 \end{bmatrix} = \begin{bmatrix} 6 & 22 & 38 \\ 10 & 46 & 82 \\ 14 & 66 & 118 \end{bmatrix},$$

but

$$\begin{bmatrix} 0 & 4 & 8 \\ 2 & 6 & 10 \end{bmatrix} \begin{bmatrix} 1 & 3 \\ 4 & 5 \\ 6 & 7 \end{bmatrix} = \begin{bmatrix} 64 & 76 \\ 86 & 106 \end{bmatrix}.$$

2. Prove that

$$\begin{bmatrix} \cos\theta & -\sin\theta \\ \sin\theta & \cos\theta \end{bmatrix} \begin{bmatrix} \cos\varphi & -\sin\varphi \\ \sin\varphi & \cos\varphi \end{bmatrix} = \begin{bmatrix} \cos(\theta+\varphi) & -\sin(\theta+\varphi) \\ \sin(\theta+\varphi) & \cos(\theta+\varphi) \end{bmatrix}.$$

3. Prove that

$$\begin{bmatrix} 1 & 0 & 0 & 0 \\ 0 & 1 & 0 & 0 \\ 0 & 0 & 1 & 0 \\ 0 & 0 & 0 & 1 \end{bmatrix} \begin{bmatrix} a & b & c \\ e & f & g \\ p & q & r \\ l & m & n \end{bmatrix} = \begin{bmatrix} a & b & c \\ e & f & g \\ p & q & r \\ l & m & n \end{bmatrix},$$

and

$$\begin{bmatrix} a & b & c \\ e & f & g \\ p & q & r \\ l & m & n \end{bmatrix} \begin{bmatrix} 1 & 0 & 0 \\ 0 & 1 & 0 \\ 0 & 0 & 1 \end{bmatrix} = \begin{bmatrix} a & b & c \\ e & f & g \\ p & q & r \\ l & m & n \end{bmatrix}.$$

The Unity Matrix

This square matrix (which appears in Exercise 3) above, may be of any size. An $n \times n$ unity matrix, usually denoted by $\mathbf{I}_n$, is defined thus:

$$\left.\begin{aligned} a_{ij} &= 0 \qquad (i \neq j), \\ a_{ii} &= 1 \qquad (i = 1, \ldots, n) \end{aligned}\right\}$$

If $\mathbf{A} = [a_{ij}]$ $(i = 1, \ldots, m;\ j = 1, \ldots, n)$ is an $m \times n$ matrix, then

$$\mathbf{I}_m\mathbf{A} = \mathbf{A}\mathbf{I}_n = \mathbf{A}. \tag{86}$$

This fundamental result should be verified by the reader. (It is illustrated in Exercise 3.)

We call the multiplication of a matrix **A** on its left by a matrix **B**, the result being **BA**, *premultiplication of* **A** *by* **B**.

We call the multiplication of a matrix **A** on its right by a matrix **B**, the result being **AB**, *postmultiplication of* **A** *by* **B**.

The result embodied in equations (86) may be stated thus: *Premultiplication or postmultiplication of a matrix* **A** *by a suitable unity matrix leaves* **A** *unchanged.*

The Elementary Matrices

These are obtained from the unity matrices by carrying out the elementary operations I, II, and III referred to in § 21, p. 100 on the rows or the columns of a given unity matrix. We first consider operations on the rows of $\mathbf{I}_m$. We shall use the resulting matrix for the *premultiplication* of a given $m \times n$ matrix **A**.

I. Interchange row i and row j of $\mathbf{I}_m$, and call the resulting matrix $\mathbf{I}_m(i, i)$. Then if we premultiply **A** by $\mathbf{I}_m(i, j)$, we interchange the rows i and j in **A**.

For example,

$$\mathbf{I}_4(2, 3) = \begin{bmatrix} 1 & 0 & 0 & 0 \\ 0 & 0 & 1 & 0 \\ 0 & 1 & 0 & 0 \\ 0 & 0 & 0 & 1 \end{bmatrix},$$

and

$$\mathbf{I}_4(2, 3)\begin{bmatrix} a_{11} & a_{12} \\ a_{21} & a_{22} \\ a_{31} & a_{32} \\ a_{41} & a_{42} \end{bmatrix} = \begin{bmatrix} a_{11} & a_{12} \\ a_{31} & a_{32} \\ a_{21} & a_{22} \\ a_{41} & a_{42} \end{bmatrix}.$$

Carrying out the calculations will convince the reader of the truth of the general statement.

II. Multiply row i of $\mathbf{I}_m$ by a scalar $k \neq 0$, and call the resulting matrix $\mathbf{I}_m(k(i))$. Then premultiplication of $\mathbf{A}$ by $\mathbf{I}_m(k(i))$ multiplies row i of $\mathbf{A}$ by k.

For example,

$$\mathbf{I}_4(k(3)) = \begin{bmatrix} 1 & 0 & 0 & 0 \\ 0 & 1 & 0 & 0 \\ 0 & 0 & k & 0 \\ 0 & 0 & 0 & 1 \end{bmatrix},$$

and

$$\mathbf{I}_4(k(3)) \begin{bmatrix} a_{11} & a_{12} \\ a_{21} & a_{22} \\ a_{31} & a_{32} \\ a_{41} & a_{42} \end{bmatrix} = \begin{bmatrix} a_{11} & a_{12} \\ a_{21} & a_{22} \\ ka_{31} & ka_{32} \\ a_{41} & a_{42} \end{bmatrix}.$$

III. To row i of $\mathbf{I}_m$ add k(row j), and call the resulting matrix

$$\mathbf{I}_m((i) + k(j)).$$

Then premultiplication of $\mathbf{A}$ by $\mathbf{I}_m((i) + k(j))$ adds k(row j) to row i of $\mathbf{A}$.

For example,

$$\mathbf{I}_4((2) + k(3)) = \begin{bmatrix} 1 & 0 & 0 & 0 \\ 0 & 1 & k & 0 \\ 0 & 0 & 1 & 0 \\ 0 & 0 & 0 & 1 \end{bmatrix},$$

and

$$\mathbf{I}_4((2) + k(3)) \begin{bmatrix} a_{11} & a_{12} \\ a_{21} & a_{22} \\ a_{31} & a_{32} \\ a_{41} & a_{42} \end{bmatrix} = \begin{bmatrix} a_{11} & a_{12} \\ a_{21} + ka_{31} & a_{22} + ka_{32} \\ a_{31} & a_{32} \\ a_{41} & a_{42} \end{bmatrix}.$$

Again, carrying out the calculations in this simple case will convince the reader of the truth of the general statement.

The matrices $\mathbf{I}_m(i, j)$, $\mathbf{I}_m(k(i))$, $\mathbf{I}_m(i + k(j))$ are called *elementary* matrices, and we shall make considerable use of them.

Postmultiplication of a given $m \times n$ matrix $\mathbf{A}$ is also our concern, and we now operate on the *columns* of $\mathbf{I}_n$.

I. Interchange column i and column j of $\mathbf{I}_n$, and call the resulting matrix $\mathbf{I}_n^*(i, j)$. Then *postmultiplication* of A by $\mathbf{I}_n^*(i, j)$ interchanges *columns* i and j in $\mathbf{A}$.

For example,

$$\mathbf{I}_4^*(2, 3) = \begin{bmatrix} 1 & 0 & 0 & 0 \\ 0 & 0 & 1 & 0 \\ 0 & 1 & 0 & 0 \\ 0 & 0 & 0 & 1 \end{bmatrix} = \mathbf{I}_4(2, 3)$$

and

$$\begin{bmatrix} a_{11} & a_{12} & a_{13} & a_{14} \\ a_{21} & a_{22} & a_{23} & a_{24} \end{bmatrix} \mathbf{I}_4^*(2, 3) = \begin{bmatrix} a_{11} & a_{13} & a_{12} & a_{14} \\ a_{21} & a_{23} & a_{22} & a_{24} \end{bmatrix}.$$

II. Multiply column i of $\mathbf{I}_n$ by a scalar $k \neq 0$, and call the resulting matrix $\mathbf{I}_n^*(k(i))$. Postmultiplication of $\mathbf{A}$ by $\mathbf{I}_n^*(k(i))$ multiplies *column* i of $\mathbf{A}$ by k.

For example,

$$\mathbf{I}_4^*(k(3)) = \begin{bmatrix} 1 & 0 & 0 & 0 \\ 0 & 1 & 0 & 0 \\ 0 & 0 & k & 0 \\ 0 & 0 & 0 & 1 \end{bmatrix} = \mathbf{I}_4(k(3)),$$

and

$$\begin{bmatrix} a_{11} & a_{12} & a_{13} & a_{14} \\ a_{21} & a_{22} & a_{23} & a_{24} \end{bmatrix} \mathbf{I}_4^*(k(3)) = \begin{bmatrix} a_{11} & a_{12} & ka_{13} & a_{14} \\ a_{21} & a_{22} & ka_{23} & a_{24} \end{bmatrix}.$$

III. To column i of $\mathbf{I}_n$ add k(column j), and call the resulting matrix $\mathbf{I}_n^*((i) + k(j))$. Postmultiplication of $\mathbf{A}$ by $\mathbf{I}_n((i) + (k(j))$ adds k(column j) to column i of $\mathbf{A}$.

For example,

$$\mathbf{I}_4^*((2) + k(3)) = \begin{bmatrix} 1 & 0 & 0 & 0 \\ 0 & 1 & 0 & 0 \\ 0 & k & 1 & 0 \\ 0 & 0 & 0 & 1 \end{bmatrix} = \mathbf{I}_4((3) + k(2)),$$

and

$$\begin{bmatrix} a_{11} & a_{12} & a_{13} & a_{14} \\ a_{21} & a_{22} & a_{23} & a_{24} \end{bmatrix} \mathbf{I}_4^*((2) + k(3))$$
$$= \begin{bmatrix} a_{11} & a_{12} + ka_{13} & a_{13} & a_{14} \\ a_{21} & a_{22} + ka_{23} & a_{23} & a_{24} \end{bmatrix}.$$

EXERCISES 29.2

1. By premultiplication by suitable elementary matrices, transform the matrix

$$\begin{bmatrix} -1 & 0 & 0 & 1 \\ -1 & 1 & 0 & 0 \\ -1 & 0 & 1 & 0 \end{bmatrix} \text{ into the matrix } \begin{bmatrix} 1 & 0 & 0 & -1 \\ 0 & 1 & 0 & -1 \\ 0 & 0 & 1 & -1 \end{bmatrix},$$

the latter matrix being in echelon form.

2. By premultiplication by suitable elementary matrices transform the matrix

$$\begin{bmatrix} 5 & 3 & 8 & 9 \\ 1 & -1 & 2 & 3 \\ 1 & 0 & 1 & 0 \\ 3 & 4 & 5 & 6 \end{bmatrix} \text{ into the echelon form } \begin{bmatrix} 1 & 3/5 & 8/5 & 9/5 \\ 0 & 1 & -1/4 & -3/4 \\ 0 & 0 & 1 & 3 \\ 0 & 0 & 0 & 0 \end{bmatrix}$$

(see Example 1, p. 126).

3. By postmultiplication of the second (echelon form) matrix in Exercise 1 by suitable elementary matrices, transform it into the matrix

$$\begin{bmatrix} 1 & 0 & 0 & 0 \\ 0 & 1 & 0 & 0 \\ 0 & 0 & 1 & 0 \end{bmatrix}.$$

4. If $\mathbf{A}$ is $m \times n$, and $\mathbf{B}$ is $n \times p$, prove that the row-vectors of the matrix $\mathbf{AB}$ are $\mathbf{R}_1\mathbf{B}, \mathbf{R}_2\mathbf{B}, \ldots, \mathbf{R}_m\mathbf{B}$, where $\mathbf{R}_1, \mathbf{R}_2, \ldots, \mathbf{R}_m$ are the row-vectors of $\mathbf{A}$; that is, linear combinations of the row-vectors of $\mathbf{B}$.

5. Prove that the column-vectors of the matrix product $\mathbf{AB}$ are $\mathbf{AC}_1, \mathbf{AC}_2, \ldots, \mathbf{AC}_p$, where $\mathbf{C}_1, \mathbf{C}_2, \ldots, \mathbf{C}_p$ are the column-vectors of $\mathbf{B}$; that is, linear combinations of the column-vectors of $\mathbf{A}$.

Properties of Matrix Multiplication

If $\mathbf{A} = [a_{ij}]$ is $m \times n$, and $\mathbf{B} = [b_{ij}]$ is $n \times p$, we prove that

$$(\mathbf{AB})^T = \mathbf{B}^T\mathbf{A}^T. \tag{86*}$$

To prove this, we note that the element in row i and column j of $(\mathbf{AB})^T$ = the element in row j and column i of $\mathbf{AB}$ = the inner product of row j of $\mathbf{A}$ and column i of $\mathbf{B}$ = the inner product of column j of $\mathbf{A}^T$ and row i of $\mathbf{B}^T$ = the inner product of row i of $\mathbf{B}^T$ and column j of $\mathbf{A}^T$ = the element in row i and column j of $\mathbf{B}^T\mathbf{A}^T$. Hence

$$(\mathbf{AB})^T = \mathbf{B}^T\mathbf{A}^T,$$

since elements in corresponding positions are equal.

With this rule to help us, we can prove all the properties of the post-multiplication of a matrix by an elementary matrix from the properties of premultiplication by an elementary matrix (see Exercise 3 which follows).

Matrix multiplication has distributive laws which follow the usual pattern. If $\mathbf{A}$ is $m \times n$, and both $\mathbf{B}$ and $\mathbf{C}$ are $n \times p$ matrices, then $\mathbf{AB}$ and $\mathbf{AC}$ are defined, and so is $\mathbf{B} + \mathbf{C}$, and we have

$$\mathbf{A}(\mathbf{B} + \mathbf{C}) = \mathbf{AB} + \mathbf{AC}. \tag{87}$$

This follows immediately from the fact that

$$\sum_{k=1}^{n} a_{ik}(b_{kj} + c_{kj}) = \sum_{k=1}^{n} a_{ik}b_{kj} + \sum_{k=1}^{n} a_{ik}c_{kj},$$

each summation representing the term in row i and column j of the matrices $\mathbf{A}(\mathbf{B} + \mathbf{C})$, $\mathbf{AB}$, and $\mathbf{AC}$ respectively.

Similarly, if both $\mathbf{B}$ and $\mathbf{C}$ are $m \times n$, and $\mathbf{A}$ is $n \times p$,

$$(\mathbf{B} + \mathbf{C})\mathbf{A} = \mathbf{BA} + \mathbf{CA} \tag{88}$$

We now come to the proof of the theorem that multiplication is *associative*; that is, that

$$\mathbf{A}(\mathbf{BC}) = (\mathbf{AB})\mathbf{C}. \tag{89}$$

For these multiplications to be possible, if $\mathbf{A}$ is an $m \times n$ matrix, $\mathbf{B}$ must be $n \times p$, and $\mathbf{C}$ must be $p \times q$, the final matrix on either side being an

$$(m \times \not{n})(\not{n} \times \not{p})(\not{p} \times q) = m \times q$$

matrix.

The term in row i and column j of $\mathbf{A}(\mathbf{BC})$ is $\sum_{k=1}^{n} a_{ik}b_{kj}{}^*$, where $b_{kj}{}^*$ is the term in row k and column j of $\mathbf{BC}$. Since

$$b_{kj}{}^* = \sum_{l=1}^{p} b_{kl}c_{lj},$$

the term in row i and column j of **A(BC)** is

$$\sum_{k=1}^{n} a_{ik} \sum_{l=1}^{p} b_{kl}c_{lj} = \left(\sum_{k=1}^{n} a_{ik}b_{kl}\right) \sum_{l=1}^{p} c_{lj},$$

and $\sum_{k=1}^{n} a_{ik}b_{kl}$ is the term in row i and column l of **AB**, and

$$\left(\sum_{k=1}^{n} a_{ik}b_{kl}\right) \sum_{l=1}^{p} c_{lj}$$

is the term in row i and column j of **(AB)C**, so that equation (89) is correct.

Finally, we note that it is possible for a product **AB** of two matrices to be a zero matrix without either being a zero matrix. For example,

$$\begin{bmatrix} 0 & 0 \\ 1 & 0 \end{bmatrix} \begin{bmatrix} 0 & 0 \\ 0 & 2 \end{bmatrix} = \begin{bmatrix} 0 & 0 \\ 0 & 0 \end{bmatrix},$$

and neither matrix appearing in the multiplication is a zero matrix.

This raises the question whether a matrix can have an *inverse*. Some matrices do; for example:

$$\begin{bmatrix} 1 & 2 \\ 3 & 4 \end{bmatrix} \begin{bmatrix} -2 & 1 \\ 3/2 & -1/2 \end{bmatrix} = \begin{bmatrix} 1 & 0 \\ 0 & 1 \end{bmatrix},$$

and

$$\begin{bmatrix} -2 & 1 \\ 3/2 & -1/2 \end{bmatrix} \begin{bmatrix} 1 & 2 \\ 3 & 4 \end{bmatrix} = \begin{bmatrix} 1 & 0 \\ 0 & 1 \end{bmatrix},$$

so that we have two matrices **A** and **B**, both 2×2, such that

$$\mathbf{AB} = \mathbf{BA} = \mathbf{I}_2,$$

where $\mathbf{I}_2$ is the unity 2×2 matrix. It is tempting to call **B** the *inverse* of **A**, and **A** is then the inverse of **B**. We discuss the conditions a matrix must satisfy to have an inverse in the next section.

EXERCISES 29.3

1. Find by trial and error, or by solving equations, matrices $\mathbf{A}^*$ and $\mathbf{B}^*$ such that $\mathbf{AA}^* = \mathbf{I}_2 = \mathbf{BB}^*$, where

$$\mathbf{A} = \begin{bmatrix} 3 & 4 \\ 2 & 3 \end{bmatrix}, \quad \mathbf{B} = \begin{bmatrix} 9 & 1 \\ 8 & 2 \end{bmatrix}, \quad \mathbf{I}_2 = \begin{bmatrix} 1 & 0 \\ 0 & 1 \end{bmatrix}.$$

Verify that $\mathbf{A}^*\mathbf{A} = \mathbf{I}_2 = \mathbf{B}^*\mathbf{B}$, and verify or prove that $\mathbf{B}^*\mathbf{A}^*\ \mathbf{AB} = \mathbf{I}_2$.

2. Show that the matrix $\mathbf{A} = \begin{bmatrix} 6 & -4 \\ 9 & -6 \end{bmatrix}$ satisfies the equation $\mathbf{A}^2 = \mathbf{0}$. Find all 2×2 matrices which satisfy this equation.

3. The matrix $\mathbf{E}$ is obtained from the unity matrix $\mathbf{I}_n$ by an elementary transformation on the rows of $\mathbf{I}_n$, so that $\mathbf{E}$ is an elementary matrix (p. 154). If $\mathbf{A}$ is an $n \times p$ matrix, so that $\mathbf{EA}$ is the matrix which arises from an elementary transformation being applied to the rows of $\mathbf{A}$, show that the identity

$$(\mathbf{EA})^T = \mathbf{A}^T\mathbf{E}^T$$

indicates that the postmultiplication of a matrix $\mathbf{A}$ by an elementary matrix obtained by operating on the columns of $\mathbf{I}_n$ effects an elementary transformation on the columns of the matrix $\mathbf{A}$.

Verify this with the matrices $\mathbf{I}_4((2) + k(3))$ and $\mathbf{I}_4{}^*((2) + k(3))$ described on pp. 155, 156.

30. Regularity and Inverse Matrices

We have discussed a regular system of equations in § 21, p. 99. This is a system of n equations in n unknowns,

$$\left.\begin{aligned} a_{11}X_1 + a_{12}X_2 + \cdots + a_{1n}X_n &= k_1, \\ a_{21}X_1 + a_{22}X_2 + \cdots + a_{2n}X_n &= k_2, \\ \cdot \qquad \cdot \qquad \cdots \qquad \cdot \quad &\quad \cdot \\ a_{n1}X_1 + a_{n2}X_2 + \cdots + a_{nn}X_n &= k_n, \end{aligned}\right\} \tag{67}$$

in which the n *column*-vectors of the matrix of coefficients

$$\mathbf{A} = \begin{bmatrix} a_{11} & a_{12} & \cdots & a_{1n} \\ a_{21} & a_{22} & \cdots & a_{2n} \\ \cdot & \cdot & \cdots & \cdot \\ a_{n1} & a_{n2} & \cdots & a_{nn} \end{bmatrix}$$

are independent. We saw that this is equivalent to the set of equations (67) with $k_1 = k_2 = \cdots = k_n = 0$ having only the trivial solution:

$$X_1 = X_2 = \cdots = X_n = 0.$$

We define the *matrix A* to be *regular by columns* if the column-vectors

$$[a_{11}, a_{21}, \ldots, a_{n1}]^T, \ldots, [a_{1n}, a_{2n}, \ldots, a_{nn}]^T$$

are linearly independent. The matrix $\mathbf{A}$ is said to be *regular by rows* if the row-vectors

$$[a_{11}, a_{12}, \ldots, a_{1n}], \ldots, [a_{n1}, a_{n2}, \ldots, a_{nn}]$$

are linearly independent.

Theorem 28. *If the matrix* $\mathbf{A}$ *is regular by columns, there exists an* $n \times n$ *matrix with entries from* R *such that* $\mathbf{BA} = \mathbf{AB} = \mathbf{I}_n$, *where* $\mathbf{I}_n$ *is the* $n \times n$ *unity matrix.*

Proof. Let us call the column-vectors of the matrix $\mathbf{A}$:

$$\mathbf{c}_1 = [a_{11}, a_{21}, \ldots, a_{n1}]^T, \ldots, \mathbf{c}_n = [a_{1n}, a_{2n}, \ldots, a_{nn}]^T.$$

Since these are independent, we may take them as a basis for $V_n(R)$, which also has as a basis the n unit vectors:

$$\mathbf{e}_1 = [1, 0, \ldots, 0], \ldots, \mathbf{e}_n = [0, 0, \ldots, 1].$$

We may express the vectors of either basis in terms of the vectors of the other basis. It is clear that

$$\begin{aligned}
\mathbf{c}_1 &= a_{11}\mathbf{e}_1 + a_{21}\mathbf{e}_2 + \cdots + a_{n1}\mathbf{e}_n, \\
\mathbf{c}_2 &= a_{12}\mathbf{e}_2 + a_{22}\mathbf{e}_2 + \cdots + a_{n2}\mathbf{e}_n, \\
&\cdot \quad \cdot \quad \cdot \quad \cdots \quad \cdot \\
\mathbf{c}_n &= a_{1n}\mathbf{e}_1 + a_{2n}\mathbf{e}_2 + \cdots + a_{nn}\mathbf{e}_n.
\end{aligned}$$

Let the expression of $\mathbf{e}_1, \ldots, \mathbf{e}_n$ in terms of $\mathbf{c}_1, \ldots, \mathbf{c}_n$ be

$$\begin{aligned}
\mathbf{e}_1 &= b_{11}\mathbf{c}_1 + b_{21}\mathbf{c}_2 + \cdots + b_{n1}\mathbf{c}_n, \\
\mathbf{e}_2 &= b_{12}\mathbf{c}_1 + b_{22}\mathbf{c}_2 + \cdots + b_{n2}\mathbf{c}_n, \\
&\cdot \quad \cdot \quad \cdot \quad \cdots \quad \cdot \\
\mathbf{e}_n &= b_{1n}\mathbf{c}_1 + b_{2n}\mathbf{c}_2 + \cdots + b_{nn}\mathbf{c}_n,
\end{aligned}$$

where all the coefficients b_{ij} are real numbers from R. Then

$$\begin{aligned}
\mathbf{e}_j &= \sum_{r=1}^{n} b_{rj}\mathbf{c}_r = \sum_{r=1}^{n} b_{rj}\left(\sum_{i=1}^{n} a_{ir}\mathbf{e}_i\right) \\
&= \sum_{i=1}^{n}\sum_{r=1}^{n} (b_{rj}a_{ir})\mathbf{e}_i.
\end{aligned}$$

Since $\mathbf{e}_1, \ldots, \mathbf{e}_n$ are linearly independent, this equation between $\mathbf{e}_j$ and $\mathbf{e}_1, \ldots, \mathbf{e}_n$, must be of the form

$$\mathbf{e}_j = 0 \cdot \mathbf{e}_1 + 0 \cdot \mathbf{e}_2 + \cdots + \mathbf{e}_j + \cdots + 0 \cdot \mathbf{e}_n,$$

so that we have the equations

$$\sum_{r=1}^{n} b_{rj}a_{ir} = \delta_{ij},$$

where $\delta_{ij} = 0$ for $i \neq j$, but $\delta_{ii} = 1$. This symbol is called the *Kronecker delta*.

If we define the matrix

$$\mathbf{B} = \begin{bmatrix} b_{11} & \cdots & b_{1n} \\ b_{21} & \cdots & b_{2n} \\ \cdot & \cdots & \cdot \\ b_{n1} & \cdots & b_{nn} \end{bmatrix},$$

this last set of equations, which can be written

$$\sum_{r=1}^{n} a_{ir}b_{rj} = \delta_{ij}$$

gives us the matrix equation

$$\mathbf{AB} = \mathbf{I}_n,$$

since the unity matrix $\mathbf{I}_n$ has δ_{ij} for the element in row i and column j. This proves the first part of the theorem.

Similarly, we have the equations

$$\mathbf{c}_j = \sum_{r=1}^{n} a_{rj}\mathbf{e}_r = \sum_{r=1}^{n} a_{rj} \sum_{i=1}^{n} b_{ir}\mathbf{c}_i$$

$$= \sum_{i=1}^{n} \left(\sum_{r=1}^{n} a_{rj}b_{ir} \right) \mathbf{c}_i,$$

giving

$$\sum_{r=1}^{n} a_{rj}b_{ir} = \sum_{r=1}^{n} b_{ir}a_{rj} = \delta_{ij},$$

which is the expression of the matrix equation

$$\mathbf{BA} = \mathbf{I}_n,$$

and this concludes the proof that regularity of $\mathbf{A}$ by columns involves the existence of an $n \times n$ matrix $\mathbf{B}$ with entries from R which is such that

$$\mathbf{BA} = \mathbf{AB} = \mathbf{I}_n,$$

where $\mathbf{I}_n$ is the $n \times n$ unity matrix.

A similar argument shows that *if* $\mathbf{A}$ *is regular by rows, then there exists an* $n \times n$ *matrix* $\mathbf{C}$ *with entries from* R *which is such that*

$$\mathbf{CA} = \mathbf{AC} = \mathbf{I}_n.$$

Our aim is to show that $\mathbf{B} = \mathbf{C}$, and that regularity by columns implies regularity by rows, and conversely. We prove Theorem 29.

Theorem 29. *If* $\mathbf{A}$ *is any* $n \times n$ *matrix with entries from* R, *and an* $n \times n$ *matrix* $\mathbf{B}$ *with entries from* R *can be found such that* $\mathbf{BA} = \mathbf{I}_n$, *then* $\mathbf{A}$ *must be regular by columns.*

Proof. If $\mathbf{A}$ were not regular by columns, these columns would be linearly dependent. Suppose that

$$\lambda_1\mathbf{c}_1 + \lambda_2\mathbf{c}_2 + \cdots + \lambda_n\mathbf{c}_n = \mathbf{0}$$

is the linear relation between them. This is

$$\lambda_1[a_{11}, a_{21}, \ldots, a_{n1}]^T + \cdots + \lambda_n[a_{1n}, a_{2n}, \ldots, a_{nn}]^T = \mathbf{0}.$$

If we pick out the entries, we obtain the n equations

$$\left.\begin{array}{l} a_{11}\lambda_1 + a_{12}\lambda_2 + \cdots + a_{1n}\lambda_n = 0, \\ a_{21}\lambda_1 + a_{22}\lambda_2 + \cdots + a_{2n}\lambda_n = 0, \\ \cdot \qquad \cdot \qquad \cdots \qquad \cdot \qquad \cdot \\ a_{n1}\lambda_1 + a_{n2}\lambda_2 + \cdots + a_{nn}\lambda_n = 0, \end{array}\right\}$$

which is the expression for the matrix equation

$$\mathbf{A}\begin{bmatrix} \lambda_1 \\ \lambda_2 \\ \cdot \\ \cdot \\ \cdot \\ \lambda_n \end{bmatrix} = \mathbf{0}.$$

We now have

$$\begin{bmatrix} \lambda_1 \\ \lambda_2 \\ \cdot \\ \cdot \\ \cdot \\ \lambda_n \end{bmatrix} = \mathbf{I}_n\begin{bmatrix} \lambda_1 \\ \lambda_2 \\ \cdot \\ \cdot \\ \cdot \\ \lambda_n \end{bmatrix} = (\mathbf{BA})\begin{bmatrix} \lambda_1 \\ \lambda_2 \\ \cdot \\ \cdot \\ \cdot \\ \lambda_n \end{bmatrix} = \mathbf{B}\left(\mathbf{A}\begin{bmatrix} \lambda_1 \\ \lambda_2 \\ \cdot \\ \cdot \\ \cdot \\ \lambda_n \end{bmatrix}\right) = \mathbf{B0} = \mathbf{0},$$

using the condition $\mathbf{BA} = \mathbf{I}_n$, and the associative law for the multiplication of matrices. Hence

$$\lambda_1 = \lambda_2 = \cdots = \lambda_n = 0,$$

and therefore the column vectors $\mathbf{c}_1, \ldots, \mathbf{c}_n$ are linearly independent.

Similarly, we have Theorem 30.

Theorem 30. *With the conditions of the previous theorem, if an $n \times n$ matrix* $\mathbf{C}$ *with entries from R can be found such that* $\mathbf{AC} = \mathbf{I}_n$, *then* $\mathbf{A}$ *is regular by rows.*

Let us now assume that $\mathbf{A}$ is regular by columns. Then $\mathbf{B}$ exists so that

$$\mathbf{BA} = \mathbf{AB} = \mathbf{I}_n.$$

But by Theorem 30, the equation $\mathbf{AB} = \mathbf{I}_n$ is sufficient to ensure that $\mathbf{A}$ is regular by rows. Similarly we prove that if $\mathbf{A}$ is regular by rows, it is also regular by columns.

We now have a new concept, that of a *regular* matrix $\mathbf{A}$.

Definition. *An $n \times n$ matrix* $\mathbf{A}$ *which is regular either by rows or by columns is called a* REGULAR *matrix.*

The theorems proved above have a number of corollaries:

1. If $\mathbf{A}$ is regular, the matrix $\mathbf{B}$ which is such that $\mathbf{BA} = \mathbf{AB} = \mathbf{I}_n$ is unique.

For suppose that $\mathbf{CA} = \mathbf{AC} = \mathbf{I}_n$. Then

$$\mathbf{B} = \mathbf{BI}_n = \mathbf{B}(\mathbf{AC}) = (\mathbf{BA})\mathbf{C} = \mathbf{I}_n\mathbf{C} = \mathbf{C}.$$

2. If $\mathbf{A}$ is given, and there exists a matrix $\mathbf{C}$ such that $\mathbf{CA} = \mathbf{I}_n$, then $\mathbf{C}$ is unique, and $\mathbf{AC} = \mathbf{I}_n$ also.

Since $\mathbf{CA} = \mathbf{I}_n$, $\mathbf{A}$ is regular by columns, and therefore regular. Therefore there is a unique $\mathbf{B}$ such that $\mathbf{BA} = \mathbf{AB} = \mathbf{I}_n$. From this we see that

$$\mathbf{C} = \mathbf{CI}_n = \mathbf{C}(\mathbf{AB}) = (\mathbf{CA})\mathbf{B} = \mathbf{I}_n\mathbf{B} = \mathbf{B}.$$

We can now define the *inverse* of a matrix. If $\mathbf{A}$ is a given $n \times n$ matrix, and there exists a matrix $\mathbf{C}$ such that $\mathbf{CA} = \mathbf{I}_n$, we have seen that $\mathbf{C}$ is unique, and that

$$\mathbf{CA} = \mathbf{I}_n = \mathbf{AC}.$$

We call $\mathbf{C}$ the *inverse* of $\mathbf{A}$, and denote it by $\mathbf{A}^{-1}$. Then

$$\mathbf{A}^{-1}\mathbf{A} = \mathbf{I}_n = \mathbf{AA}^{-1}.$$

The preceding theorems give us Theorem 31.

Theorem 31. *A matrix* $\mathbf{A}$ *has an inverse if, and only if, it is regular.*

We began this section with a regular system of equations:

$$\left.\begin{aligned} a_{11}X_1 + \cdots + a_{1n}X_n &= k_1, \\ a_{21}X_1 + \cdots + a_{2n}X_n &= k_2, \\ \cdot \quad \cdots \quad &\cdot \quad \cdot \\ a_{n1}X_1 + \cdots + a_{nn}X_n &= k_n, \end{aligned}\right\} \tag{67}$$

which can be written in matrix form as

$$\mathbf{AX} = \mathbf{k},$$

where $\mathbf{A} = [a_{ij}]$ is now seen to be a *regular* matrix, and

$$\mathbf{X} = [X_1, \ldots, X_n]^T, \qquad \mathbf{k} = [k_1, \ldots, k_n]^T.$$

To solve this system of equations, we premultiply by $\mathbf{A}^{-1}$, and obtain

$$\begin{aligned} \mathbf{A}^{-1}(\mathbf{AX}) &= \mathbf{A}^{-1}\mathbf{k}, \\ (\mathbf{A}^{-1}\mathbf{A})\mathbf{X} &= \mathbf{A}^{-1}\mathbf{k}, \\ \mathbf{I}_n\mathbf{X} &= \mathbf{A}^{-1}\mathbf{k}, \\ \mathbf{X} &= \mathbf{A}^{-1}\mathbf{k}. \end{aligned}$$

Hence, if we evaluate $\mathbf{A}^{-1}$, the *inverse* matrix, we have the solution of the set of equations.

Methods for doing this will be given later [p. 182]. A matrix which is not regular is called *singular*. Regular matrices are also called *non-singular* matrices.

Example 1

The equations

$$\begin{aligned} X_1 + 2X_2 &= 3, \\ 3X_1 + 4X_2 &= 5, \end{aligned}$$

may be written:

$$\begin{bmatrix} 1 & 2 \\ 3 & 4 \end{bmatrix}\begin{bmatrix} X_1 \\ X_2 \end{bmatrix} = \begin{bmatrix} 3 \\ 5 \end{bmatrix},$$

and since

$$\begin{bmatrix} 1 & 2 \\ 3 & 4 \end{bmatrix}\begin{bmatrix} -2 & +1 \\ +3/2 & -1/2 \end{bmatrix} = \begin{bmatrix} 1 & 0 \\ 0 & 1 \end{bmatrix},$$

we have:

$$\begin{bmatrix} 1 & 0 \\ 0 & 1 \end{bmatrix}\begin{bmatrix} X_1 \\ X_2 \end{bmatrix} = \begin{bmatrix} -2 & 1 \\ 3/2 & -1/2 \end{bmatrix}\begin{bmatrix} 3 \\ 5 \end{bmatrix},$$

that is,

$$\begin{bmatrix} X_1 \\ X_2 \end{bmatrix} = \begin{bmatrix} -1 \\ 2 \end{bmatrix},$$

$$X_1 = -1, \qquad X_2 = 2.$$

Example 2

For regular matrices of order 3 we can easily determine the inverse matrix. If the matrix

$$\mathbf{A} = \begin{bmatrix} a_{11} & a_{12} & a_{13} \\ a_{21} & a_{22} & a_{23} \\ a_{31} & a_{32} & a_{33} \end{bmatrix}$$

is regular, the equations

$$\left.\begin{aligned} a_{11}X_1 + a_{12}X_2 + a_{13}X_3 &= 0, \\ a_{21}X_1 + a_{22}X_2 + a_{23}X_3 &= 0, \\ a_{31}X_1 + a_{32}X_2 + a_{33}X_3 &= 0 \end{aligned}\right\}$$

have only the trivial solution, and therefore the *determinant*

$$\Delta = \det(\mathbf{A}) = |\mathbf{A}| \neq 0.$$

To find the inverse $\mathbf{B} = \mathbf{A}^{-1} = [b_{ij}]$, we must solve the equations $\mathbf{AB} = \mathbf{I}_3$, of which there are nine. We pick out the equations containing b_{11}, b_{21}, b_{31}:

$$\left.\begin{aligned} a_{11}b_{11} + a_{12}b_{21} + a_{13}b_{31} &= 1. \\ a_{21}b_{11} + a_{22}b_{21} + a_{23}b_{31} &= 0, \\ a_{31}b_{11} + a_{32}b_{21} + a_{33}b_{31} &= 0. \end{aligned}\right\}$$

We solve these equations by multiplying by the cofactors A_{11}, A_{21}, A_{31} respectively in $\det(\mathbf{A})$. Then

$$b_{11}\Delta = A_{11}.$$

Similarly,

$$b_{21}\Delta = A_{12},$$

$$b_{31}\Delta = A_{13}.$$

This pattern of solution holds all through, and we see that

$$\mathbf{B} = \mathbf{A}^{-1} = \begin{bmatrix} A_{11}/\Delta & A_{21}/\Delta & A_{31}/\Delta \\ A_{12}/\Delta & A_{22}/\Delta & A_{32}/\Delta \\ A_{13}/\Delta & A_{23}/\Delta & A_{33}/\Delta \end{bmatrix}, \tag{90}$$

and the rules for determinants enable us to verify that

$$\mathbf{A}^{-1}\mathbf{A} = \mathbf{I}_3 = \mathbf{A}\mathbf{A}^{-1}.$$

This formula generalises for $n \times n$ determinants (see Exercises 35, No. 3).

In Example 1,

$$\Delta = \begin{vmatrix} 1 & 2 \\ 3 & 4 \end{vmatrix} = -2$$

$$A_{11} = 4,\ A_{21} = -2,\ A_{12} = -3,\ A_{22} = 1,$$

and

$$\mathbf{A}^{-1} = \begin{bmatrix} -2 & 1 \\ 3/2 & -1/2 \end{bmatrix}.$$

EXERCISES 30.1

1. If $a \neq 0$, $b \neq 0$, prove that $\begin{bmatrix} a & 0 \\ 0 & b \end{bmatrix}$ is regular and $\begin{bmatrix} a^{-1} & 0 \\ 0 & b^{-1} \end{bmatrix}$ is its inverse.

2. Prove that the matrix $\begin{bmatrix} a & b \\ c & d \end{bmatrix}$ is regular if and only if the determinant $\begin{vmatrix} a & b \\ c & d \end{vmatrix} \neq 0$, and then its inverse is $\dfrac{1}{ad - bc}\begin{bmatrix} d & -b \\ -c & a \end{bmatrix}$.

3. If $\mathbf{A}$ is a square matrix, and $\mathbf{A}^k = \mathbf{I}_n$, the unity matrix, show that $\mathbf{A}$ is regular, and $\mathbf{A}^{-1} = \mathbf{A}^{k-1}$, k being a positive integer.

4. If $\mathbf{A}$ is an $n \times n$ matrix and $\mathbf{A}\mathbf{A}^T = \mathbf{I}_n$, prove that $\mathbf{A}$ is regular, and also that $\mathbf{A}^T\mathbf{A} = \mathbf{I}_n$ (The matrix $\mathbf{A}$ is said to be *orthogonal* in this case).

5. Find, by any method, the inverse of the matrix

$$\begin{bmatrix} 1 & 5 & 2 \\ 1 & 1 & 7 \\ 0 & -3 & 4 \end{bmatrix}$$

and hence solve the equations

$$\begin{aligned} X_1 + 5X_2 + 2X_3 &= 1, \\ X_1 + X_2 + 7X_3 &= 2, \\ -3X_2 + 4X_3 &= 3. \end{aligned}$$

We conclude this section with some deductions from the theorem on the existence of an inverse.

If $\mathbf{A}$ *and* $\mathbf{B}$ *are both regular and* $n \times n$, *then* $\mathbf{AB}$ *is regular, and its inverse is* $\mathbf{B}^{-1}\mathbf{A}^{-1}$.

We know that $\mathbf{B}^{-1}$ and $\mathbf{A}^{-1}$ both exist, and since

$$(\mathbf{B}^{-1}\mathbf{A}^{-1})(\mathbf{AB}) = \mathbf{B}^{-1}(\mathbf{A}^{-1}\mathbf{A})\mathbf{B} = \mathbf{B}^{-1}\mathbf{B} = \mathbf{I}_n,$$

it follows that $\mathbf{B}^{-1}\mathbf{A}^{-1}$ is the inverse of $\mathbf{AB}$, which is therefore regular.

The transpose of the inverse is the inverse of the transpose.

That is

$$(\mathbf{A}^{-1})^T = (\mathbf{A}^T)^{-1}.$$

Since

$$\mathbf{AA}^{-1} = \mathbf{I}_n,$$

and $\mathbf{I}_n$ is symmetric, on taking the transpose of both sides of this matrix equation,

$$(\mathbf{I}_n)^T = \mathbf{I}_n = (\mathbf{AA}^{-1})^T = (\mathbf{A}^{-1})^T\mathbf{A}^T,$$

so that the inverse of $\mathbf{A}^T$ is $(\mathbf{A}^{-1})^T$.

If $\mathbf{A}$ *is* $n \times n$ *and regular, and* $\mathbf{B}$ *is* $n \times p$, *then* $\mathbf{AB} = \mathbf{0}$ *implies* $\mathbf{B} = \mathbf{0}$.

If $\mathbf{AB} = \mathbf{0}$, then

$$\mathbf{B} = \mathbf{I}_n\mathbf{B} = (\mathbf{A}^{-1}\mathbf{A})\mathbf{B} = \mathbf{A}^{-1}(\mathbf{AB}) = \mathbf{A}^{-1}\mathbf{0} = \mathbf{0}.$$

If $\mathbf{C}$ *is* $m \times n$ *and* $\mathbf{A}$ *is* $n \times n$ *and regular, then* $\mathbf{CA} = \mathbf{0}$ *implies that* $\mathbf{C} = \mathbf{0}$.

$$\mathbf{C} = \mathbf{CI}_n = \mathbf{C}(\mathbf{AA}^{-1}) = (\mathbf{CA})\mathbf{A}^{-1} = (\mathbf{0})\mathbf{A}^{-1} = \mathbf{0}.$$

EXERCISES 30.2

1. Show that the inverses of the elementary matrices considered in § 29, p. 154 are, respectively:

$$\mathbf{I}_4(2, 3)^{-1} = \mathbf{I}_4(2, 3);$$
$$\mathbf{I}_4(k(3))^{-1} = \mathbf{I}_4(k^{-1}(3));$$
$$\mathbf{I}_4((2) + k(3))^{-1} = \mathbf{I}_4((2) - k(3)).$$

2. If the sum of the elements in each row (column) of a regular matrix is $k \neq 0$, prove that the sum of the elements in each row (column) of the inverse matrix is k^{-1}.

3. If $\mathbf{A}$ is a given matrix, and we are told that $\mathbf{AX} = \mathbf{XA}$ for every $\mathbf{X}$, show that we must have $\mathbf{A} = a\mathbf{I}$, where a is a scalar, and $\mathbf{I}$ is a unity matrix.

4. If $\mathbf{A} = \begin{bmatrix} -1 & 2 \\ 4 & 1 \end{bmatrix}$, find a regular matrix $\mathbf{B}$ of the form $\begin{bmatrix} 1 & 1 \\ p & q \end{bmatrix}$ such that $\mathbf{B}^{-1}\mathbf{AB}$ has non-zero elements only on the principal diagonal.

Hence, or otherwise, express $\mathbf{A}^n$, where n is a positive integer, in the form of a 2×2 matrix.

5. $\mathbf{A}$ is a square $n \times n$ matrix whose elements are all 0, 1, or -1, and in each row or column there is exactly one element which is not zero. Prove that $\mathbf{A}^2, \mathbf{A}^3, \ldots$ are of the same type, and hence show that for some positive integer h we have $\mathbf{A}^h = \mathbf{I}_n$, where $\mathbf{I}_n$ is the unity matrix.

CHAPTER EIGHT

The Concept of Rank

31. The Rank of a Matrix

A connection between the number of linearly independent row-vectors and the number of linearly independent column-vectors of a matrix

$$\mathbf{A} = \begin{bmatrix} a_{11} & a_{12} & \cdots & a_{1n} \\ a_{21} & a_{22} & \cdots & a_{2n} \\ \cdot & \cdot & \cdots & \cdot \\ a_{m1} & a_{m2} & \cdots & a_{mn} \end{bmatrix}$$

has been suspected on a number of occasions in preceding sections (§ 20, p. 96, § 22, p. 105, § 26, p. 130). We now know that if $\mathbf{A}$ is $n \times n$ and its rows are independent vectors, so are its columns, and conversely (Theorems 29, 30, § 30, p. 163). In this section we shall prove that the number of independent row-vectors of $\mathbf{A}$ is *equal* to the number of independent column-vectors of $\mathbf{A}$.

The row-vectors

$$\mathbf{R}_1 = [a_{11}, a_{12}, \ldots, a_{1n}] \ldots, \mathbf{R}_m = [a_{m1}, a_{m2}, \ldots, a_{mn}]$$

of $\mathbf{A}$ generate a vector subspace, which we shall refer to as the *row-space*, of V_n, and the column-vectors

$$\mathbf{c}_1 = [a_{11}, a_{21}, \ldots, a_{m1}]^T, \ldots, \mathbf{c}_n = [a_{1n}, a_{2n}, \ldots, a_{mn}]^T$$

generate a vector subspace, which we shall refer to as the *column-space*, of V_m.

The dimension r of the row-space is called the *row rank* of $\mathbf{A}$.

The dimension c of the column-space is called the *column rank* of $\mathbf{A}$.

Our aim is to show that $r = c$ for any matrix $\mathbf{A}$.

Example I

The matrix

$$\begin{bmatrix} 1 & 2 & 3 & 4 \\ 0 & 6 & 7 & 8 \\ 0 & 0 & 9 & 5 \end{bmatrix}$$

is already in echelon form, and therefore the three rows are independent. In fact, if

$$\lambda[1, 2, 3, 4] + \mu[0, 6, 7, 8] + \nu[0, 0, 9, 5] = \mathbf{0},$$

then comparison of the entries on both sides of this equation gives us

$$\lambda = \mu = \nu = 0.$$

Similarly, the first three columns are independent, since

$$\lambda[1, 0, 0] + \mu[2, 6, 0] + \nu[3, 7, 9] = \mathbf{0}$$

gives us, in the reverse order,

$$\nu = \mu = \lambda = 0,$$

on comparing entries. Since the column-vectors are in V_3, the fourth column must be linearly dependent on them, and $r = c = 3$ for this matrix.

We now prove a theorem which connects the vector space of solutions of the equations

$$\left.\begin{array}{c} a_{11}X_1 + a_{12}X_2 + \cdots + a_{1n}X_n = 0, \\ \cdot \quad \cdot \quad \cdots \quad \cdot \quad \cdot \\ a_{m1}X_1 + a_{m2}X_2 + \cdots + a_{mn}X_n = 0 \end{array}\right\}$$

with the column rank c of the matrix $\mathbf{A} = [a_{ij}]$.

These equations may be written in matrix form as

$$\mathbf{AX} = \mathbf{0},$$

where $\mathbf{X} = [X_1, X_2, \ldots, X_n]^T$, and it is then clear that if $\mathbf{X}$ and $\mathbf{Y}$ satisfy this equation,

$$\mathbf{A}(\mathbf{X} + \mathbf{Y}) = \mathbf{AX} + \mathbf{AY} = \mathbf{0},$$

so that $\mathbf{X} + \mathbf{Y}$ satisfies the equation, and

$$\mathbf{A}(k\mathbf{X}) = k(\mathbf{AX}) = \mathbf{0},$$

so that $k\mathbf{X}$ also satisfies the equation.

Hence the solution vectors of m homogeneous linear equations in n unknowns form a vector subspace of V_n. Call this subspace S, and suppose that its dimension is s.

Theorem 32. $c + s = n.$

Proof. The column-space of **A** consists of the set of vectors given by

$$X_1\begin{bmatrix} a_{11} \\ \cdot \\ \cdot \\ \cdot \\ a_{m1} \end{bmatrix} + X_2\begin{bmatrix} a_{12} \\ \cdot \\ \cdot \\ \cdot \\ a_{m2} \end{bmatrix} + \cdots + X_n\begin{bmatrix} a_{1n} \\ \cdot \\ \cdot \\ \cdot \\ a_{mn} \end{bmatrix},$$

and this is equal to the matrix

$$\begin{bmatrix} a_{11}X_1 + a_{12}X_2 + \cdots + a_{1n}X_n \\ \cdot \quad\quad \cdot \quad\quad \cdots \quad\quad \cdot \\ a_{m1}X_1 + a_{m2}X_2 + \cdots + a_{mn}X_n \end{bmatrix},$$

which is just the matrix **AX**.

Let the solution-space S have a basis $\mathbf{u}_1, \ldots, \mathbf{u}_s$. This can be amplified (Theorem 19, § 25, p. 121) to a basis

$$\mathbf{u}_1, \ldots, \mathbf{u}_s, \mathbf{u}_{s+1}, \ldots, \mathbf{u}_n$$

for V_n.

Every vector **X** in V_n has a unique representation:

$$\mathbf{X} = \lambda_1\mathbf{u}_1 + \cdots + \lambda_s\mathbf{u}_s + \lambda_{s+1}\mathbf{u}_{s+1} + \cdots + \lambda_n\mathbf{u}_n$$

in terms of this basis for V_n. Now

$$\mathbf{AX} = \lambda_1(\mathbf{Au}_1) + \cdots + \lambda_s(\mathbf{Au}_s) + \lambda_{s+1}(\mathbf{Au}_{s+1}) + \cdots + \lambda_n(\mathbf{Au}_n),$$

and since $\mathbf{u}_1, \ldots, \mathbf{u}_s$ lie in the solution space S,

$$\mathbf{Au}_1 = \mathbf{Au}_2 = \cdots = \mathbf{Au}_n = \mathbf{0},$$

so that any vector **AX** in the column-space has the form

$$\mathbf{AX} = \lambda_{s+1}(\mathbf{Au}_{s+1}) + \cdots + \lambda_n(\mathbf{Au}_n).$$

Hence the column-space is generated by the vectors

$$\mathbf{Au}_{s+1}, \mathbf{Au}_{s+2}, \ldots, \mathbf{Au}_n.$$

In fact, we have a basis, for if these vectors were dependent, so that

$$\mu_{s+1}(\mathbf{Au}_{s+1}) + \mu_{s+2}(\mathbf{Au}_{s+2}) + \cdots + \mu_n(\mathbf{Au}_n) = \mathbf{0},$$

then
$$\mathbf{A}(\mu_{s+1}\mathbf{u}_{s+1} + \cdots + \mu_n\mathbf{u}_n) = \mathbf{0},$$

so that

$$\mu_{s+1}\mathbf{u}_{s+1} + \cdots + \mu_n\mathbf{u}_n$$

belongs to the solution-space. But since the set of vectors

$$\mathbf{u}_1, \ldots, \mathbf{u}_s, \mathbf{u}_{s+1}, \ldots, \mathbf{u}_n$$

are linearly independent, the only common vector of the two sets

$$\{\mathbf{u}_1, \ldots, \mathbf{u}_s\}$$

and $\{\mathbf{u}_{s+1}, \ldots, \mathbf{u}_n\}$ is the zero vector, and therefore $\mu_{s+1} = \cdots = \mu_n = 0$, and the vectors $\mathbf{Au}_{s+1}, \ldots, \mathbf{Au}_n$ are independent. Hence the dimension of the column-space is $n - s$, and so

$$c = n - s,$$

which proves the theorem.

Example 2

We have had many illustrations of this theorem. Consider, for instance, the equations

$$\left.\begin{aligned} a_1X_1 + a_2X_2 + a_3X_3 &= 0, \\ b_1X_1 + b_2X_2 + b_3X_3 &= 0. \end{aligned}\right\}$$

The column-vectors lie in V_2, and so not more than two of them can be independent. If two are independent, $n = 3$, $c = 2$, and $s = n - c = 1$, and in fact the solution-space of these equations is

$$L\{[a_2b_3 - a_3b_2, a_3b_1 - a_1b_3, a_1b_2 - a_2b_1]\},$$

and of dimension 1.

EXERCISES 31.1

1. Prove that row rank = column rank = 2 for the matrix $\begin{bmatrix} 5 & 6 & 7 \\ 7 & 3 & 4 \end{bmatrix}$.

2. Find the row rank and the column rank for the matrix

$$\begin{bmatrix} 1 & 2 & 3 & 4 \\ 0 & 8 & 9 & 10 \\ 0 & 0 & 5 & 6 \end{bmatrix}.$$

3. Prove that the equations $cX_2 - bX_3 = aX_3 - cX_1 = bX_1 - aX_2 = 0$ have a non-trivial solution, and that this is of the form

$$X_1 = a\theta, \qquad X_2 = b\theta, \qquad X_3 = c\theta.$$

4. Prove that the vectors $\mathbf{Y}$ in V_m which satisfy the equations $\mathbf{YA} = \mathbf{0}$ fill a vector subspace of V_m of dimension $m - r$, where r is the row rank of $\mathbf{A}$.

We now consider elementary row operations on a matrix **A**, and their effect on the row and column-rank of **A**. These transformations, once more, are:

I. The interchange of two rows of **A**.
II. The multiplication of a row by a scalar $k \neq 0$.
III. The addition to a row of a multiple of another row.

We saw that each of these operations may be effected by the premultiplication of **A** by a suitable elementary matrix (§ 29, p. 154). Such an elementary matrix is obtained from the unity matrix $\mathbf{I}_m$ by carrying out the desired operation on the unity matrix itself.

For convenience, and to avoid confusion, we denote the elementary matrices used in a sequence of elementary row-operations on **A** by the symbols $\mathbf{E}_1, \mathbf{E}_2, \ldots, \mathbf{E}_k$. After the first operation, **A** becomes $\mathbf{E}_1\mathbf{A}$. After the second operation, $\mathbf{E}_1\mathbf{A}$ becomes $\mathbf{E}_2(\mathbf{E}_1\mathbf{A})$, and so on, the final matrix obtained from **A** being $\mathbf{E}_k\mathbf{E}_{k-1} \cdots \mathbf{E}_1\mathbf{A}$.

Such a matrix is said to be *row-equivalent* to **A**.

Example 3

Let us reduce the matrix **A** to echelon form, where

$$\mathbf{A} = \begin{bmatrix} 1 & 5 & 2 \\ 1 & 1 & 7 \\ 0 & -3 & 4 \end{bmatrix}$$

by first subtracting the first row from the second. We premultiply by

$$\mathbf{E}_1 = \mathbf{I}_3((2) - (1)) = \begin{bmatrix} 1 & 0 & 0 \\ -1 & 1 & 0 \\ 0 & 0 & 1 \end{bmatrix},$$

using the notation of p. 155, and

$$\mathbf{E}_1\mathbf{A} = \begin{bmatrix} 1 & 5 & 2 \\ 0 & -4 & 5 \\ 0 & -3 & 4 \end{bmatrix}.$$

We now divide the second row of this matrix by -4, so that we premultiply $\mathbf{E}_1\mathbf{A}$ by

$$\mathbf{E}_2 = \mathbf{I}_3\left(-\frac{1}{4}(2)\right) = \begin{bmatrix} 1 & 0 & 0 \\ 0 & -1/4 & 0 \\ 0 & 0 & 1 \end{bmatrix},$$

and

$$\mathbf{E}_2\mathbf{E}_1\mathbf{A} = \begin{bmatrix} 1 & 5 & 2 \\ 0 & 1 & -5/4 \\ 0 & -3 & 4 \end{bmatrix}.$$

Add 3 (second row) to the third row. To do this we premultiply $\mathbf{E}_2\mathbf{E}_1\mathbf{A}$ by

$$\mathbf{E}_3 = \mathbf{I}_3((3) + 3(2)) = \begin{bmatrix} 1 & 0 & 0 \\ 0 & 1 & 0 \\ 0 & 3 & 1 \end{bmatrix},$$

and

$$\mathbf{E}_3\mathbf{E}_2\mathbf{E}_1\mathbf{A} = \begin{bmatrix} 1 & 5 & 2 \\ 0 & 1 & -5/4 \\ 0 & 0 & 1/4 \end{bmatrix}.$$

Finally, we multiply the last row of this matrix by 4 so as to make the only non-zero element unity. We therefore premultiply by

$$\mathbf{E}_4 = \mathbf{I}_3(4(3)) = \begin{bmatrix} 1 & 0 & 0 \\ 0 & 1 & 0 \\ 0 & 0 & 4 \end{bmatrix},$$

and

$$\mathbf{E}_4\mathbf{E}_3\mathbf{E}_2\mathbf{E}_1\mathbf{A} = \begin{bmatrix} 1 & 5 & 2 \\ 0 & 1 & -5/4 \\ 0 & 0 & 1 \end{bmatrix}.$$

For the definition of row-equivalence to satisfy the usual mathematical notions of equivalence, we must prove that, using $\sim$ as a symbol for equivalence:

1. $\mathbf{A}$ is row-equivalent to itself: ($\mathbf{A} \sim \mathbf{A}$).
2. If $\mathbf{A}$ is row-equivalent to $\mathbf{B}$, then $\mathbf{B}$ is row-equivalent to $\mathbf{A}$ (if $\mathbf{A} \sim \mathbf{B}$, then $\mathbf{B} \sim \mathbf{A}$).
3. If $\mathbf{A}$ is row-equivalent to $\mathbf{B}$, and $\mathbf{B}$ is row-equivalent to $\mathbf{C}$, then $\mathbf{A}$ is row-equivalent to $\mathbf{C}$ (if $\mathbf{A} \sim \mathbf{B}$, and $\mathbf{B} \sim \mathbf{C}$, then $\mathbf{A} \sim \mathbf{C}$).

Condition 1 is evident, since $\mathbf{A} = \mathbf{I}_m\mathbf{A}$, and $\mathbf{I}_m$ itself is an elementary matrix.

To prove condition 2 we note that *all elementary matrices have inverses* (see Exercise 1, p. 168). This is clear, since we find the inverse by performing the *inverse* operation on $\mathbf{I}_m$, and premultiplication by the resulting matrix brings the elementary matrix considered back to its original state, namely back to $\mathbf{I}_m$.

Now, if $\mathbf{A}$ is row-equivalent to $\mathbf{B}$, then

$$\mathbf{B} = \mathbf{E}_k\mathbf{E}_{k-1}\cdots\mathbf{E}_1\mathbf{A},$$

and we can premultiply by $\mathbf{E}_1^{-1}\mathbf{E}_2^{-1}\cdots\mathbf{E}_k^{-1}$,

$$\begin{aligned}\mathbf{E}_1^{-1}\mathbf{E}_2^{-1}\cdots\mathbf{E}_k^{-1}\mathbf{B} &= \mathbf{E}_1^{-1}\mathbf{E}_2^{-1}\cdots\mathbf{E}_k^{-1}\mathbf{E}_k\mathbf{E}_{k-1}\cdots\mathbf{E}_1\mathbf{A}\\ &= \mathbf{E}_1^{-1}\mathbf{E}_2^{-1}\cdots\mathbf{I}_m\mathbf{E}_{k-1}\cdots\mathbf{E}_1\mathbf{A}\\ &= \mathbf{E}_1^{-1}\mathbf{E}_2^{-1}\cdots\mathbf{E}_{k-1}^{-1}\mathbf{E}_{k-1}\cdots\mathbf{E}_1\mathbf{A}\\ &= \mathbf{A},\end{aligned}$$

after all inverses $\mathbf{E}_i^{-1}$ and $\mathbf{E}_i$ have come together. Since $\mathbf{E}_1^{-1}, \mathbf{E}_2^{-1}, \ldots \mathbf{E}_k^{-1}$ are also elementary matrices, $\mathbf{B}$ is row-equivalent to $\mathbf{A}$.

To prove condition 3 we assume that

$$\mathbf{B} = \mathbf{E}_k\mathbf{E}_{k-1}\cdots\mathbf{E}_1\mathbf{A}, \qquad (\mathbf{A} \sim \mathbf{B}),$$

$$\mathbf{C} = \mathbf{E}_j^*\mathbf{E}_{j-1}^*\cdots\mathbf{E}_1^*\mathbf{B}, \qquad (\mathbf{B} \sim \mathbf{C}),$$

where all $\mathbf{E}_i$, $\mathbf{E}_i^*$ are elementary matrices. Hence

$$\mathbf{C} = \mathbf{E}_j^*\mathbf{E}_{j-1}^*\cdots\mathbf{E}_1^*\mathbf{E}_k\mathbf{E}_{k-1}\cdots\mathbf{E}_1\mathbf{A},$$

so that $\mathbf{A} \sim \mathbf{C}$.

Having justified the term row-equivalence, we wish to prove:

1. Row-equivalent matrices have the same row rank,
2. Row-equivalent matrices have the same column rank.

The first statement is contained in the more general Theorem 33.

Theorem 33. *Elementary operations on the generating vectors* $\mathbf{X}_1, \ldots, \mathbf{X}_p$ *of the vector space*

$$L\{\mathbf{X}_1, \mathbf{X}_2, \ldots, \mathbf{X}_p\}$$

do not alter the space.

In other words, if $\mathbf{X}_1', \mathbf{X}_2', \ldots, \mathbf{X}_p'$ arise from $\mathbf{X}_1, \mathbf{X}_2, \ldots, \mathbf{X}_p$ by elementary operations, then

$$L\{\mathbf{X}_1', \mathbf{X}_2', \ldots, \mathbf{X}_p'\} = L\{\mathbf{X}_1, \mathbf{X}_2, \ldots, \mathbf{X}_p\}.$$

If we can prove this, it will follow, in particular, that the dimension of the space is unchanged, and therefore row-equivalent matrices have the same row rank.

Proof. We show that carrying out each elementary operation in turn does not affect the *totality* of vectors in $L\{\mathbf{X}_1, \mathbf{X}_2, \ldots, \mathbf{X}_p\}$. This means that the totality of vectors given by

$$a_1\mathbf{X}_1 + a_2\mathbf{X}_2 + \cdots + a_p\mathbf{X}_p \qquad (a_i \in R)$$

is unaffected if any of the $\mathbf{X}_i$ undergo elementary transformations.

Put in this form, the theorem is almost self-evident. Operation I, interchanging $\mathbf{X}_i$ and $\mathbf{X}_j$, does not affect the totality. Nor does operation II, since if

$$\mathbf{X}_i' = k\mathbf{X}_i,$$

then
$$a_1\mathbf{X}_1 + a_2\mathbf{X}_2 + \cdots + a_i\mathbf{X}_i + \cdots + a_p\mathbf{X}_p$$
is matched by

$$a_1\mathbf{X}_1 + a_2\mathbf{X}_2 + \cdots + a_ik^{-1}\mathbf{X}_i' + \cdots + a_p\mathbf{X}_p,$$

so that $L\{\mathbf{X}_1, \mathbf{X}_2, \ldots, \mathbf{X}_i, \ldots, \mathbf{X}_p\} = L\{\mathbf{X}_1, \mathbf{X}_2, \ldots, \mathbf{X}_i', \ldots, \mathbf{X}_p\}$. Let operation III produce

$$\mathbf{X}_i' = \mathbf{X}_i + k\mathbf{X}_j.$$

Then
$$a_1\mathbf{X}_1 + a_2\mathbf{X}_2 + \cdots + a_i\mathbf{X}_i + \cdots + a_j\mathbf{X}_j + \cdots + a_p\mathbf{X}_p$$
is matched by

$$a_1\mathbf{X}_1 + a_2\mathbf{X}_2 + \cdots + a_i\mathbf{X}_i' + \cdots + (a_j - ka_i)\mathbf{X}_j + \cdots + a_p\mathbf{X}_p,$$

and
$$b_1\mathbf{X}_1 + b_2\mathbf{X}_2 + \cdots + b_i\mathbf{X}_i' + \cdots + b_j\mathbf{X}_j + \cdots + b_p\mathbf{X}_p$$
is matched by

$$b_1\mathbf{X}_1 + b_2\mathbf{X}_2 + \cdots + b_i\mathbf{X}_i + \cdots + (b_j + kb_i)\mathbf{X}_j + \cdots + b_p\mathbf{X}_p.$$

Hence for any one of the three operations, and therefore for any sequence of them,

$$L\{\mathbf{X}_1', \mathbf{X}_2', \ldots, \mathbf{X}_p'\} = L\{\mathbf{X}_1, \mathbf{X}_2, \ldots, \mathbf{X}_p\},$$

where $\mathbf{X}_1', \mathbf{X}_2', \ldots, \mathbf{X}_p'$ arise from $\mathbf{X}_1, \mathbf{X}_2, \ldots, \mathbf{X}_p$ by means of elementary operations. This completes the proof.

We now have the justification for our assertion that transforming a matrix by elementary row-transformations into echelon form produces a basis for the row-space (p. 126).

Since the number of non-zero row-vectors in the final echelon form is equal to the dimension of the row-space, which is fixed, the number of non-zero vectors is fixed, however we carry out the elementary operations on the rows. Hence we have Theorem 34.

Theorem 34. *Any $m \times n$ matrix $\mathbf{A}$ of row-rank r is row-equivalent to an $m \times n$ echelon matrix with just r non-zero rows.*

We now prove Theorem 35.

Theorem 35. *Row-equivalent matrices have the same column rank.*

Proof. Suppose that $\mathbf{B} = \mathbf{E}_k\mathbf{E}_{k-1} \cdots \mathbf{E}_1\mathbf{A}$ is row-equivalent to $\mathbf{A}$. Let $\mathbf{R} = \mathbf{E}_k\mathbf{E}_{k-1} \cdots \mathbf{E}_1$. Then since every elementary matrix $\mathbf{E}_i$ in the product is regular, so is their product (p. 167).

Hence $\mathbf{R}$ is regular, and it has an inverse:

$$\mathbf{R}^{-1} = \mathbf{E}_1^{-1}\mathbf{E}_2^{-1} \cdots \mathbf{E}_k^{-1}.$$

(This proves, of course, that $\mathbf{R}$ is regular.)

Now let $\mathbf{X}$ be any (column) vector such that $\mathbf{AX} = \mathbf{0}$. Then we have

$$\mathbf{BX} = (\mathbf{RA})\mathbf{X} = \mathbf{R}(\mathbf{AX}) = \mathbf{R0} = \mathbf{0}.$$

Again, if $\mathbf{X}$ is any column vector such that $\mathbf{BX} = \mathbf{0}$, then

$$\mathbf{AX} = (\mathbf{R}^{-1}\mathbf{B})\mathbf{X} = \mathbf{R}^{-1}(\mathbf{BX}) = \mathbf{R}^{-1}\mathbf{0} = \mathbf{0}.$$

Hence the solution-spaces of the equations

$$\mathbf{AX} = \mathbf{0}$$

and $\mathbf{BX} = \mathbf{0}$ coincide. By Theorem 32, p. 171, the column ranks of $\mathbf{A}$ and $\mathbf{B}$ are therefore equal. This proves the theorem.

We must also use elementary *column*-transformations on the matrix $\mathbf{A}$ to achieve our goal. These have already been defined (§ 29, p. 156). Very similar proofs to those given above show that:

1. Column-equivalent matrices have the column rank,
2. Column-equivalent matrices have the same row rank.

Since column-transformations are achieved by postmultiplication by a succession of elementary matrices, and the product of such a succession is regular, we can finally give the following definition.

Definition. *Two matrices* $\mathbf{A}$ *and* $\mathbf{B}$, *either of which can be derived from the other by a finite succession of row and column-transformations are called rationally equivalent.*

Then $\mathbf{B} = \mathbf{RAS}$, where both $\mathbf{R}$ and $\mathbf{S}$ are regular, and products of elementary matrices, and $\mathbf{A}$ and $\mathbf{B}$ have the same row rank r, and the same column rank c.

We now take the final step to proving that $r = c$ for any matrix $\mathbf{A}$. We do this by showing that $\mathbf{A}$ is rationally equivalent to a matrix in which it is clear that $r = c$.

The matrix looks like this:

$$
\mathbf{A}_r^* = \left[\begin{array}{cccc|ccc}
1 & 0 & \cdot\cdot & 0 & 0 & \cdot\cdot & 0 \\
0 & 1 & \cdot\cdot & 0 & 0 & \cdot\cdot & 0 \\
\cdot & \cdot & \cdot\cdot & \cdot & \cdot & \cdot\cdot & \cdot \\
0 & \cdot & \cdot\cdot & 1 & 0 & \cdot\cdot & 0 \\
\hline
0 & \cdot & \cdot\cdot & 0 & 0 & \cdot\cdot & 0 \\
\cdot & \cdot & \cdot\cdot & \cdot & \cdot & \cdot\cdot & \cdot \\
0 & \cdot & \cdot\cdot & 0 & 0 & \cdot\cdot & 0
\end{array}\right] \tag{91}
$$

(The first r columns and the first r rows are marked r; the remaining $n - r$ columns and $m - r$ rows are marked $n - r$ and $m - r$.)

The matrix in the top left-hand corner is $\mathbf{I}_r$, the unity matrix of r rows and columns, and all other entries are zero. It is clear that the first r rows of this matrix, and only these, are independent, and the first r columns, and only these, are independent. Both the row rank and column rank of the matrix $\mathbf{A}_r^*$ given by (91) are equal to r. We now prove Theorem 36.

Theorem 36. *Any $m \times n$ matrix $\mathbf{A}$ of row rank r is rationally equivalent to the matrix $\mathbf{A}_r^*$ shown in* (91).

Proof. We know already that $\mathbf{A}$ is row-equivalent to an echelon matrix with only r non-zero rows, and unity entries as the first non-zero entries encountered as we move along the non-zero rows. By interchange of columns of the echelon matrix we can transform it into a matrix of the form

$$
\left[\begin{array}{ccccc|ccc}
1 & b_{12} & b_{13} & \cdot\cdot & b_{1r} & b_{1,r+1} & \cdot\cdot & b_{1n} \\
0 & 1 & b_{23} & \cdot\cdot & b_{2r} & b_{2,r+1} & \cdot\cdot & b_{2n} \\
\cdot & \cdot & \cdot & \cdot\cdot & \cdot & \cdot & \cdot\cdot & \cdot \\
0 & 0 & 0 & \cdot\cdot & 1 & b_{r,r+1} & \cdot\cdot & b_{rn} \\
\hline
0 & 0 & 0 & \cdot\cdot & 0 & 0 & \cdot\cdot & 0 \\
\cdot & \cdot & \cdot & \cdot\cdot & \cdot & \cdot & \cdot\cdot & \cdot \\
0 & 0 & 0 & \cdot\cdot & 0 & 0 & \cdot\cdot & 0
\end{array}\right],
$$

(The first r columns and the first r rows are marked r; the remaining $n - r$ columns and $m - r$ rows are marked $n - r$ and $m - r$.)

and by column operations of type III we can now, by subtracting suitable multiples of the first column from the others, make every element in the first row *after* the first not already zero equal to zero. Then use the second column and subtract suitable multiples from the succeeding columns. In this way we obtain the matrix $\mathbf{A}_r^*$ of (91), and we have proved Theorem 37.

Theorem 37. *The row rank of any matrix $\mathbf{A}$ is equal to its column rank.*

If this be equal to r for a given matrix $\mathbf{A}$, we say that *the rank of $\mathbf{A}$ is equal to r*, and we have also proved Theorem 38.

Theorem 38. *If* $\mathbf{A}$ *is* $m \times n$ *and of rank* r, *there exists a regular* $m \times m$ *matrix* $\mathbf{R}$ *and a regular* $n \times n$ *matrix* $\mathbf{S}$ *such that* $\mathbf{RAS} = \mathbf{A}_r{}^*$.

The matrix $\mathbf{A}_r{}^*$ given by (91) is called *the first rational canonical* (*standard*) *form of a matrix which is* $m \times n$ *and of rank* r.

Example 4

In Example 3, p. 173, we reduced the matrix

$$\mathbf{A} = \begin{bmatrix} 1 & 5 & 2 \\ 1 & 1 & 7 \\ 0 & -3 & 4 \end{bmatrix}$$

to the echelon form

$$\mathbf{E}_4\mathbf{E}_3\mathbf{E}_2\mathbf{E}_1\mathbf{A} = \begin{bmatrix} 1 & 5 & 2 \\ 0 & 1 & -5/4 \\ 0 & 0 & 1 \end{bmatrix}$$

by premultiplication by suitable elementary matrices. To reduce further the echelon form to canonical form we may:

(1) subtract 5 (first column) from the second column,
(2) subtract 2 (first column) from the third column.

This leaves us with the matrix

$$\begin{bmatrix} 1 & 0 & 0 \\ 0 & 1 & -5/4 \\ 0 & 0 & 1 \end{bmatrix}.$$

We now
(3) add 5/4 (second column) to the third column, and we have the rational canonical form

$$\begin{bmatrix} 1 & 0 & 0 \\ 0 & 1 & 0 \\ 0 & 0 & 1 \end{bmatrix}.$$

Operations (1), (2), and (3) can be effected by postmultiplication of the echelon form by suitable elementary matrices $\mathbf{E}_1{}^*$, $\mathbf{E}_2{}^*$, $\mathbf{E}_3{}^*$, and the final canonical form is

$$\mathbf{E}_4\mathbf{E}_3\mathbf{E}_2\mathbf{E}_1\mathbf{A}\mathbf{E}_1{}^*\mathbf{E}_2{}^*\mathbf{E}_3{}^*,$$

where $\mathbf{E}_1^* = \mathbf{I}_3^*((2) - 5(1))$, $\mathbf{E}_2^* = \mathbf{I}_3^*((3) - 2(1))$, and

$$\mathbf{E}_3^* = \mathbf{I}_3^*((3) + 5/4(2)).$$

In fact, *since* **A** *is regular, row-operations alone could have been used.* At the stage

$$\mathbf{E}_4\mathbf{E}_3\mathbf{E}_2\mathbf{E}_1\mathbf{A} = \begin{bmatrix} 1 & 5 & 2 \\ 0 & 1 & -5/4 \\ 0 & 0 & 1 \end{bmatrix}$$

we may:

(1) subtract 2 (third row) from first row,
(2) add 5/4 (third row) to the second row.

This leaves us with the matrix

$$\begin{bmatrix} 1 & 5 & 0 \\ 0 & 1 & 0 \\ 0 & 0 & 1 \end{bmatrix}.$$

Finally we
(3) subtract 5 (second row) from the first row,
and we are left with the unity matrix

$$\mathbf{I}_3 = \begin{bmatrix} 1 & 0 & 0 \\ 0 & 1 & 0 \\ 0 & 0 & 1 \end{bmatrix}.$$

Hence
$$\mathbf{I}_3 = \mathbf{E}_7\mathbf{E}_6\mathbf{E}_5\mathbf{E}_4\mathbf{E}_3\mathbf{E}_2\mathbf{E}_1\mathbf{A},$$

where $\mathbf{E}_5 = \mathbf{I}_3((1) - 2(3))$, $\mathbf{E}_6 = \mathbf{I}_3((2) + 5/4(3))$, and $\mathbf{E}_7 = \mathbf{I}_3((1) - 5(2))$. We shall return to this regular case on p. 181.

EXERCISES 31.2

1. Prove that the relation "rational equivalence" between matrices satisfies the equivalence criteria: (1) $\mathbf{A} \sim \mathbf{A}$, (2) if $\mathbf{A} \sim \mathbf{B}$, then $\mathbf{B} \sim \mathbf{A}$, and (3) if $\mathbf{A} \sim \mathbf{B}$ and $\mathbf{B} \sim \mathbf{C}$, then $\mathbf{A} \sim \mathbf{C}$, where the symbol $\sim$ stands for "is rationally equivalent to".
2. Prove that **A** and $\mathbf{A}^T$ have the same rank.
3. Prove that every regular $n \times n$ matrix, and in particular $\mathbf{I}_n$, has rank n.
4. If **A** is a regular $n \times n$ matrix, deduce from the fact that the rational canonical form for **A** is $\mathbf{I}_n$ that **A** can be written as a finite product of elementary matrices.

5. If **A** is $m \times n$ and has rank 1, deduce from the fact that regular matrices **R** and **S** exist such that

$$\mathbf{RAS} = \begin{bmatrix} 1 & 0 & \cdots & 0 \\ 0 & 0 & \cdots & 0 \\ \cdot & \cdot & \cdots & \cdot \\ 0 & 0 & \cdots & 0 \end{bmatrix}$$

that
$$\mathbf{A} = \mathbf{P}\begin{bmatrix} 1 & 0 & \cdots & 0 \\ 0 & 0 & \cdots & 0 \\ \cdot & \cdot & \cdots & \cdot \\ 0 & 0 & \cdots & 0 \end{bmatrix}\mathbf{Q} = \begin{bmatrix} p_1q_1 & p_1q_2 & \cdots & p_1q_n \\ p_2q_1 & p_2q_2 & \cdots & p_2q_n \\ \cdot & \cdot & \cdots & \cdot \\ p_mq_1 & p_mq_2 & \cdots & p_mq_n \end{bmatrix}.$$

($[p_1, \ldots, p_m]^T$ is the first column of **P**, and $[q_1, \ldots, q_n]$ is the first row of **Q**).

If an $n \times n$ matrix **A** is regular, the corresponding canonical form is the unity matrix $\mathbf{I}_n$, and we have the matrix relation

$$\mathbf{RAS} = \mathbf{I}_n,$$

where **R** and **S** are suitable regular matrices. Now, this can be written:

$$\mathbf{A} = \mathbf{R}^{-1}\mathbf{I}_n\mathbf{S}^{-1} = \mathbf{R}^{-1}\mathbf{S}^{-1} = (\mathbf{SR})^{-1},$$

so that
$$\mathbf{SRA} = \mathbf{I}_n,$$

which indicates that **A** *can be transformed to the unity matrix by premultiplication only, that is, by operations on the rows only.*

In fact, the first stage in the transformation, which is to an echelon matrix, gives us a matrix of the form

$$\begin{bmatrix} 1 & b_{12} & b_{13} & \cdots & b_{1n} \\ 0 & 1 & b_{23} & \cdots & b_{2n} \\ \cdot & \cdot & \cdot & \cdots & \cdot \\ 0 & 0 & 0 & \cdots & 1 \end{bmatrix},$$

and we can now use the last row to nullify all the non-zero elements in the last column above the last row. Then we can use the $(n - 1)$th row to nullify all the elements in the $(n - 1)$th column above the $(n - 1)$th row, and so on, until, by row operations alone we obtain the unity matrix $\mathbf{I}_n$.

This procedure has an important application toward finding the inverse of a regular $n \times n$ matrix **A**. We now know that there exist elementary matrices $\mathbf{E}_1, \ldots, \mathbf{E}_k$ such that

$$\mathbf{E}_1\mathbf{E}_2 \cdots \mathbf{E}_k\mathbf{A} = \mathbf{I}_n.$$

Hence $$\mathbf{E}_1\mathbf{E}_2 \cdots \mathbf{E}_k\mathbf{I}_n = \mathbf{I}_n\mathbf{A}^{-1} = \mathbf{A}^{-1},$$

which shows that *the same sequence of row-operations which transforms* **A** *into the unity matrix* $\mathbf{I}_n$ *will, if applied to the unity matrix, produce* $\mathbf{A}^{-1}$, *the inverse of* **A**.

Example 5

$$\begin{bmatrix} 3 & 2 \\ 4 & 3 \end{bmatrix} \rightarrow \begin{bmatrix} 1 & 2/3 \\ 4 & 3 \end{bmatrix} \rightarrow \begin{bmatrix} 1 & 2/3 \\ 0 & 1/3 \end{bmatrix} \rightarrow \begin{bmatrix} 1 & 2/3 \\ 0 & 1 \end{bmatrix} \rightarrow \begin{bmatrix} 1 & 0 \\ 0 & 1 \end{bmatrix},$$

by a sequence of operations which, by now, should be evident to the reader. The same sequence applied to $\mathbf{I}_2$ gives us

$$\begin{bmatrix} 1 & 0 \\ 0 & 1 \end{bmatrix} \rightarrow \begin{bmatrix} 1/3 & 0 \\ 0 & 1 \end{bmatrix} \rightarrow \begin{bmatrix} 1/3 & 0 \\ -4/3 & 1 \end{bmatrix} \rightarrow \begin{bmatrix} 1/3 & 0 \\ -4 & 3 \end{bmatrix} \rightarrow \begin{bmatrix} 3 & -2 \\ -4 & 3 \end{bmatrix},$$

which is, indeed, the inverse matrix.

EXERCISE 31.3

1. Find the inverse of the matrix

$$\begin{bmatrix} 0 & 1 & 2 \\ 1 & 0 & 2 \\ 1 & 2 & 0 \end{bmatrix},$$

and also of the matrix

$$\begin{bmatrix} 1 & 5 & 2 \\ 1 & 1 & 7 \\ 0 & -3 & 4 \end{bmatrix}.$$

32. Properties Involving the Rank of a Matrix

Theorem 39. *If* **A** *and* **B** *have the same shape and the same rank, then they are rationally equivalent.*

Proof. If $\mathbf{A}$ and $\mathbf{B}$ are both $m \times n$ and of rank r, we can find regular matrices $\mathbf{R}$ and $\mathbf{S}$ such that $\mathbf{RAS} = \mathbf{A}_r^*$, and regular matrices $\mathbf{P}$ and $\mathbf{Q}$ such that $\mathbf{PBQ} = \mathbf{A}_r^*$, where $\mathbf{A}_r^*$ is the canonical form for $m \times n$ matrices of rank r given by (91), p. 178.

Hence
$$\mathbf{RAS} = \mathbf{PBQ},$$
and since $\mathbf{R}$ and $\mathbf{S}$ are both regular, their inverses $\mathbf{R}^{-1}$ and $\mathbf{S}^{-1}$ exist, and
$$\mathbf{A} = \mathbf{R}^{-1}\mathbf{PBQS}^{-1}.$$
The matrices $\mathbf{R}^{-1}\mathbf{P}$ and $\mathbf{QS}^{-1}$ are both regular, and therefore $\mathbf{A}$ is rationally equivalent to $\mathbf{B}$.

We could, of course, shorten this proof by making use of the result of Exercise 1, p. 180, and assume that "rational equivalence" is an equivalence relation. It should also be noted that there is no restriction in assuming that the matrices $\mathbf{R}$, $\mathbf{S}$, $\mathbf{P}$, and $\mathbf{Q}$ used in the foregoing proof are merely regular, rather than specified as the product of elementary matrices in each case, since Exercise 4, p. 180 shows that every regular matrix can be written as the product of elementary matrices.

EXERCISE 32.1

1. Show that the two 3×4 matrices given below are rationally equivalent:

$$\begin{bmatrix} 1 & 2 & 3 & 4 \\ 5 & 6 & 7 & 8 \\ 7 & 10 & 13 & 16 \end{bmatrix}, \quad \begin{bmatrix} 0 & 0 & 1 & 0 \\ -1 & 1 & 0 & 1 \\ 1 & -1 & 1 & -1 \end{bmatrix}.$$

Theorem 40. *If* $\mathbf{A}$ *and* $\mathbf{B}$ *are both* $m \times n$, *then*

$$\textit{rank}(\mathbf{A} + \mathbf{B}) \leqslant \textit{rank}\ \mathbf{A} + \textit{rank}\ \mathbf{B}.$$

Proof. We know by Theorem 32, p. 171, that the column n-vectors $\mathbf{X}$ which satisfy the equations $\mathbf{AX} = \mathbf{0}$ and $\mathbf{BX} = \mathbf{0}$ form subspaces in V_n of respective dimension $n - \text{rank}\ \mathbf{A}$ and $n - \text{rank}\ \mathbf{B}$. By the dimension theorem, Theorem 22, p. 134,

$$\begin{aligned} &\text{dimension (join)} + \text{dimension (intersection)} \\ &\qquad = \text{sum of dimensions}, \end{aligned}$$

and since dimension (join) $\leqslant n$, this gives us

$$\begin{aligned} &\text{dimension (intersection)} \\ &\qquad \geqslant \text{sum of dimensions} - n. \end{aligned}$$

In the above case this formula becomes:

$$\begin{aligned}&\text{dimension (intersection)}\\&\quad\geqslant (n - \text{rank } \mathbf{A}) + (n - \text{rank } \mathbf{B}) - n\\&\quad= n - \text{rank } \mathbf{A} - \text{rank } \mathbf{B}.\end{aligned}$$

The intersection of the solution spaces of $\mathbf{AX} = \mathbf{0}$ and $\mathbf{BX} = \mathbf{0}$ contains all vectors $\mathbf{X}$ which satisfy both $\mathbf{AX} = \mathbf{0}$ and $\mathbf{BX} = \mathbf{0}$. Such vectors also satisfy the equations $(\mathbf{A} + \mathbf{B})\mathbf{X} = \mathbf{0}$, and the solution space of these equations has dimension $n - \text{rank}(\mathbf{A} + \mathbf{B})$. Therefore

$$\begin{aligned}n - \text{rank}(\mathbf{A} + \mathbf{B}) &\geqslant \text{dimension (intersection)}\\&\geqslant n - \text{rank } \mathbf{A} - \text{rank } \mathbf{B},\end{aligned}$$

so that

$$\text{rank}(\mathbf{A} + \mathbf{B}) \leqslant \text{rank } \mathbf{A} + \text{rank } \mathbf{B}.$$

Example 1

If

$$\mathbf{A} = \begin{bmatrix} 1 & 2 \\ 3 & 4 \end{bmatrix} \qquad \mathbf{B} = \begin{bmatrix} -1 & -2 \\ 3 & 4 \end{bmatrix}$$

then rank $\mathbf{A}$ = rank $\mathbf{B}$ = 2, but $\text{rank}(\mathbf{A} + \mathbf{B}) = 1$.

EXERCISE 32.2

1. Write two 2×2 matrices $\mathbf{A}$ and $\mathbf{B}$, each of rank 2 such that $\text{rank}(\mathbf{A} + \mathbf{B}) = 0$.

Theorem 41. *Rank*$(\mathbf{AB}) \leqslant$ *min.* (*rank* $\mathbf{A}$, *rank* $\mathbf{B}$).

Proof. If we look once again at the way the matrix product $\mathbf{AB}$ is formed, we see that the column-vectors of $\mathbf{AB}$ are linear combinations of the column-vectors of $\mathbf{A}$. The column-space of $\mathbf{AB}$ is therefore a subspace of the column-space of $\mathbf{A}$, so that $\text{rank}(\mathbf{AB}) \leqslant \text{rank } \mathbf{A}$ (cf. Exercises 4, 5, p. 157).

Again, the row-vectors of $\mathbf{AB}$ are linear combinations of the row-vectors of $\mathbf{B}$. The row-space of $\mathbf{AB}$ is therefore a subspace of the row-space of $\mathbf{B}$. Since row rank = column rank, we deduce that $\text{rank}(\mathbf{AB}) \leqslant \text{rank } \mathbf{B}$.

EXERCISES 32.3

1. From the fact that every $\mathbf{X}$ satisfying $\mathbf{BX} = \mathbf{0}$ also satisfies $\mathbf{ABX} = \mathbf{0}$, and every $\mathbf{Y}$ satisfying $\mathbf{YA} = \mathbf{0}$ also satisfies $\mathbf{YAB} = \mathbf{0}$, and Theorem 32, p. 171, together with Exercise 4, p. 172, deduce Theorem 41.

2. If $\mathbf{A}$ is regular, deduce from $\mathbf{B} = \mathbf{A}^{-1}\mathbf{AB}$ that $\text{rank}(\mathbf{AB}) = \text{rank } \mathbf{B}$. Deduce also that $\text{rank}(\mathbf{CA}) = \text{rank } \mathbf{C}$.

Definition. *If in an $m \times n$ matrix* **A** *we delete p rows* $(0 \leqslant p \leqslant m)$ *and q columns* $(0 \leqslant q \leqslant n)$, *the remaining* $(m - p) \times (n - q)$ *matrix is called a* SUBMATRIX *of* **A**.

Example 2

If

$$\mathbf{A} = \begin{bmatrix} a_{11} & a_{12} & a_{13} & a_{14} \\ a_{21} & a_{22} & a_{23} & a_{24} \\ a_{31} & a_{32} & a_{33} & a_{34} \end{bmatrix},$$

and we delete the second row and the second and fourth columns, we are left with the submatrix

$$\begin{bmatrix} a_{11} & a_{13} \\ a_{31} & a_{33} \end{bmatrix}.$$

Theorem 42. *A matrix has rank r if and only if it contains at least one regular $k \times k$ submatrix for each of the values $k = 1, 2, \ldots, r$, but none for $k > r$.*

Proof. Let **A** have rank r, and let **B** be any regular $k \times k$ submatrix. Then the k row-vectors of **B** are linearly independent. If these row-vectors occur in the rows $i_1, i_2, \ldots, i_k$ of the matrix **A**, we may affirm that the row-vectors of **A** in the rows $i_1, i_2, \ldots, i_k$ of **A** are also linearly independent. For if they were dependent, their dependence would imply the dependence of the row-vectors of **B**. Hence $k \leqslant r$.

On the other hand, because **A** has rank r, we can find k linearly independent row-vectors in **A** whenever $k \leqslant r$. These rows form a k-rowed submatrix **C** of rank k. Since **C** has rank k, **C** contains k linearly independent columns. These k columns of **C** form a $k \times k$ submatrix of **C**, and therefore of **A**, and this $k \times k$ submatrix is regular.

This proves that the given condition is a *necessary* condition.

To prove that the condition is sufficient, suppose that **A** contains a regular $k \times k$ submatrix for $k \leqslant r$, but not for $k > r$. The row-vectors of such an $r \times r$ matrix are linearly independent, and by the argument given earlier, the r corresponding rows of **A** are also independent. Hence rank $\mathbf{A} \geqslant r$.

If rank $\mathbf{A} > r$, the proof of the necessity of the theorem given above would imply that **A** contains a regular $k \times k$ submatrix, where $k > r$. This is contrary to hypothesis. Hence rank $\mathbf{A} = r$.

We shall see later (p. 198) the connection between this theorem and the concept of *determinantal rank*.

Corollary. *If a $k \times k$ submatrix of* **A** *is regular, there exist regular $h \times h$ submatrices for all the values $h = 1, 2, \ldots, k - 1$.*

In fact, we need only apply the theorem to the given submatrix to obtain this corollary. Hence, if we are testing a matrix for rank, the detection of a regular $k \times k$ submatrix assures us that the rank $\geqslant k$, and we need not investigate submatrices of smaller size. But reduction to echelon form is usually the quickest procedure for the determination of rank.

Before we go on to the final theorem in this section we discuss the *partitioning* of matrices, or *the division into blocks.*

If we are merely adding matrices of the same shape, say

$$\mathbf{A} = \left[\begin{array}{ccc|c} a_{11} & a_{12} & a_{13} & a_{14} \\ a_{21} & a_{22} & a_{23} & a_{24} \\ \hline a_{31} & a_{32} & a_{33} & a_{34} \end{array}\right], \qquad \mathbf{B} = \left[\begin{array}{ccc|c} b_{11} & b_{12} & b_{13} & b_{14} \\ b_{21} & b_{22} & b_{23} & b_{24} \\ \hline b_{31} & b_{32} & b_{33} & b_{34} \end{array}\right],$$

and we divide each matrix into blocks in the same way, calling the submatrices

$$\mathbf{A}_{11} = \begin{bmatrix} a_{11} & a_{12} & a_{13} \\ a_{21} & a_{22} & a_{23} \end{bmatrix}, \qquad \mathbf{A}_{12} = \begin{bmatrix} a_{14} \\ a_{24} \end{bmatrix},$$

$$\mathbf{A}_{21} = [a_{31} \quad a_{32} \quad a_{33}], \qquad \mathbf{A}_{22} = [a_{34}],$$

then we write

$$\mathbf{A} = \begin{bmatrix} \mathbf{A}_{11} & \mathbf{A}_{12} \\ \mathbf{A}_{21} & \mathbf{A}_{22} \end{bmatrix},$$

and if

$$\mathbf{B}_{11} = \begin{bmatrix} b_{11} & b_{12} & b_{13} \\ b_{21} & b_{22} & b_{23} \end{bmatrix}, \qquad \mathbf{B}_{12} = \begin{bmatrix} b_{14} \\ b_{24} \end{bmatrix},$$

$$\mathbf{B}_{21} = [b_{31} \quad b_{32} \quad b_{33}], \qquad \mathbf{B}_{22} = [b_{34}],$$

we also write

$$\mathbf{B} = \begin{bmatrix} \mathbf{B}_{11} & \mathbf{B}_{12} \\ \mathbf{B}_{21} & \mathbf{B}_{22} \end{bmatrix},$$

and it is clear that

$$\mathbf{A} + \mathbf{B} = \left[\begin{array}{ccc|c} a_{11} + b_{11} & a_{12} + b_{12} & a_{13} + b_{13} & a_{14} + b_{14} \\ a_{21} + b_{21} & a_{22} + b_{22} & a_{23} + b_{23} & a_{24} + b_{24} \\ \hline a_{31} + b_{31} & a_{32} + b_{32} & a_{33} + b_{33} & a_{34} + b_{34} \end{array}\right]$$

$$= \begin{bmatrix} \mathbf{A}_{11} + \mathbf{B}_{11} & \mathbf{A}_{12} + \mathbf{B}_{12} \\ \mathbf{A}_{21} + \mathbf{B}_{21} & \mathbf{A}_{22} + \mathbf{B}_{22} \end{bmatrix},$$

so that the block matrices can be added as if they were mere matrix elements. This result is easily extended to two $m \times n$ matrices.

If multiplication is being considered, the division into blocks must conform to the necessary pattern which makes multiplication possible. Let

$$\mathbf{A} = \left[\begin{array}{ccc|c} a_{11} & a_{12} & a_{13} & a_{14} \\ a_{21} & a_{22} & a_{23} & a_{24} \\ \hline a_{31} & a_{32} & a_{33} & a_{34} \end{array}\right],$$

$$\mathbf{B} = \left[\begin{array}{cc|c} b_{11} & b_{12} & b_{13} \\ b_{21} & b_{22} & b_{23} \\ b_{31} & b_{32} & b_{33} \\ \hline b_{41} & b_{42} & b_{43} \end{array}\right].$$

Then if $\mathbf{A}$ is 3×4, $\mathbf{B}$ must be $4 \times q$ (in this case it is 4×3) for multiplication to be possible. If we divide $\mathbf{A}$ into blocks as in the first example, then $\mathbf{B}$ must be divided into blocks with the *rows* of $\mathbf{B}$ conforming to the pattern of subdivision of the *columns* of $\mathbf{A}$. One such subdivision is indicated. If we write

$$\mathbf{B}_{11} = \begin{bmatrix} b_{11} & b_{12} \\ b_{21} & b_{22} \\ b_{31} & b_{32} \end{bmatrix}, \qquad \mathbf{B}_{12} = \begin{bmatrix} b_{13} \\ b_{23} \\ b_{33} \end{bmatrix},$$

$$\mathbf{B}_{21} = [b_{41} \quad b_{42}], \qquad \mathbf{B}_{22} = [b_{43}],$$

then

$$\mathbf{AB} = \begin{bmatrix} \mathbf{A}_{11}\mathbf{B}_{11} + \mathbf{A}_{12}\mathbf{B}_{21} & \mathbf{A}_{11}\mathbf{B}_{12} + \mathbf{A}_{12}\mathbf{B}_{22} \\ \mathbf{A}_{21}\mathbf{B}_{11} + \mathbf{A}_{22}\mathbf{B}_{21} & \mathbf{A}_{21}\mathbf{B}_{12} + \mathbf{A}_{22}\mathbf{B}_{22} \end{bmatrix},$$

as the reader should verify.

We could also subdivide $\mathbf{B}$ thus:

$$\mathbf{B} = \left[\begin{array}{c|c|c} b_{11} & b_{12} & b_{13} \\ b_{21} & b_{22} & b_{23} \\ b_{31} & b_{32} & b_{33} \\ \hline b_{41} & b_{42} & b_{43} \end{array}\right] = \begin{bmatrix} \mathbf{B}_{11} & \mathbf{B}_{12} & \mathbf{B}_{13} \\ \mathbf{B}_{21} & \mathbf{B}_{22} & \mathbf{B}_{23} \end{bmatrix}$$

and again

$$\begin{aligned} \mathbf{AB} &= \begin{bmatrix} \mathbf{A}_{11} & \mathbf{A}_{12} \\ \mathbf{A}_{21} & \mathbf{A}_{22} \end{bmatrix} \begin{bmatrix} \mathbf{B}_{11} & \mathbf{B}_{12} & \mathbf{B}_{13} \\ \mathbf{B}_{21} & \mathbf{B}_{22} & \mathbf{B}_{23} \end{bmatrix} \\ &= \begin{bmatrix} \mathbf{A}_{11}\mathbf{B}_{11} + \mathbf{A}_{12}\mathbf{B}_{21} & \mathbf{A}_{11}\mathbf{B}_{12} + \mathbf{A}_{12}\mathbf{B}_{22} & \mathbf{A}_{11}\mathbf{B}_{13} + \mathbf{A}_{12}\mathbf{B}_{23} \\ \mathbf{A}_{21}\mathbf{B}_{11} + \mathbf{A}_{22}\mathbf{B}_{21} & \mathbf{A}_{21}\mathbf{B}_{12} + \mathbf{A}_{22}\mathbf{B}_{22} & \mathbf{A}_{21}\mathbf{B}_{13} + \mathbf{A}_{22}\mathbf{B}_{23} \end{bmatrix}. \end{aligned}$$

This should also be verified.

The process described can also be extended to the multiplication of any $m \times n$ matrix by an $n \times p$ matrix.

With this division into blocks the rational canonical form $\mathbf{A}_r^*$, given by (91) p. 178, for an $m \times n$ matrix of rank r may be written

$$\mathbf{A}_r^* = \begin{array}{r} \\ m-r\updownarrow \end{array}\left[\begin{array}{c|c} \mathbf{I}_r & \mathbf{0} \\ \hline \mathbf{0} & \mathbf{0} \end{array}\right], \quad \text{with the right-hand columns of width } n-r \ (\longleftrightarrow)$$

where $\mathbf{I}_r$ is the $r \times r$ unity matrix, and the three zero matrices shown have the sizes indicated.

Example 3

If $\mathbf{P}$ and $\mathbf{R}$ are regular matrices, not necessarily of the same size, prove that

$$\begin{bmatrix} \mathbf{P} & \mathbf{Q} \\ \mathbf{0} & \mathbf{R} \end{bmatrix}^{-1} = \begin{bmatrix} \mathbf{P}^{-1} & -\mathbf{P}^{-1}\mathbf{Q}\mathbf{R}^{-1} \\ \mathbf{0} & \mathbf{R}^{-1} \end{bmatrix}.$$

In fact

$$\begin{bmatrix} \mathbf{P} & \mathbf{Q} \\ \mathbf{0} & \mathbf{R} \end{bmatrix}\begin{bmatrix} \mathbf{P}^{-1} & -\mathbf{P}^{-1}\mathbf{Q}\mathbf{R}^{-1} \\ \mathbf{0} & \mathbf{R}^{-1} \end{bmatrix} = \begin{bmatrix} \mathbf{P}\mathbf{P}^{-1} & -\mathbf{P}\mathbf{P}^{-1}\mathbf{Q}\mathbf{R}^{-1} + \mathbf{Q}\mathbf{R}^{-1} \\ \mathbf{0} & \mathbf{R}\mathbf{R}^{-1} \end{bmatrix}$$

$$= \begin{bmatrix} \mathbf{I} & -\mathbf{Q}\mathbf{R}^{-1} + \mathbf{Q}\mathbf{R}^{-1} \\ \mathbf{0} & \mathbf{I} \end{bmatrix} = \begin{bmatrix} \mathbf{I} & \mathbf{0} \\ \mathbf{0} & \mathbf{I} \end{bmatrix},$$

where the two unity matrices shown are of the same size as $\mathbf{P}$ and $\mathbf{R}$ respectively. Since this last matrix is just a unity matrix of the size of the original matrices we have been multiplying together, the result follows.

EXERCISE 32.4

1. Find the inverse of the matrix

$$\begin{bmatrix} \cos\alpha & \sin\alpha & \cos\beta & \sin\beta \\ -\sin\alpha & \cos\alpha & -\sin\beta & \cos\beta \\ 0 & 0 & \cos\gamma & \sin\gamma \\ 0 & 0 & -\sin\gamma & \cos\gamma \end{bmatrix}.$$

We can now prove Theorem 43.

Theorem 43. *If* **A** *is* $p \times q$ *and* **B** *is* $q \times r$ *and* $\mathbf{C} = \mathbf{AB}$, *then*

$$\text{rank } \mathbf{C} \geqslant \text{rank } \mathbf{A} + \text{rank } \mathbf{B} - q$$

Proof. We write $r_{\mathbf{A}} = \text{rank } \mathbf{A}$, $r_{\mathbf{B}} = \text{rank } \mathbf{B}$ and $r_{\mathbf{C}} = \text{rank } \mathbf{C}$. Since **B** is of rank $r_{\mathbf{B}}$ there exist regular matrices **Q** (of type $q \times q$) and **R** (of type $r \times r$) such that

$$\mathbf{B} = \mathbf{Q}\begin{bmatrix} \mathbf{I}_{r_{\mathbf{B}}} & \mathbf{0} \\ \mathbf{0} & \mathbf{0} \end{bmatrix}\mathbf{R}.$$

This follows immediately from Theorem 38, p. 179. We also know that premultiplication or postmultiplication by a regular matrix leaves the rank of a matrix unchanged (Exercise 2, p. 184). Hence

$$\mathbf{C}^* = \mathbf{CR}^{-1}, \qquad \mathbf{A}^* = \mathbf{AQ}$$

are of ranks $r_{\mathbf{C}}$ and $r_{\mathbf{A}}$ respectively. We divide $\mathbf{A}^*$ into blocks thus:

$$\mathbf{A}^* = [\mathbf{A}_{11}^* \quad \mathbf{A}_{12}^*],$$

where $\mathbf{A}_{11}^*$ is a $p \times r_{\mathbf{B}}$ matrix and $\mathbf{A}_{12}^*$ is a $p \times (q - r_{\mathbf{B}})$ matrix.

Now $\mathbf{A}^*$ is of rank $r_{\mathbf{A}}$, and therefore has $r_{\mathbf{A}}$ linearly independent columns. We consider the number of these linearly independent columns which can occur amongst the columns of $\mathbf{A}_{11}^*$. Since $\mathbf{A}_{12}^*$ has $q - r_{\mathbf{B}}$ columns, even if all these were independent there are still $r_{\mathbf{A}} - (q - r_{\mathbf{B}})$ of the original $r_{\mathbf{A}}$ columns in $\mathbf{A}^*$ which must occur amongst the columns of $\mathbf{A}_{11}^*$. Hence the rank of $[\mathbf{A}_{11}^* \ \mathbf{0}]$ is at least

$$r_{\mathbf{A}} - (q - r_{\mathbf{B}}) = r_{\mathbf{A}} + r_{\mathbf{B}} - q.$$

Now

$$[\mathbf{A}_{11}^* \quad \mathbf{0}] = [\mathbf{A}_{11}^* \quad \mathbf{A}_{12}^*]\begin{bmatrix} \mathbf{I}_{r_{\mathbf{B}}} & \mathbf{0} \\ \mathbf{0} & \mathbf{0} \end{bmatrix}$$

$$= \mathbf{AQ}\begin{bmatrix} \mathbf{I}_{r_{\mathbf{B}}} & \mathbf{0} \\ \mathbf{0} & \mathbf{0} \end{bmatrix},$$

and since

$$\mathbf{B} = \mathbf{Q}\begin{bmatrix} \mathbf{I}_{r_{\mathbf{B}}} & \mathbf{0} \\ \mathbf{0} & \mathbf{0} \end{bmatrix}\mathbf{R},$$

$$\mathbf{AQ}\begin{bmatrix} \mathbf{I}_{r_{\mathbf{B}}} & \mathbf{0} \\ \mathbf{0} & \mathbf{0} \end{bmatrix} = \mathbf{ABR}^{-1}$$

and

$$\mathbf{ABR}^{-1} = (\mathbf{AB})\mathbf{R}^{-1} = \mathbf{CR}^{-1} = \mathbf{C}^*.$$

But $\mathbf{C}^*$ is of rank $r_{\mathbf{C}}$, and since

$$[\mathbf{A}_{11}^* \quad \mathbf{0}] = \mathbf{C}^*,$$

it follows that

$$\begin{aligned} r_{\mathbf{C}} &= \operatorname{rank}[\mathbf{A}_{11}^* \quad \mathbf{0}] \\ &\geqslant r_{\mathbf{A}} + r_{\mathbf{B}} - q. \end{aligned}$$

33. Homogeneous Linear Equations

We have seen in Theorem 32, p. 171 that the solution-vectors of the homogeneous linear equations

$$\left.\begin{array}{l} a_{11}X_1 + a_{12}X_2 + \cdots + a_{1n}X_n = 0, \\ \cdot \quad \cdot \quad \cdot \quad \cdots \quad \cdot \quad \cdot \\ a_{m1}X_1 + a_{m2}X_2 + \cdots + a_{mn}X_n = 0 \end{array}\right\}$$

fill a vector subspace of V_n which is of dimension $n - c$, where c is the column rank of $\mathbf{A}$, and $\mathbf{A} = [a_{ij}]$ is the matrix of the coefficients of the set of equations.

We now know that c is also the row rank of $\mathbf{A}$, and we replace c by $r = \operatorname{rank} \mathbf{A}$, so that the solution-space of the set of equations has a basis which consists of $n - r$ linearly independent vectors. If we can find such a basis, say

$$\mathbf{f}_1, \mathbf{f}_2, \ldots, \mathbf{f}_{n-r},$$

any solution of the set of equations $\mathbf{AX} = \mathbf{0}$ can be written in the form

$$\mathbf{X} = \lambda_1\mathbf{f}_1 + \lambda_2\mathbf{f}_2 + \cdots + \lambda_{n-r}\mathbf{f}_{n-r}.$$

In practice, if $\mathbf{A}$ is of rank r we pick out a regular $r \times r$ submatrix, and, by renumbering the unknowns $X_1, \ldots, X_n$ and reordering the equations, we contrive that this regular submatrix is up in the top left-hand corner of the matrix of coefficients, so that it is

$$[a_{ij}] \qquad (i = 1, \ldots, r;\ j = 1, \ldots, r).$$

We now know that the first r row-vectors of $\mathbf{A}$ are independent, and that if there are any further row-vectors, these are linearly dependent on the first r. This means that we solve the first r equations and ignore the remainder, knowing that they will be automatically satisfied by the solutions of the first r equations. We therefore consider the set of equations

$$\left.\begin{array}{l} a_{11}X_1 + \cdots + a_{1r}X_r + a_{1,r+1}X_{r+1} + \cdots + a_{1n}X_n = 0, \\ \cdot \quad \cdots \cdot \quad \cdot \qquad \cdot \qquad \cdots \qquad \cdot \quad \cdot \\ a_{r1}X_1 + \cdots + a_{rr}X_r + a_{r,r+1}X_{r+1} + \cdots + a_{rn}X_n = 0. \end{array}\right\}$$

We write these in the form

$$\begin{bmatrix} a_{11} & a_{12} & \cdots & a_{1r} \\ \cdot & \cdot & \cdots & \cdot \\ a_{r1} & a_{r2} & \cdots & a_{rr} \end{bmatrix} \begin{bmatrix} X_1 \\ \cdot \\ X_r \end{bmatrix} = - \begin{bmatrix} a_{1,r+1} & \cdots & a_{1n} \\ \cdot & \cdots & \cdot \\ a_{r,r+1} & \cdots & a_{rn} \end{bmatrix} \begin{bmatrix} X_{r+1} \\ \cdot \\ X_n \end{bmatrix},$$

and we *solve* for $X_1, X_2, \ldots, X_r$ in terms of $X_{r+1}, X_{r+2}, \ldots, X_n$, regarding this last set as a set of parameters. We can do this because the $r \times r$ matrix on the left is regular, and has an inverse. We therefore obtain the solution of the given set of equations in terms of $n - r$ independent parameters, to which any arbitrary values can be assigned *independently of each other*, and we can pick out a basis for the complete set of solutions. For if we write, for clearness,

$$X_{r+1} = \lambda_{r+1},\ X_{r+2} = \lambda_{r+2}, \ldots, X_n = \lambda_n,$$

solving the foregoing equations gives us

$$\left.\begin{matrix} X_1 = c_{1,r+1}\lambda_{r+1} + \cdots + c_{1n}\lambda_n, \\ \cdot \quad \cdot \quad \cdot \quad \cdots \quad \cdot \\ X_r = c_{r,r+1}\lambda_{r+1} + \cdots + c_{rn}\lambda_n, \end{matrix}\right\}$$

where the c_{ij} are numbers which can be found in a unique manner. Hence the solution of the equations is

$$\begin{aligned} \mathbf{X} &= [X_1, \ldots, X_r, X_{r+1}, \ldots, X_n] = [X_1, \ldots, X_r, \lambda_{r+1}, \ldots, \lambda_n] \\ &= \lambda_{r+1}\mathbf{Y}_{r+1} + \lambda_{r+2}\mathbf{Y}_{r+2} + \cdots + \lambda_n\mathbf{Y}_n, \end{aligned}$$

on picking out the coefficients of the parameters, where

$$\begin{aligned} \mathbf{Y}_{r+1} &= [c_{1,r+1}, c_{2,r+1}, \ldots, c_{r,r+1}, 1, 0, 0, \ldots, 0], \\ \mathbf{Y}_{r+2} &= [c_{1,r+2}, c_{2,r+2}, \ldots, c_{r,r+2}, 0, 1, 0, \ldots, 0], \\ &\cdot \quad \cdot \quad \cdot \quad \cdots \quad \cdot \quad \cdots \\ \mathbf{Y}_n &= [\ c_{1,n},\ c_{2,n},\ \ldots,\ c_{r,n},\ 0, 0, 0, \ldots, 1]. \end{aligned}$$

The $\mathbf{Y}_{r+1}, \mathbf{Y}_{r+2}, \ldots, \mathbf{Y}_n$ are clearly linearly independent (see Exercise 3, p. 128) and form a basis for the set of solutions.

Example 1

Solve the equations

$$\begin{aligned} X_1 + 2X_2 + 3X_3 + 4X_4 &= 0, \\ 2X_1 + 5X_2 + X_3 + X_4 &= 0. \end{aligned}$$

We may write the equations in the form

$$\begin{bmatrix} 1 & 2 \\ 2 & 5 \end{bmatrix} \begin{bmatrix} X_1 \\ X_2 \end{bmatrix} = - \begin{bmatrix} 3 & 4 \\ 1 & 1 \end{bmatrix} \begin{bmatrix} X_3 \\ X_4 \end{bmatrix}.$$

The inverse of the regular 2×2 matrix on the left is $\begin{bmatrix} 5 & -2 \\ -2 & 1 \end{bmatrix}$.

Hence
$$\begin{bmatrix} X_1 \\ X_2 \end{bmatrix} = -\begin{bmatrix} 5 & -2 \\ -2 & 1 \end{bmatrix}\begin{bmatrix} 3 & 4 \\ 1 & 1 \end{bmatrix}\begin{bmatrix} X_3 \\ X_4 \end{bmatrix},$$
giving
$$\begin{bmatrix} X_1 \\ X_2 \end{bmatrix} = \begin{bmatrix} -13X_3 - 18X_4 \\ 5X_3 + 7X_4 \end{bmatrix} = \begin{bmatrix} -13\lambda_3 - 18\lambda_4 \\ 5\lambda_3 + 7\lambda_4 \end{bmatrix},$$
and
$$\begin{aligned} \mathbf{X} = [X_1, X_2, X_3, X_4] &= [-13\lambda_3 - 18\lambda_4, 5\lambda_3 + 7\lambda_4, \lambda_3, \lambda_4] \\ &= \lambda_3[-13, 5, 1, 0] + \lambda_4[-18, 7, 0, 1], \end{aligned}$$
which gives a basis for the solution vectors of the equations.

EXERCISE 33

1. Solve the equations

$$3X_1 + 4X_2 + 5X_3 + 6X_4 = 0,$$
$$2X_1 + 3X_2 + 4X_3 + 5X_4 = 0.$$

34. Non-homogeneous Linear Equations

Consider the set of non-homogeneous linear equations

$$\begin{aligned} a_{11}X_1 + a_{12}X_2 + \cdots + a_{1n}X_n &= k_1, \\ a_{21}X_1 + a_{22}X_2 + \cdots + a_{2n}X_n &= k_2, \\ \cdot \quad \cdot \quad \cdot \quad \cdots \quad & \cdot \quad \cdot \\ a_{m1}X_1 + a_{m2}X_2 + \cdots + a_{mn}X_n &= k_m. \end{aligned}$$

We have already considered the case $m = n$, when the equations are also regular, in § 21, p. 99.

Here we write once more $\mathbf{k} = [k_1, k_2, \ldots, k_m]^T$, and the equations can be written in matrix notation as

$$\mathbf{AX} = \mathbf{k}.$$

We now introduce the matrix

$$\begin{bmatrix} a_{11} & a_{12} & \cdots & a_{1n} & k_1 \\ a_{21} & a_{22} & \cdots & a_{2n} & k_2 \\ \cdot & \cdot & \cdots & \cdot & \cdot \\ a_{m1} & a_{m2} & \cdots & a_{mn} & k_m \end{bmatrix},$$

which we can also write as $[\mathbf{A}\ \mathbf{k}]$, and we call this the *augmented matrix* of $\mathbf{A}$. We now prove

Theorem 44. *The equations* $\mathbf{AX} = \mathbf{k}$ *have a solution if, and only if, the matrices* $\mathbf{A}$ *and* $[\mathbf{A}\ \mathbf{k}]$ *have the same rank.*

Proof. The matrices $\mathbf{A}$ and $[\mathbf{A}\ \mathbf{k}]$ have the same rank if, and only if, they have the same column-space, that is, if and only if $\mathbf{k}$ is linearly dependent on the column vectors $\mathbf{c}_1, \mathbf{c}_2, \ldots, \mathbf{c}_n$ of $\mathbf{A}$. This is the case if and only if for some $\lambda_1, \lambda_2, \ldots, \lambda_n$ in R we have the relation

$$\begin{aligned}\mathbf{k} &= \lambda_1\mathbf{c}_1 + \lambda_2\mathbf{c}_2 + \cdots + \lambda_n\mathbf{c}_n \\ &= [\mathbf{c}_1\ \mathbf{c}_2 \cdots \mathbf{c}_n]\begin{bmatrix}\lambda_1\\ \lambda_2\\ \cdot\\ \cdot\\ \cdot\\ \lambda_n\end{bmatrix} = \mathbf{A}\begin{bmatrix}\lambda_1\\ \lambda_2\\ \cdot\\ \cdot\\ \cdot\\ \lambda_n\end{bmatrix},\end{aligned}$$

and this is the condition that the equations $\mathbf{AX} = \mathbf{k}$ should have the solution $\mathbf{X} = [\lambda_1, \lambda_2, \ldots, \lambda_n]^T$.

If the given set of equations can be solved, they are said to be *consistent*, or *compatible*.

EXERCISE 34.1

1. Show that the equations

$$X_1 + 2X_2 = 3, \qquad X_2 - X_3 = 2, \qquad X_1 + X_2 + X_3 = 1$$

are compatible, but that the equations

$$X_1 + 2X_2 = 3, \qquad X_2 - X_3 = 2, \qquad X_1 + X_2 + X_3 = 2$$

are not compatible, and interpret the two sets of equations geometrically (cf. Example 3, § 20, p. 96).

If the given set of equations is compatible, let $\mathbf{X} = \mathbf{U}$ be any particular solution, found by any method. Then $\mathbf{X} = \mathbf{V}$ is a solution if and only if

$$\mathbf{AV} = \mathbf{k} = \mathbf{AU},$$

that is if, and only if,

$$\mathbf{A}(\mathbf{V} - \mathbf{U}) = \mathbf{0}.$$

This implies that $\mathbf{V} - \mathbf{U}$ is a solution of the set of *homogeneous* equations $\mathbf{AX} = \mathbf{0}$. We know that all the solutions of the homogeneous set are given by

$$\mathbf{X} = \lambda_1\mathbf{f}_1 + \lambda_2\mathbf{f}_2 + \cdots + \lambda_{n-r}\mathbf{f}_{n-r},$$

so that $$\mathbf{V} - \mathbf{U} = \lambda_1'\mathbf{f}_1 + \lambda_2'\mathbf{f}_2 + \cdots + \lambda_{n-r}'\mathbf{f}_{n-r},$$

and $$\mathbf{V} = \mathbf{U} + \lambda_1'\mathbf{f}_1 + \cdots + \lambda_{n-r}'\mathbf{f}_{n-r} \qquad (92)$$

for particular values of the parameters $\lambda_1, \lambda_2, \ldots, \lambda_{n-r}$.

Conversely,

$$\mathbf{V} = \mathbf{U} + \lambda_1\mathbf{f}_1 + \cdots + \lambda_{n-r}\mathbf{f}_{n-r}$$

satisfies the equations $\mathbf{AX} = \mathbf{k}$ for arbitrary values of $\lambda_1, \lambda_2, \ldots, \lambda_{n-r}$, and it therefore follows that all solutions of $\mathbf{AX} = \mathbf{k}$ can be written in the form (92).

We considered the special case for planes intersecting in space of three dimensions in § 15, p. 61.

Example 2

The equations
$$X_1 + X_2 + X_3 = 1,$$
$$X_1 + 2X_2 = 3$$

have the particular solution (3, 0, −2), and the homogeneous equations

$$X_1 + X_2 + X_3 = 0 = X_1 + 2X_2$$

have the general solution

$$\mathbf{X} = [X_1, X_2, X_3] = \lambda[-2, 1, 1].$$

Hence the general solution of the non-homogeneous equations is

$$\mathbf{X} = [X_1, X_2, X_3] = [3, 0, -2] + \lambda[-2, 1, 1].$$

The fact that we can find a particular solution is sufficient to show that the matrices $\mathbf{A}$ and $[\mathbf{A}\ \mathbf{k}]$ have the same rank.

EXERCISE 34.2

1. Solve the equations

$$X_1 + 2X_2 + 3X_3 + 4X_4 = 10,$$
$$2X_1 + 5X_2 + X_3 + X_4 = 3$$

in the form

$$\mathbf{X} = [44, -17, 0, 0] + \lambda[-13, 5, 1, 0] + \mu[-18, 7, 0, 1].$$

35. Determinants of Order n

We have already encountered determinants of orders 2 and 3 (§ 17, p. 70). We now introduce determinants of order n.

Let

$$\mathbf{A} = \begin{bmatrix} a_{11} & a_{12} & \cdots & a_{1n} \\ a_{21} & a_{22} & \cdots & a_{2n} \\ \cdot & \cdot & \cdots & \cdot \\ a_{n1} & a_{n2} & \cdots & a_{nn} \end{bmatrix}$$

be an $n \times n$ matrix. We consider all possible products of elements of **A** formed by multiplying together n elements, where no two elements come from the same row or column of **A**. A typical product of this kind is

$$a_{1i_1}a_{2i_2} \cdots a_{ni_n},$$

where $i_1, i_2, \ldots, i_n$ is some permutation (rearrangement) of the numbers $1, 2, \ldots, n$. Writing the product in this way ensures that our requirement is satisfied that no two elements come from the same row or column, since the row subscripts $1, 2, \ldots, n$ are all distinct, and the column subscripts $i_1, i_2, \ldots, i_n$ are all distinct. The number of such products is equal to the number of permutations $i_1, i_2, \ldots, i_n$ of the numbers $1, 2, \ldots, n$, and this is $n! = n(n-1)(n-2) \cdots 2 \cdot 1$.

The *determinant* of the matrix **A**, which we write *det* **A** or $|\mathbf{A}|$ is defined thus:

$$|\mathbf{A}| = \sum \pm a_{1i_1}a_{2i_2} \cdots a_{ni_n},$$

where the summation is over the $n!$ distinct products arising from the $n!$ permutations of the numbers $1, 2, \ldots, n$, and the sign of a product-term is *plus* if the permutation is *even*, and *minus* if the permutation is *odd*, which notions we shall now explain.

In the permutation $i_1, i_2, \ldots, i_n$ an *inversion* is said to occur whenever a larger number *precedes* a smaller number. For example, if $n = 6$, the permutation

$$3, 6, 2, 1, 4, 5$$

of the numbers 1, 2, 3, 4, 5, 6 contains seven inversions, because 3 precedes 1 and 2 (two inversions), 6 precedes 2, 1, 4 and 5 (four inversions), and 2 precedes 1 (one inversion). A permutation $i_1, i_2, \ldots, i_n$ of the numbers $1, 2, \ldots, n$ is said to be *even* or *odd* according as the number of inversions occurring in the permutation is *even* or *odd*.

We note that in

$$|\mathbf{A}| = \begin{vmatrix} a_{11} & a_{12} & \cdots & a_{1n} \\ a_{21} & a_{22} & \cdots & a_{2n} \\ \cdot & \cdot & \cdots & \cdot \\ a_{n1} & a_{n2} & \cdots & a_{nn} \end{vmatrix} = \sum \pm a_{1i_1}a_{2i_2} \cdots a_{ni_n},$$

the term $a_{11}a_{22} \cdots a_{nn}$ has a plus sign attached to it, and this term arises from the multiplication of elements on the *principal diagonal* of **A**.

It is now possible to prove for determinants of *order n* (determinants of $n \times n$ matrices $\mathbf{A}$) the same set of rules which we proved for $n = 3$ on pp. 73–79.

Rules for Evaluating Determinants

1. The determinant of a matrix $\mathbf{A}$ is equal to the determinant of the transpose matrix $\mathbf{A}^T$ (obtained by interchanging rows and columns of $\mathbf{A}$).

2. If two rows (or columns) of the matrix $\mathbf{A}$ are interchanged, the determinant of the resulting matrix is equal to $-|\mathbf{A}|$.

3. If two rows (or columns) of a matrix $\mathbf{A}$ are identical, then $|\mathbf{A}| = 0$.

4. If every element of a row (or column) of $\mathbf{A}$ is multiplied by k, the determinant of the resulting matrix is equal to $k\,|\mathbf{A}|$.

5. If a multiple of any row of $\mathbf{A}$ is added to another row (or a multiple of any column is added to another column), the determinant of the matrix thus formed is equal to $|\mathbf{A}|$.

Before stating the other rules for evaluating determinants, we once more define the *minor* of the element a_{ij} in $|\mathbf{A}|$ as the determinant of the submatrix of $\mathbf{A}$ obtained by striking out the row and the column of $\mathbf{A}$ which contain the element a_{ij}. If we represent this submatrix by the symbol $\mathbf{A}_{ij}$, then its determinant, which is the minor of a_{ij}, is $|\mathbf{A}_{ij}|$, and the *cofactor* of a_{ij} is defined to be $(-1)^{i+j}\,|\mathbf{A}_{ij}|$. If we now write $\mathbf{A}_{ij}{}^* = (-1)^{i+j}\,|\mathbf{A}_{ij}|$, we have the rule:

6.
$$\begin{aligned} |\mathbf{A}| &= a_{i1}\mathbf{A}_{i1}{}^* + a_{i2}\mathbf{A}_{i2}{}^* + \cdots + a_{in}\mathbf{A}_{in}{}^* \\ &= a_{1j}\mathbf{A}_{1j}{}^* + a_{2j}\mathbf{A}_{2j}{}^* + \cdots + a_{nj}\mathbf{A}_{nj}{}^*. \end{aligned}$$

This gives the rule for evaluating $|\mathbf{A}|$ in terms of the elements of any row or column.

If $k \neq i$, rule 3 shows that

7.
$$a_{i1}\mathbf{A}_{k1}{}^* + a_{i2}\mathbf{A}_{k2}{}^* + \cdots + a_{in}\mathbf{A}_{kn}{}^* = 0.$$

Similarly, if $k \neq j$, we have

$$a_{1j}\mathbf{A}_{1k}{}^* + a_{2j}\mathbf{A}_{2k}{}^* + \cdots + a_{nj}\mathbf{A}_{nk}{}^* = 0.$$

If we use the useful Kronecker delta symbol δ_{ij}, defined thus:

$$\delta_{ij} = 0 \qquad (i \neq j),$$

$$\delta_{ij} = 1 \qquad (i = j),$$

we may state rules 6 and 7 thus:

$$a_{i1}\mathbf{A}_{k1}{}^* + a_{i2}\mathbf{A}_{k2}{}^* + \cdots + a_{in}\mathbf{A}_{kn}{}^* = |\mathbf{A}|\,\delta_{ik},$$

$$a_{1j}\mathbf{A}_{1k}{}^* + a_{2j}\mathbf{A}_{2k}{}^* + \cdots + a_{nj}\mathbf{A}_{nk}{}^* = |\mathbf{A}|\,\delta_{jk}.$$

We shall not prove these rules here. They are not difficult to prove from the definition of a determinant, and can well be left for another course. But, as we have already seen, knowing how determinants work is useful.

We evaluate some determinants which are of frequent occurrence.

If $\mathbf{I}_n$ is the $n \times n$ unity matrix, which we can now write with the help of the Kronecker delta as

$$\mathbf{I}_n = [\delta_{ij}] \qquad (i, j = 1, 2, \ldots, n),$$

then, since the first row contains only one non-zero element, and its cofactor is $|\mathbf{I}_{n-1}|$,

$$|\mathbf{I}_n| = |\mathbf{I}_{n-1}|,$$

and continuing thus,

$$|\mathbf{I}_n| = |\mathbf{I}_{n-1}| = |\mathbf{I}_{n-2}| = \cdots = |\mathbf{I}_1| = 1.$$

More generally,

$$\begin{vmatrix} c & \mathbf{0} \\ \mathbf{K} & \mathbf{B} \end{vmatrix} = c\,|\mathbf{B}|,$$

if the first row consists of zeros except for the first term, which is c. It follows that the purely diagonal determinant:

$$\begin{vmatrix} a_1 & 0 & 0 & \cdots & 0 \\ 0 & a_2 & 0 & \cdots & 0 \\ \cdot & \cdot & \cdot & \cdots & \cdot \\ 0 & 0 & \cdot & \cdots & a_n \end{vmatrix} = a_1 a_2 \cdots a_n.$$

We now look at the determinants of the elementary matrices, defined in § 29, p. 154. We obtain $\mathbf{I}_n(i, j)$ by interchanging rows i and j of $\mathbf{I}_n$, so that

$$|\mathbf{I}_n\,(i, j)| = -|\mathbf{I}_n| = -1.$$

$\mathbf{I}_n(k(i))$ is obtained from $\mathbf{I}_n$ by multiplying row i by k. Hence

$$|\mathbf{I}_n(k(i))| = k\,|\mathbf{I}_n| = k.$$

$\mathbf{I}_n((i) + k(j))$ is obtained from $\mathbf{I}_n$ by adding k(row j) to row i, and

$$|\mathbf{I}_n\,((i) + k(j))| = |\mathbf{I}_n| = 1.$$

If $\mathbf{A}$ is any $n \times n$ matrix, and $\mathbf{E}$ refers to any one of the elementary matrices we are considering, the matrix $\mathbf{EA}$ can be obtained from the matrix $\mathbf{A}$ by one of the following procedures:

1. Interchanging row i and row j.
2. Multiplying row i by k.
3. Adding k(row j) to row i.

By our rules, $|\mathbf{EA}|$ is $-|\mathbf{A}|$ in the first case, $k\,|\mathbf{A}|$ in the second case, and $|\mathbf{A}|$ in the third case. Similar arguments apply to $\mathbf{AE}$, substituting *columns* for *rows*, so that we have Theorem 45.

Theorem 45. *If* $\mathbf{E}$ *is an elementary matrix,*

$$|\mathbf{EA}| = |\mathbf{E}|\,|\mathbf{A}| = |\mathbf{AE}|.$$

We use this theorem to obtain a connection between the regularity of an $n \times n$ matrix $\mathbf{A}$ and its determinant. We prove Theorem 46.

Theorem 46. *An* $n \times n$ *matrix* $\mathbf{A}$ *is regular if and only if* $|A| \neq 0$.

Proof. If $\mathbf{A}$ is of rank r, we can write

$$\mathbf{A} = \mathbf{E}_k\mathbf{E}_{k-1}\cdots\mathbf{E}_1\mathbf{A}_r{}^*\mathbf{E}_1{}^*\mathbf{E}_2{}^*\cdots\mathbf{E}_l{}^*,$$

where $\mathbf{A}_r{}^*$ is the canonical form given in (91) on p. 178, and the $\mathbf{E}_i$ and $\mathbf{E}_j{}^*$ are all elementary matrices. By applying Theorem 45 we have, in succession:

$$\begin{aligned}
|\mathbf{A}| &= |\mathbf{E}_k\mathbf{E}_{k-1}\cdots\mathbf{E}_1\mathbf{A}_r{}^*\mathbf{E}_1{}^*\mathbf{E}_2{}^*\cdots\mathbf{E}_l{}^*| \\
&= |\mathbf{E}_k\mathbf{E}_{k-1}\cdots\mathbf{E}_1\mathbf{A}_r{}^*\mathbf{E}_1{}^*\mathbf{E}_2{}^*\cdots|\,|\mathbf{E}_l{}^*| \\
&= |\mathbf{E}_k\mathbf{E}_{k-1}\cdots\mathbf{E}_1\mathbf{A}_r{}^*|\,|\mathbf{E}_1{}^*|\,|\mathbf{E}_2{}^*|\,|\cdots|\,|\mathbf{E}_l{}^*| \\
&= |\mathbf{E}_k|\,|\mathbf{E}_{k-1}\cdots\mathbf{E}_1\mathbf{A}_r{}^*|\,|\mathbf{E}_1{}^*|\,|\mathbf{E}_2{}^*|\,|\cdots|\,|\mathbf{E}_l{}^*| \\
&= |\mathbf{E}_k|\,|\mathbf{E}_{k-1}|\,|\cdots\mathbf{E}_1\mathbf{A}_r{}^*|\,|\mathbf{E}_1{}^*|\,|\mathbf{E}_2{}^*|\,|\cdots|\,|\mathbf{E}_l{}^*| \\
&= |\mathbf{E}_k|\,|\mathbf{E}_{k-1}|\cdots|\mathbf{E}_1|\,|\mathbf{A}_r{}^*|\,|\mathbf{E}_1{}^*|\,|\mathbf{E}_2{}^*|\,|\cdots|\,|\mathbf{E}_l{}^*|.
\end{aligned}$$

Since each $|\mathbf{E}_i| \neq 0$, and each $|\mathbf{E}_j{}^*| \neq 0$, $|\mathbf{A}| \neq 0$ if and only if $|\mathbf{A}_r{}^*| \neq 0$. But the canonical form $\mathbf{A}_r{}^*$ has exactly r entries $= 1$ along the principal diagonal, where $r = \text{rank}\,(\mathbf{A})$, and $|\mathbf{A}_r{}^*| =$ the product of the n entries on the principal diagonal. Hence $|\mathbf{A}_r{}^*| \neq 0$ if and only if $r = n$, so that there are no zero entries on the principal diagonal. Since $r = n$ implies the regularity of $\mathbf{A}$, this proves the theorem.

We proved in Theorem 42 that a matrix $\mathbf{A}$ has rank r if and only if it contains at least one regular $k \times k$ submatrix for each of the values $k = 1, 2, \ldots, r$, but none for $k > r$. Since by Theorem 46 the determinants of these regular submatrices are not zero, whereas determinants of all $k \times k$ submatrices for $k > r$ are zero, we can test the rank of a matrix $\mathbf{A}$ by finding the determinants of its $k \times k$ submatrices, and we have Theorem 47.

Theorem 47. *The rank of a matrix* $\mathbf{A}$ *is equal to the order of the greatest* $k \times k$ *submatrix which can be extracted from* $\mathbf{A}$ *for which the determinant is not zero.*

This shows that rank can be tested by the use of determinants, and if we call the rank determined thus the *determinantal rank*, we have shown that:

$$\textit{Determinantal rank} = \textit{rank}.$$

We now prove a theorem of which Theorem 45 is a special case.

Theorem 48. *The determinant of a matrix product of two $n \times n$ matrices is the product of the determinants, that is:*

$$|\mathbf{AB}| = |\mathbf{A}|\,|\mathbf{B}|.$$

Proof. Since, by Theorem 41, rank $(\mathbf{AB}) \leqslant$ min. (rank $\mathbf{A}$, rank $\mathbf{B}$), if either $\mathbf{A}$ or $\mathbf{B}$ is not regular then rank $(\mathbf{AB}) < n$, so that $\mathbf{AB}$ is not regular, and by Theorem 46 we have $|\mathbf{AB}| = 0$. In this case one of the quantities $|\mathbf{A}|$, $|\mathbf{B}|$ is also zero, so that

$$|\mathbf{AB}| = 0 = |\mathbf{A}|\,|\mathbf{B}|.$$

We now assume that both $\mathbf{A}$ and $\mathbf{B}$ are regular. We can write

$$\mathbf{A} = \mathbf{E}_k\mathbf{E}_{k-1}\cdots\mathbf{E}_1,$$
$$\mathbf{B} = \mathbf{E}_l{}^*\mathbf{E}_{l-1}^*\cdots\mathbf{E}_1{}^*,$$

where the $\mathbf{E}_i$ and $\mathbf{E}_j{}^*$ are all elementary. Then

$$\begin{aligned}|\mathbf{A}| &= |\mathbf{E}_k\mathbf{E}_{k-1}\cdots\mathbf{E}_2|\,|\mathbf{E}_1| \\ &= |\mathbf{E}_k|\,|\mathbf{E}_{k-1}|\cdots|\mathbf{E}_2|\,|\mathbf{E}_1|,\end{aligned}$$

using Theorem 45, and similarly

$$|\mathbf{B}| = |\mathbf{E}_l{}^*|\,|\mathbf{E}_{l-1}^*|\cdots|\mathbf{E}_2{}^*|\,|\mathbf{E}_1{}^*|,$$

and finally

$$\mathbf{AB} = \mathbf{E}_k\mathbf{E}_{k-1}\cdots\mathbf{E}_1\mathbf{E}_l{}^*\mathbf{E}_{l-1}^*\cdots\mathbf{E}_1{}^*,$$

and, as above,

$$\begin{aligned}|\mathbf{AB}| &= |\mathbf{E}_k|\,|\mathbf{E}_{k-1}|\cdots|\mathbf{E}_1|\,|\mathbf{E}_l{}^*|\,|\mathbf{E}_{l-1}^*|\cdots|\mathbf{E}_1{}^*| \\ &= |\mathbf{A}|\,|\mathbf{B}|.\end{aligned}$$

Example 1

Let $\mathbf{A} = \begin{bmatrix} a & b & c \\ c & a & b \\ b & c & a \end{bmatrix}$, and $\mathbf{B} = \begin{bmatrix} p & q & r \\ r & p & q \\ q & r & p \end{bmatrix}$.

Then
$$\begin{aligned}|\mathbf{A}| &= a(a^2 - bc) + b(b^2 - ac) + c(c^2 - ab) \\ &= a^3 + b^3 + c^3 - 3abc,\end{aligned}$$

and similarly

$$|\mathbf{B}| = p^3 + q^3 + r^3 - 3pqr.$$

If we consider

$$\mathbf{AB} = \begin{bmatrix} a & b & c \\ c & a & b \\ b & c & a \end{bmatrix} \begin{bmatrix} p & q & r \\ r & p & q \\ q & r & p \end{bmatrix}$$

$$= \begin{bmatrix} ap + br + cq & aq + bp + cr & ar + bq + cp \\ ar + bq + cp & ap + br + cq & aq + bp + cr \\ aq + bp + cr & ar + bq + cp & ap + br + cq \end{bmatrix}$$

we see that it is of the same form as **A** and **B**, so that

$$|\mathbf{AB}| = (ap + br + cq)^3 + (aq + bp + cr)^3 + (ar + bq + cp)^3$$
$$- 3(ap + br + cq)(aq + bp + cr)(ar + bq + cp).$$

But since $|\mathbf{AB}| = |\mathbf{A}|\,|\mathbf{B}|$, we deduce that

$$(a^3 + b^3 + c^3 - 3abc)(p^3 + q^3 + r^3 - 3pqr)$$
$$= (ap + br + cq)^3 + (aq + bp + cr)^3 + (ar + bq + cp)^3$$
$$- 3(ap + br + cq)(aq + bp + cr)(ar + bq + cp).$$

EXERCISES 35

1. If **A** is $n \times n$ and such that $\mathbf{AA}^T = \mathbf{I}_n$, prove that $|\mathbf{A}| = \pm 1$.
2. If **A** is regular, prove that $|\mathbf{A}^{-1}| = |\mathbf{A}|^{-1}$.
3. If **A** is $n \times n$ and regular, and $\Delta = |\mathbf{A}|$ prove, from rules 6 and 7 (p. 196) that the matrix $\mathbf{A}^* = [a_{ij}^*]$, where $a_{ij}^* = A_{ji}^*/\Delta$, A_{ij}^* being the cofactor of a_{ij} in $|\mathbf{A}|$, satisfies the equation $\mathbf{AA}^* = \mathbf{A}^*\mathbf{A} = \mathbf{I}_n$, so that $\mathbf{A}^* = \mathbf{A}^{-1}$ (compare p. 166).
4. If **A** is a skew-symmetric matrix of odd order (see p. 150), prove that $|\mathbf{A}| = -|\mathbf{A}|$, so that $|\mathbf{A}| = 0$.

CHAPTER NINE

Linear Mappings and Matrices

In this final chapter we discuss an important concept which motivated our discussion of matrices, namely the notion of a *linear mapping* or *linear transformation* between two vector spaces. The two vector spaces need not be distinct.

36. Linear Mappings

Let V_n and V_m be two vector spaces, not necessarily distinct, of respective dimensions n and m over the field R of real numbers, and suppose that to any given vector $\mathbf{X}$ in V_n there is assigned a unique vector $\mathbf{Y}$ in V_m. We then say that V_n is *mapped* on to V_m, and denote this either by the symbolism

$$\mathbf{X} \rightarrow \mathbf{Y},$$

or, if T represents the mapping, by

$$T(\mathbf{X}) = \mathbf{Y}.$$

If every vector in V_m is the map of some vector in V_n, we say that the mapping is an *onto* mapping, and that V_n is mapped *onto* V_m.

If this is not the case, so that not all vectors in V_m are maps of vectors in V_n, the mapping T is said to be a mapping of V_n *into* V_m.

It is very easy to give an example of an *into* mapping. Let the mapping T be such that for all $\mathbf{X} \in V_n$

$$\mathbf{X} \rightarrow \mathbf{0},$$

where $\mathbf{0}$ is the zero vector in V_m. Then if the dimension of V_m is greater than zero, there are vectors in V_m which are not the maps of vectors in V_n, so that the mapping is an *into* mapping.

For a simple example of an *onto* mapping, we need only take $V_n = V_m$ and consider the mapping (called the *identity* mapping)

$$\mathbf{X} \rightarrow \mathbf{X}$$

for all $\mathbf{X} \in V_n$. A less trivial example is given by the mapping

$$\mathbf{X} \rightarrow k\mathbf{X} \qquad (k \neq 0)$$

for fixed k. Any vector $\mathbf{Y} \in V_n$ is the map of the vector $k^{-1}\mathbf{Y}$ in V_n.

All the examples considered so far are examples of *linear mappings*, which we now define.

Definition. *If V_n is mapped on V_m, and $\mathbf{X} \rightarrow \mathbf{Y}$, $\mathbf{X}' \rightarrow \mathbf{Y}'$, then if*

$$a\mathbf{X} + b\mathbf{X}' \rightarrow a\mathbf{Y} + b\mathbf{Y}'$$

for all real a and b, and all $\mathbf{X}$, $\mathbf{X}' \in V_n$, the mapping is said to be LINEAR, *or* A LINEAR MAPPING *of V_n on V_m.*

This definition looks different if we use the functional notation and write:

if $$T(\mathbf{X}) = \mathbf{Y}, \quad \text{and} \quad T(\mathbf{X}') = \mathbf{Y}',$$

then $$T(a\mathbf{X} + b\mathbf{X}') = a\mathbf{Y} + b\mathbf{Y}'.$$

More concisely, we may even write this in the form:

$$T(a\mathbf{X} + b\mathbf{X}') = aT(\mathbf{X}) + bT(\mathbf{X}').$$

If we take $a = b = 0$, this definition gives

$$T(\mathbf{0}) = \mathbf{0},$$

so that in a linear mapping the zero vector of V_n is mapped on the zero vector of V_m.

To verify that $\mathbf{X} \rightarrow k\mathbf{X}$ $(k \neq 0)$ is a linear mapping of V_n onto itself, we note that

$$\begin{aligned} T(a\mathbf{X} + b\mathbf{X}') &= k(a\mathbf{X} + b\mathbf{X}') \\ &= a(k\mathbf{X}) + b(k\mathbf{X}') \\ &= aT(\mathbf{X}) + bT(\mathbf{X}'), \end{aligned}$$

which verifies that the mapping is linear. The proof is also valid for $k = 0$ as well as for $k = 1$, so that we have verified that all the examples considered earlier are linear. We now consider further examples of linear mappings.

Example I

If $\mathbf{X} = [X_1, X_2, X_3]$ is a vector of V_3, suppose that

$$T(\mathbf{X}) = \mathbf{Y} = [X_1, X_2, 0].$$

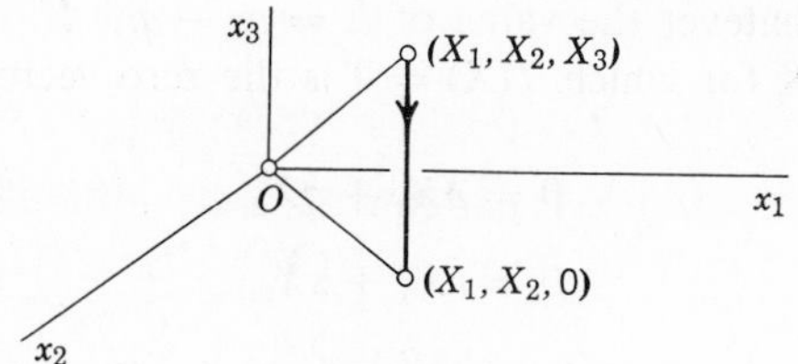

Figure 22

Then if

$$T(\mathbf{X}') = \mathbf{Y}' = [X_1', X_2', 0],$$

$$\begin{aligned} T(a\mathbf{X} + b\mathbf{X}') &= [aX_1 + bX_1', aX_2 + bX_2', 0] \\ &= a[X_1, X_2, 0] + b[X_1', X_2', 0] \\ &= aT(\mathbf{X}) + bT(\mathbf{X}'), \end{aligned}$$

so that the mapping is linear.

The point $\mathbf{X} = (X_1, X_2, X_3)$ is projected orthogonally on to the plane Ox_1x_2, and the infinity of points (X_1, X_2, k), where k is variable, are all projected down on to the same point $(X_1, X_2, 0)$. In particular, the infinity of vectors $[0, 0, k]$ are all mapped on to the zero vector $\mathbf{0} = [0, 0, 0]$. The space of the mapped vectors is the Ox_1x_2 plane which, regarded as a vector space, has dimension 2. We note that the dimension of the vector space which consists of the vectors $[0, 0, k]$ is 1, and $1 + 2 = 3 =$ dimension of V_3, the space being mapped. This illustrates Theorem 49, p. 207, which we shall prove later.

Example 2

$\mathbf{X} = [X_1, X_2]$ is a vector of V_2, and we consider the mapping on to V_2 given by $T(\mathbf{X}) = \mathbf{Y}$, where

$$\mathbf{Y} = [pX_1 + qX_2, rX_1 + sX_2],$$

and $\Delta = ps - qr \neq 0$.

Here, if

$$T(\mathbf{X}') = \mathbf{Y}' = [pX_1' + qX_2', rX_1' + sX_2'],$$

then

$$\begin{aligned} T(a\mathbf{X} + b\mathbf{X}') &= T([aX_1 + bX_1', aX_2 + bX_2']) \\ &= [p(aX_1 + bX_1') + q(aX_2 + bX_2'), \\ &\qquad r(aX_1 + bX_1') + s(aX_2 + bX_2')] \\ &= [a(pX_1 + qX_2) + b(pX_1' + qX_2'), \\ &\qquad a(rX_1 + sX_2) + b(rX_1' + sX_2')] \\ &= a[(pX_1 + qX_2), (rX_1 + sX_2)] \\ &\qquad + b[(pX_1' + qX_2'), (rX_1' + sX_2')] \\ &= aT(\mathbf{X}) + bT(\mathbf{X}'), \end{aligned}$$

so that the mapping is linear.

This is true whatever the value of $\Delta = ps - qr$. If, however, $\Delta \neq 0$, the only vector $\mathbf{X}$ for which $T(\mathbf{X}) = \mathbf{0}$ is the zero vector. For we have the equations

$$0 = pX_1 + qX_2,$$
$$0 = rX_1 + sX_2,$$

and since $\Delta \neq 0$, these equations have only the trivial solution. In this case $T(\mathbf{X})$ may be any vector of V_2, since the equations

$$Y_1 = pX_1 + qX_2,$$
$$Y_2 = rX_1 + sX_2$$

always have a solution for X_1 and X_2, whatever Y_1 and Y_2, the system of equations being regular. Hence when the mapping is *onto* V_2, so that the whole space is covered by the vectors $T(\mathbf{X})$, the only vector which maps on to the zero vector is the zero vector.

Suppose now that $\Delta = ps - qr = 0$, so that the rank of the matrix

$$\mathbf{A} = \begin{bmatrix} p & q \\ r & s \end{bmatrix}$$

is less than 2. If rank $\mathbf{A} = 1$, we suppose that the row-vector $[p, q] \neq [0, 0]$, so that $[r, s]$ is linearly dependent on it. If this is the case, we shall have

$$r = kp, \qquad s = kq.$$

To find the vectors which map on the zero vector, we solve the equations

$$0 = pX_1 + qX_2,$$
$$0 = rX_1 + sX_2.$$

We need only solve the first equation, since the second equation is a multiple of the first. We deduce that all vectors $[X_1, X_2]$ with their end-points on the line

$$0 = pX_1 + qX_2$$

are mapped on to $[0, 0]$. The dimension of the vector space filled by these vectors is 1.

On the other hand, V_2 is not filled by the vectors $T(\mathbf{X})$, since

$$rX_1 + sX_2 = k(pX_1 + qX_2),$$

so that only the vectors

$$\mathbf{Y} = [Y_1, kY_1]$$

arise from the mapping. These vectors fill a one-dimensional vector space, and once again Theorem 49 is satisfied, since $1 + 1 = 2$.

In a linear mapping $T(\mathbf{X}) = \mathbf{Y}$, the vectors $\mathbf{X}$ for which $T(\mathbf{X}) = \mathbf{0}$ fill a vector space, which is called the *null space* of the mapping.

In fact, if $T(\mathbf{X}) = \mathbf{0}$ and $T(\mathbf{X}') = \mathbf{0}$,

then $$T(a\mathbf{X} + b\mathbf{X}') = aT(\mathbf{X}) + bT(\mathbf{X}') = a \cdot \mathbf{0} + b \cdot \mathbf{0} = \mathbf{0},$$

so that with $\mathbf{X}$ and $\mathbf{X}'$ also $a\mathbf{X} + b\mathbf{X}'$ lies in the null space, and it is therefore a vector space (p. 117).

The space filled by the vectors $T(\mathbf{X}) = \mathbf{Y}$ is also a vector space, and this space is called the *range* of the transformation T.

To prove that this space is a vector space we must show that if $T(\mathbf{X}) = \mathbf{Y}$ and $T(\mathbf{X}') = \mathbf{Y}'$, then $a\mathbf{Y} + b\mathbf{Y}'$ is also a vector of the range. But by the definition of linear mapping,

$$T(a\mathbf{X} + b\mathbf{X}') = a\mathbf{Y} + b\mathbf{Y}',$$

which proves that $a\mathbf{Y} + b\mathbf{Y}'$ is a vector of the range, since $a\mathbf{X} + b\mathbf{X}'$ is a vector of the vector space V_n.

It is now fitting that we give some examples of *non*-linear mappings.

Example 3

Let $$T[X_1, X_2] = [X_1, X_2 + 1].$$

Since $T[0, 0] = [0, 1] \neq \mathbf{0}$, the mapping cannot be linear.

Example 4

Let $$T[X_1, X_2] = [X_1^2, X_2].$$

Here we do have $T[0, 0] = [0, 0]$, but of course this is not a *sufficient* condition for a mapping to be linear. But since

$$T[aX_1, aX_2] = T(a\mathbf{X}) = [a^2X_1^2, aX_2] \neq aT(\mathbf{X}) \quad (a \neq 1),$$

the mapping is not linear.

EXERCISES 36.1

1. Determine which of the following mappings are linear mappings:
(*a*) $T[X_1, X_2] = [X_1 + 2, 2X_2]$,
(*b*) $T[X_1, X_2] = [X_1 - X_2, -X_2]$,
(*c*) $T[X_1, X_2, X_3] = [2X_1, X_2 + X_3, 3X_3, X_1 + X_2]$,
(*d*) $T[X_1, X_2] = [X_1 \cos\theta - X_2 \sin\theta, X_1 \sin\theta + X_2 \cos\theta]$.

2. Prove that the mappings (*a*), (*b*), and (*d*) in Exercise 1 are one–one onto mappings, but that (*c*) is an *into* mapping of V_3 into V_4.

3. Prove that the linear mapping T of vectors $\mathbf{X}$ in V_n which lie on the line $t\mathbf{X}_1 + (1 - t)\mathbf{X}_2$ is

$$tT(\mathbf{X}_1) + (1 - t)T(\mathbf{X}_2),$$

and that this is a line if $T(\mathbf{X}_1) \neq T(\mathbf{X}_2)$, but that the map is a point independent of t if $T(\mathbf{X}_1) = T(\mathbf{X}_2)$.

4. Prove that if T is a linear mapping, then

$$T(a\mathbf{X}_1 + b\mathbf{X}_2 + \cdots + s\mathbf{X}_r) = aT(\mathbf{X}_1) + bT(\mathbf{X}_2) + \cdots + sT(\mathbf{X}_r).$$

One of the most familiar applications of one–one onto linear mappings occurs in coordinate geometry when we change the coordinate axes.

Example 5

Suppose that we rotate the coordinate axes (assumed to be rectangular) in the Ox_1x_2 plane through an angle θ, and let us call the new axes $Ox_1{}^*$ and $Ox_2{}^*$ respectively. If P is the point (X_1, X_2), let OP make an angle α with Ox_1. Then

$$X_1{}^* = OP\cos(\alpha - \theta) = OP(\cos\alpha\cos\theta + \sin\alpha\sin\theta) = X_1\cos\theta + X_2\sin\theta,$$

and

$$X_2{}^* = OP\sin(\alpha - \theta) = OP(\sin\alpha\cos\theta - \cos\alpha\sin\theta) = X_2\cos\theta - X_1\sin\theta.$$

We may regard the mapping

$$X_1{}^* = X_1\cos\theta + X_2\sin\theta,$$
$$X_2{}^* = -X_1\sin\theta + X_2\cos\theta,$$

as a linear mapping of V_2 onto itself. The mapping is one–one, since the matrix

$$\mathbf{A} = \begin{bmatrix} \cos\theta & \sin\theta \\ -\sin\theta & \cos\theta \end{bmatrix}$$

is regular, having the inverse

$$\mathbf{A}^{-1} = \begin{bmatrix} \cos\theta & -\sin\theta \\ \sin\theta & \cos\theta \end{bmatrix},$$

and the inverse mapping is

$$X_1 = X_1{}^*\cos\theta - X_2{}^*\sin\theta,$$
$$X_2 = X_1{}^*\sin\theta + X_2{}^*\cos\theta.$$

EXERCISES 36.2

1. Show that after rotating the coordinate axes through a suitable angle θ, the equation

$$aX_1^2 + 2hX_1X_2 + bX_2^2 = 1$$

assumes the form

$$a^*X_1^{*2} + b^*X_2^{*2} = 1,$$

where a^* and b^* are constants which satisfy the equations

$$a^* + b^* = a + b, \qquad a^*b^* = ab - h^2.$$

2. If $P = (X_1, X_2)$, $Q = (Y_1, Y_2)$, and

$$[X_1, X_2] \to [X_1^*, X_2^*], \qquad [Y_1, Y_2] \to [Y_1^*, Y_2^*]$$

under rotation of the coordinate axes through an angle θ, show that

$$\begin{bmatrix} X_1^* & X_2^* \\ Y_1^* & Y_2^* \end{bmatrix} = \begin{bmatrix} X_1 & X_2 \\ Y_1 & Y_2 \end{bmatrix} \begin{bmatrix} \cos\theta & -\sin\theta \\ \sin\theta & \cos\theta \end{bmatrix},$$

so that

$$\begin{vmatrix} X_1^* & X_2^* \\ Y_1^* & Y_2^* \end{vmatrix} = \begin{vmatrix} X_1 & X_2 \\ Y_1 & Y_2 \end{vmatrix}.$$

By choosing Ox_1^* to pass through P, so that

$$\begin{vmatrix} X_1^* & X_2^* \\ Y_1^* & Y_2^* \end{vmatrix} = \begin{vmatrix} X_1^* & 0 \\ Y_1^* & Y_2^* \end{vmatrix} = X_1^*Y_2^*$$

$$= OP \times (\text{distance of } Q \text{ from } OP)$$

deduce that

$$\begin{vmatrix} X_1 & X_2 \\ Y_1 & Y_2 \end{vmatrix} = 2(\text{area of triangle } OPQ).$$

We now prove Theorem 49.

Theorem 49. *The dimension n of the vector space V_n is equal to the sum of the dimensions of the range and the null space of any linear mapping from V_n on to any vector space V_m.*

Proof. Let $\mathbf{X}_1, \mathbf{X}_2, \ldots, \mathbf{X}_n$ be a basis for V_n, and let

$$T(\mathbf{X}_i) = \mathbf{Y}_i \qquad (i = 1, 2, \ldots, n).$$

Then the range of the linear mapping T is the vector space spanned by $\mathbf{Y}_1, \mathbf{Y}_2, \ldots, \mathbf{Y}_n$. That is

$$\text{Range of } T = L\{\mathbf{Y}_1, \mathbf{Y}_2, \ldots, \mathbf{Y}_n\}.$$

Let the dimension of the range be r, and let us assume, as we may, that it is the vectors $\mathbf{Y}_1, \mathbf{Y}_2, \ldots, \mathbf{Y}_r$ which are linearly independent, and therefore span the range. Then the vectors $\mathbf{Y}_{r+1}, \ldots, \mathbf{Y}_n$ are linearly dependent on $\mathbf{Y}_1, \mathbf{Y}_2, \ldots, \mathbf{Y}_r$, and we have relations

$$\mathbf{Y}_{r+i} = a_{i1}\mathbf{Y}_1 + a_{i2}\mathbf{Y}_2 + \cdots + a_{ir}\mathbf{Y}_r \quad (i = 1, \ldots, n - r),$$

that is

$$T(\mathbf{X}_{r+i}) = a_{i1}\mathbf{Y}_1 + a_{i2}\mathbf{Y}_2 + \cdots + a_{ir}\mathbf{Y}_r,$$

or

$$T(\mathbf{X}_{r+i}) = a_{i1}T(\mathbf{X}_1) + a_{i2}T(\mathbf{X}_2) + \cdots + a_{ir}T(\mathbf{X}_r).$$

Since T is a linear mapping, Exercise 4, p. 206 shows that

$$T(\mathbf{X}_{r+i} - a_{i1}\mathbf{X}_1 - a_{i2}\mathbf{X}_2 - \cdots - a_{ir}\mathbf{X}_r) = \mathbf{0}.$$

Hence, if we write

$$\mathbf{Z}_i = \mathbf{X}_{r+i} - a_{i1}\mathbf{X}_1 - a_{i2}\mathbf{X}_2 - \cdots - a_{ir}\mathbf{X}_r,$$

then $T(\mathbf{Z}_i) = \mathbf{0}$ for $i = 1, 2, \ldots, n - r$. The vectors $\mathbf{Z}_i$ are in V_n, and lie in the null space of T, by definition of the null space. We prove that these vectors $\mathbf{Z}_i$ *form a basis* for the null space. This will prove the theorem, since the dimension of the null space will be $n - r$, where r is the bimension of the range.

We first prove that the vectors $\mathbf{Z}_1, \mathbf{Z}_2, \ldots, \mathbf{Z}_{n-r}$ are linearly independent. If

$$c_1\mathbf{Z}_1 + c_2\mathbf{Z}_2 + \cdots + c_{n-r}\mathbf{Z}_{n-r} = \mathbf{0}$$

then, expressing the $\mathbf{Z}_i$ in terms of the $\mathbf{X}_i$,

$$c_1\mathbf{X}_{r+1} + c_2\mathbf{X}_{r+2} + \cdots + c_{n-r}\mathbf{X}_n + \sum_{j=1}^{r} d_j\mathbf{X}_j = \mathbf{0},$$

where the d_j are definite combinations of the a_{ij} and the c_i which do not concern us, since this last equation gives us

$$c_1 = c_2 = \cdots = c_{n-r} = 0,$$

the $\mathbf{X}_1, \ldots, \mathbf{X}_r, \mathbf{X}_{r+1}, \ldots, \mathbf{X}_n$ being independent. Hence the vectors $\mathbf{Z}_1, \mathbf{Z}_2, \ldots, \mathbf{Z}_{n-r}$ are linearly independent. We must now show that if $T(\mathbf{Z}) = \mathbf{0}$, then $\mathbf{Z}$ lies in the space spanned by $\mathbf{Z}_1, \mathbf{Z}_2, \ldots, \mathbf{Z}_{n-r}$.

We know that $\mathbf{Z}$ lies in V_n, so that

$$\mathbf{Z} = b_1\mathbf{X}_1 + b_2\mathbf{X}_2 + \cdots + b_n\mathbf{X}_n.$$

Consider the vector

$$\mathbf{Z}' = \mathbf{Z} - b_{r+1}\mathbf{Z}_1 - b_{r+2}\mathbf{Z}_2 - \cdots - b_n\mathbf{Z}_{n-r},$$

where the $\mathbf{Z}_1, \mathbf{Z}_2, \ldots, \mathbf{Z}_{n-r}$ are as defined above. Then since

$$T(\mathbf{Z}) = T(\mathbf{Z}_1) = \cdots = T(\mathbf{Z}_{n-r}) = \mathbf{0},$$

$$T(\mathbf{Z}') = \mathbf{0}.$$

But if we look at the definition of $\mathbf{Z}_i$ given previously, we see that $\mathbf{Z}'$ is a linear combination of the vectors $\mathbf{X}_1, \mathbf{X}_2, \ldots, \mathbf{X}_r$ only, say:

$$\mathbf{Z}' = p_1\mathbf{X}_1 + p_2\mathbf{X}_2 + \cdots + p_r\mathbf{X}_r.$$

Then

$$T(\mathbf{Z}') = p_1T(\mathbf{X}_1) + \cdots + p_rT(\mathbf{X}_r) = p_1\mathbf{Y}_1 + \cdots + p_r\mathbf{Y}_r = \mathbf{0},$$

and since $\mathbf{Y}_1, \ldots, \mathbf{Y}_r$ are independent,

$$p_1 = \cdots = p_r = 0,$$

so that $\mathbf{Z}' = 0$. Hence

$$\mathbf{Z} - b_{r+1}\mathbf{Z}_1 - \cdots - b_n\mathbf{Z}_{n-r} = \mathbf{0},$$

$$\mathbf{Z} = b_{r+1}\mathbf{Z}_1 + \cdots + b_n\mathbf{Z}_{n-r},$$

and therefore $\mathbf{Z}$ lies in the space spanned by $\mathbf{Z}_1, \ldots, \mathbf{Z}_{n-r}$. This concludes the proof of the theorem.

The examples worked earlier (1 and 2) are illustrations of this theorem.

It is clear that the range of a vector space V_n under a linear mapping T can never be of dimension greater than n. We consider what happens when the dimension of the range is equal to n. Then, by the theorem we have just proved, the dimension of the null space must be zero. This means that the only vector $\mathbf{X} \in V_n$ for which $T(\mathbf{X}) = \mathbf{0}$ is the vector $\mathbf{X} = \mathbf{0}$.

It now follows that if

$$\mathbf{Y} = T(\mathbf{X}) = T(\mathbf{X}'),$$

then $\mathbf{X} = \mathbf{X}'$. For

$$T(\mathbf{X} - \mathbf{X}') = \mathbf{0},$$

from which it follows that

$$\mathbf{X} - \mathbf{X}' = \mathbf{0}.$$

The mapping T is therefore a one–one mapping, with no two distinct vectors in V_n mapping on to the same vector in V_m. If the mapping T is from V_n on to itself, and the dimension of the range is n, the mapping is an onto mapping, and, as we have just seen, it is then also a one–one mapping.

If the mapping T of V_n on to itself were not one–one, there would be at least two vectors $\mathbf{X}, \mathbf{X}'$, where $\mathbf{X} \neq \mathbf{X}'$ such that

$$T(\mathbf{X}) = T(\mathbf{X}').$$

But then

$$T(\mathbf{X} - \mathbf{X}') = \mathbf{0},$$

where $\mathbf{X} - \mathbf{X}' \neq \mathbf{0}$, so that the null space of T would be of dimension greater than zero. Hence, summing up, we have Theorem 50.

Theorem 50. *A linear mapping of a vector space V on to itself is one–one onto if, and only if, either of the following conditions holds: (a) the null space of T is the zero vector, (b) the range of T is V.*

37. Linear Mappings and Matrices

We now show how a matrix inevitably arises from the consideration of a linear mapping between vector spaces. As an example, let T be a linear mapping of V_3 on to V_2. Then a basis for vectors in V_3 is given by the vectors

$$\mathbf{e}_1 = [1, 0, 0], \qquad \mathbf{e}_2 = [0, 1, 0], \qquad \mathbf{e}_3 = [0, 0, 1],$$

and a basis for vectors in V_2 is given by the vectors

$$\mathbf{E}_1 = [1, 0], \qquad \mathbf{E}_2 = [0, 1].$$

If we know the maps under T of the basis vectors of V_3, these maps can be expressed as linear multiples of the basis vectors of V_2, and we shall know how any vector in V_3 is mapped. To be more precise:

Let
$$T[1, 0, 0] = a_{11}[1, 0] + a_{21}[0, 1],$$
$$T[0, 1, 0] = a_{12}[1, 0] + a_{22}[0, 1],$$
$$T[0, 0, 1] = a_{13}[1, 0] + a_{23}[0, 1].$$

Then if
$$\mathbf{X} = X_1[1, 0, 0] + X_2[0, 1, 0] + X_3[0, 0, 1],$$

$$\begin{aligned} T(\mathbf{X}) &= X_1T[1, 0, 0] + X_2T[0, 1, 0] + X_3T[0, 0, 1] \\ &= (a_{11}X_1 + a_{12}X_2 + a_{13}X_3)[1, 0] \\ &\quad + (a_{21}X_1 + a_{22}X_2 + a_{23}X_3)[0, 1]. \end{aligned}$$

If we also write

$$T(\mathbf{X}) = X_1^*[1, 0] + X_2^*[0, 1] = [X_1^*, X_2^*],$$

we have the equations

$$X_1^* = a_{11}X_1 + a_{12}X_2 + a_{13}X_3,$$
$$X_2^* = a_{21}X_1 + a_{22}X_2 + a_{23}X_3,$$

for the linear mapping T. These equations can be written in the form

$$\begin{bmatrix} X_1^* \\ X_2^* \end{bmatrix} = \begin{bmatrix} a_{11} & a_{12} & a_{13} \\ a_{21} & a_{22} & a_{23} \end{bmatrix} \begin{bmatrix} X_1 \\ X_2 \\ X_3 \end{bmatrix}. \tag{93}$$

Suppose now that the mapping T from V_3 on to V_2 is followed by a mapping S from V_2 on to a vector space V_2', and that

$$\begin{aligned} S[1, 0] &= b_{11}[1, 0] + b_{21}[0, 1], \\ S[0, 1] &= b_{12}[1, 0] + b_{22}[0, 1]. \end{aligned}$$

Then

$$\begin{aligned} S[X_1^*, X_2^*] &= S(X_1^*[1, 0] + X_2^*[0, 1]) \\ &= X_1^*(b_{11}[1, 0] + b_{21}[0, 1]) \\ &\quad + X_2^*(b_{12}[1, 0] + b_{22}[0, 1]) \\ &= (b_{11}X_1^* + b_{12}X_2^*)[1, 0] \\ &\quad + (b_{21}X_1^* + b_{22}X_2^*)[0, 1]. \end{aligned}$$

If

$$S[X_1^*, X_2^*] = X_1'[1, 0] + X_2'[0, 1] = [X_1', X_2']$$

we now have

$$\begin{aligned} X_1' &= b_{11}X_1^* + b_{12}X_2^*, \\ X_2' &= b_{21}X_1^* + b_{22}X_2^* \end{aligned}$$

or

$$\begin{bmatrix} X_1' \\ X_2' \end{bmatrix} = \begin{bmatrix} b_{11} & b_{12} \\ b_{21} & b_{22} \end{bmatrix} \begin{bmatrix} X_1^* \\ X_2^* \end{bmatrix}.$$

On the other hand, if we express X_1^*, X_2^* in terms of X_1, X_2, and X_3 by means of the relations (93), we have

$$\begin{aligned} X_1' &= b_{11}(a_{11}X_1 + a_{12}X_2 + a_{13}X_3) \\ &\quad + b_{12}(a_{21}X_1 + a_{22}X_2 + a_{23}X_3) \\ &= (b_{11}a_{11} + b_{12}a_{21})X_1 \\ &\quad + (b_{11}a_{12} + b_{11}a_{22})X_2 \\ &\quad + (b_{11}a_{13} + b_{12}a_{23})X_3, \end{aligned}$$

and

$$\begin{aligned} X_2' &= b_{21}(a_{11}X_1 + a_{12}X_2 + a_{13}X_3) \\ &\quad + b_{22}(a_{21}X_1 + a_{22}X_2 + a_{23}X_3) \\ &= (b_{21}a_{11} + b_{22}a_{21})X_1 \\ &\quad + (b_{21}a_{12} + b_{22}a_{22})X_2 \\ &\quad + (b_{21}a_{13} + b_{22}a_{23})X_3. \end{aligned}$$

But we also have

$$\begin{aligned} \begin{bmatrix} X_1' \\ X_2' \end{bmatrix} &= \begin{bmatrix} b_{11} & b_{12} \\ b_{21} & b_{22} \end{bmatrix} \begin{bmatrix} X_1^* \\ X_2^* \end{bmatrix} \\ &= \begin{bmatrix} b_{11} & b_{12} \\ b_{21} & b_{22} \end{bmatrix} \begin{bmatrix} a_{11} & a_{12} & a_{13} \\ a_{21} & a_{22} & a_{23} \end{bmatrix} \begin{bmatrix} X_1 \\ X_2 \\ X_3 \end{bmatrix}, \end{aligned}$$

and we now see the motivation for the definition of matrix multiplication given on p. 152. In the foregoing example,

$$\begin{bmatrix} b_{11} & b_{12} \\ b_{21} & b_{22} \end{bmatrix} \begin{bmatrix} a_{11} & a_{12} & a_{13} \\ a_{21} & a_{22} & a_{23} \end{bmatrix}$$
$$= \begin{bmatrix} b_{11}a_{11} + b_{12}a_{21} & b_{11}a_{12} + b_{12}a_{22} & b_{11}a_{13} + b_{12}a_{23} \\ b_{21}a_{11} + b_{22}a_{21} & b_{21}a_{12} + b_{22}a_{22} & b_{21}a_{13} + b_{22}a_{23} \end{bmatrix}$$

and this agrees with the expression for X_1', X_2' in terms of X_1, X_2, X_3.

The mapping T from V_3 on to V_2 has been represented by the matrix

$$\mathbf{A} = \begin{bmatrix} a_{11} & a_{12} & a_{13} \\ a_{21} & a_{22} & a_{23} \end{bmatrix}$$

and the mapping S from V_2 on to V_2' has been represented by the matrix

$$\mathbf{B} = \begin{bmatrix} b_{11} & b_{12} \\ b_{21} & b_{22} \end{bmatrix}.$$

In these mappings,

$$T(\mathbf{X}) = \mathbf{X}^*,$$

and

$$S(\mathbf{X}^*) = \mathbf{X}',$$

which may be written

$$S(T(\mathbf{X})) = \mathbf{X}',$$

or

$$ST(\mathbf{X}) = \mathbf{X}'.$$

The *product mapping* ST *of* $\mathbf{X}$ on to $\mathbf{X}'$ is represented by the matrix $\mathbf{BA}$.

It will be found that some texts represent the mapping $T(\mathbf{X})$ by the symbol $\mathbf{X}T$. Then the product mapping is written

$$(\mathbf{X}T)S = \mathbf{X}(TS).$$

EXERCISES 37

1. In a linear mapping T from V_3 on to V_2,

$$T[1, 0, 0] = [3, 1],$$
$$T[0, 1, 0] = [0, 1],$$
$$T[0, 0, 1] = [1, 1].$$

Find $T(\mathbf{X})$, where $\mathbf{X} = [X_1, X_2, X_3]$ is any vector of V_3, and determine the null space and the range of T.

2. In the linear mapping $T(\mathbf{X}) = \mathbf{X}'$ from V_3 on to V_3,

$$\begin{aligned} T(\mathbf{e}_1) &= \mathbf{e}_1 + \mathbf{e}_2 + \mathbf{e}_3 \\ T(\mathbf{e}_2) &= \qquad \mathbf{e}_2 + \mathbf{e}_3 \\ T(\mathbf{e}_3) &= \mathbf{e}_1 + \mathbf{e}_2 + 2\mathbf{e}_3 \end{aligned}$$

where $\mathbf{e}_1 = [1, 0, 0]$, $\mathbf{e}_2 = [0, 1, 0]$, and $\mathbf{e}_3 = [0, 0, 1]$. Show that this mapping is a one–one mapping of V_3 onto V_3.

3. In Exercise 2, determine the matrix of the mapping $T(\mathbf{X}) = \mathbf{X}'$ when $\mathbf{X}$ is referred to the basis $\mathbf{e}_1, \mathbf{e}_2, \mathbf{e}_3$, but $\mathbf{X}'$ is referred to the basis

$$\mathbf{e}_1' = [1, 0, 0], \qquad \mathbf{e}_2' = [0, 1, 1], \qquad \mathbf{e}_3' = [0, -2, 1].$$

It is not difficult to express the ideas developed previously in more general terms. Let T be a linear mapping from V_n on to V_m, and suppose that $\mathbf{e}_1, \mathbf{e}_2, \ldots, \mathbf{e}_n$ is a basis for V_n, and $\mathbf{E}_1, \mathbf{E}_2, \ldots, \mathbf{E}_m$ is a basis for V_m, and that

$$\begin{aligned} T(\mathbf{e}_1) &= a_{11}\mathbf{E}_1 + a_{21}\mathbf{E}_2 + \cdots + a_{m1}\mathbf{E}_m, \\ T(\mathbf{e}_2) &= a_{12}\mathbf{E}_1 + a_{22}\mathbf{E}_2 + \cdots + a_{m2}\mathbf{E}_m, \\ &\cdot \quad \cdot \quad \cdot \qquad \cdot \qquad \cdots \quad \cdot \\ T(\mathbf{e}_n) &= a_{1n}\mathbf{E}_1 + a_{2n}\mathbf{E}_2 + \cdots + a_{mn}\mathbf{E}_m. \end{aligned}$$

Then

$$\begin{aligned} T(X_1\mathbf{e}_1 &+ X_2\mathbf{e}_2 + \cdots + X_n\mathbf{e}_n) \\ &= X_1(a_{11}\mathbf{E}_1 + a_{21}\mathbf{E}_2 + \cdots + a_{m1}\mathbf{E}_m) \\ &\quad + X_2(a_{12}\mathbf{E}_1 + a_{22}\mathbf{E}_2 + \cdots + a_{m2}\mathbf{E}_m) \\ &\quad + \cdot \quad \cdot \quad \cdot \quad \cdot \quad \cdots \quad \cdot \\ &\quad + X_n(a_{1n}\mathbf{E}_1 + a_{2n}\mathbf{E}_2 + \cdots + a_{mn}\mathbf{E}_m) \\ &= (a_{11}X_1 + a_{12}X_2 + \cdots + a_{1n}X_n)\mathbf{E}_1 \\ &\quad + (a_{21}X_1 + a_{22}X_2 + \cdots + a_{2n}X_n)\mathbf{E}_2 \\ &\quad + \cdot \quad \cdot \quad \cdots \quad \cdot \\ &\quad + (a_{m1}X_1 + a_{m2}X_2 + \cdots + a_{mn}X_n)\mathbf{E}_m, \end{aligned}$$

so that if

$$T[X_1, X_2, \ldots, X_n] = [X_1^*, X_2^*, \ldots, X_m^*],$$

$$\begin{aligned} X_1^* &= a_{11}X_1 + a_{12}X_2 + \cdots + a_{1n}X_n \\ X_2^* &= a_{21}X_1 + a_{22}X_2 + \cdots + a_{2n}X_n \\ &\cdot \quad \cdot \qquad \cdot \qquad \cdots \quad \cdot \\ X_m^* &= a_{m1}X_1 + a_{m2}X_2 + \cdots + a_{mn}X_n, \end{aligned} \tag{94}$$

and the linear mapping T is realized by the $m \times n$ matrix

$$\mathbf{A} = [a_{ij}] \qquad (i = 1, \ldots, m;\ j = 1, \ldots, n),$$

and

$$\begin{bmatrix} X_1^* \\ X_2^* \\ \cdot \\ \cdot \\ X_m^* \end{bmatrix} = \mathbf{A} \begin{bmatrix} X_1 \\ X_2 \\ \cdot \\ \cdot \\ X_n \end{bmatrix}$$

is the matrix equation of the linear mapping.

We can now proceed more rapidly, and say that since the foregoing equation represents a mapping T of V_n on to V_m, a mapping S of V_m on to V_p will be represented by a matrix equation

$$\begin{bmatrix} X_1' \\ X_2' \\ \cdot \\ \cdot \\ X_p' \end{bmatrix} = \mathbf{B} \begin{bmatrix} X_1^* \\ X_2^* \\ \cdot \\ \cdot \\ X_m^* \end{bmatrix}$$

where $\mathbf{B}$ is the $p \times m$ matrix

$$\mathbf{B} = [b_{ij}] \qquad (i = 1, \ldots, p;\ j = 1, \ldots, m),$$

and the mapping of V_n on V_p

$$\mathbf{X}' = S(T(\mathbf{X})) = S(\mathbf{X}^*)$$

is represented by the matrix equation

$$\begin{bmatrix} X_1' \\ X_2' \\ \cdot \\ \cdot \\ \cdot \\ X_p' \end{bmatrix} = \mathbf{B}\left(\mathbf{A} \begin{bmatrix} X_1 \\ X_2 \\ \cdot \\ \cdot \\ \cdot \\ X_n \end{bmatrix}\right) = (\mathbf{BA}) \begin{bmatrix} X_1 \\ X_2 \\ \cdot \\ \cdot \\ \cdot \\ X_n \end{bmatrix},$$

where $\mathbf{B}$ is $p \times m$ and $\mathbf{A}$ is $m \times n$, and the matrix product $\mathbf{BA}$ is $p \times n$.

This last equation shows that the product of linear mappings is indeed a linear mapping, and motivates the rule we have been using for the product $\mathbf{C} = \mathbf{BA}$ of a $p \times m$ matrix $\mathbf{B}$ and an $m \times n$ matrix $\mathbf{A}$. In fact, if we find

X' directly in terms of X, using equations (94) and the similar ones connecting X' and X^*, we find that

$$\begin{bmatrix} X_1' \\ X_2' \\ \cdot \\ \cdot \\ \cdot \\ X_p' \end{bmatrix} = \mathbf{C} \begin{bmatrix} X_1 \\ X_2 \\ \cdot \\ \cdot \\ \cdot \\ X_n \end{bmatrix}$$

where

$$\mathbf{C} = (c_{ij}) \qquad (i = 1, \ldots, p; j = 1, \ldots, n),$$

and

$$c_{ij} = \sum_{k=1}^{m} b_{ik} a_{kj}.$$

In fact,

$$\begin{aligned} X_i' &= \sum b_{ik} X_k^* \\ &= \sum b_{ik} (\sum a_{kj} X_j) \\ &= \sum \{\sum (b_{ik} a_{kj})\} X_j \\ &= \sum_{j=1}^{n} c_{ij} X_j, \end{aligned}$$

where

$$c_{ij} = \sum_{k=1}^{m} b_{ik} a_{kj}.$$

The linear mapping of V_n on V_m is a more fundamental tool than the matrix which represents it with respect to given bases or coordinate systems in the respective spaces V_n and V_m. The *associative law* for matrix multiplication is a fairly cumbrous thing to prove (see p. 158), but it can be deduced from the associative law for mappings, which is almost intuitive.

If $T(\mathbf{X}) = \mathbf{X}^*$ maps V_n on V_m, and $S(\mathbf{X}^*) = \mathbf{X}'$ maps V_m on V_p, and finally $R(\mathbf{X}') = \mathbf{Y}$ maps V_p on V_q, then

$$\begin{aligned} \mathbf{Y} = R(\mathbf{X}') &= R(S(\mathbf{X}^*)) \\ &= R(S(T(\mathbf{X}))). \end{aligned}$$

By the previous definition of the product of two linear mappings, we may write

$$\mathbf{Y} = (RS)(\mathbf{X}^*),$$

and we may also write

$$\mathbf{X}' = (ST)(\mathbf{X}),$$

so that we have

$$\mathbf{Y} = R(ST)(\mathbf{X}) = (RS)(T)(\mathbf{X}),$$

so that

$$R(ST) = (RS)(T),$$

since we naturally define linear mappings to be equal if they have the same effect on all vectors in the space being mapped.

The foregoing proof does not use any of the fundamental properties of linear mappings, and it therefore holds for more general mappings.

Finally, a word must be said about the results of changing the basis, or coordinate system, in a vector space V_n. We saw in Example 5, p. 206 that this is equivalent to a linear invertible mapping of the space onto itself. In fact, if $\mathbf{X}$ becomes $\mathbf{X}'$ in the new coordinate system, and

$$\mathbf{X} = \mathbf{A}\mathbf{X}',$$

then we must be able to represent $\mathbf{X}'$ in terms of $\mathbf{X}$, say by the matrix equation

$$\mathbf{X}' = \mathbf{B}\mathbf{X},$$

and therefore

$$\mathbf{X}' = \mathbf{B}\mathbf{X} = \mathbf{B}(\mathbf{A}\mathbf{X}') = (\mathbf{B}\mathbf{A})\mathbf{X}',$$

and $\mathbf{BA}$ must be the unity matrix, so that the matrix $\mathbf{A}$ has an inverse. In fact, one–one onto linear mappings of a space V_n on to itself are always associated with regular matrices, which have inverses (Theorem 31, p. 164).

If there is a linear mapping of V_n on to V_m which is expressed by the matrix equation $\mathbf{Y} = \mathbf{A}\mathbf{X}$, where $\mathbf{X} \in V_n$ and $\mathbf{Y} \in V_m$, let us suppose that the coordinate systems in both spaces are changed, so that

$$\mathbf{X} = \mathbf{P}\mathbf{X}', \qquad \mathbf{Y} = \mathbf{Q}\mathbf{Y}',$$

where both $\mathbf{P}$ and $\mathbf{Q}$ are regular matrices. Then the relation between $\mathbf{X}$ and $\mathbf{Y}$ is given by the matrix equation

$$\mathbf{Y} = \mathbf{Q}\mathbf{Y}' = \mathbf{A}\mathbf{X} = \mathbf{A}(\mathbf{P}\mathbf{X}') = (\mathbf{A}\mathbf{P})\mathbf{X}',$$

so that

$$\mathbf{Y}' = (\mathbf{Q}^{-1}\mathbf{A}\mathbf{P})\mathbf{X}'.$$

If $\mathbf{A}$ is $m \times n$ of rank r, we can choose $\mathbf{Q}$ and $\mathbf{P}$ so that the matrix $\mathbf{Q}^{-1}\mathbf{A}\mathbf{P}$ is in canonical form [(91), p. 178], and then the mapping between the two vector spaces assumes the simple form

$$Y_i' = X_i' \qquad (i = 1, \ldots, r),$$

$$Y_i' = 0 \qquad (i = r + 1, \ldots, m).$$

ANSWERS TO EXERCISES

Exercises 3, p. 13

2. $X_1 = 0$ and $X_1 - X_2\sqrt{3} + 3\sqrt{3} = 0$.
3. $\cos^{-1} 11/\sqrt{221}$.

Exercises 4, p. 16

4. $(0, \lambda a)$.

Exercises 6, p. 25

1. (*a*) $[3, 14]$; (*b*) $[-32, -30]$; (*c*) $[-3p, 4p]$.
3. (*a*) $\mathbf{X} = t[5, -6] + (1 - t)[1, 3]$.
   (*b*) $\mathbf{X} = t[0, 8] + (1 - t)[-2, 9]$.

Exercises 7.3, p. 32

1. $(-9\theta, 18\theta, 0)$; 2. $(-(3\varphi + \theta)/9, \varphi, \theta)$; 3. $(-2\theta, 10\theta, -9\theta)$.

Exercises 9, p. 41

1. (*a*) $(45°, 60°, 60°)$ (*b*) $(\pi - \cos^{-1} 1/3, \cos^{-1} 2/3, \cos^{-1} 2/3)$;
   (*c*) $(\cos^{-1} 2/7, \pi - \cos^{-1} 3/7, \cos^{-1} 6/7)$.
2. $60°$ or $120°$.
3. radius $= 3$.

Exercises 10, p. 44

1. $120°$;
2. $\cos^{-1} \dfrac{a^2 + b^2}{\sqrt{a^2 + b^2 + c^2}}, \cos^{-1} \dfrac{c^2}{\sqrt{a^2 + c^2}\sqrt{b^2 + c^2}}$.
3. $-8:10:11$, $-8/q$, $10/q$, $11/q$, where $q = \sqrt{285}$.

Exercises 11, p. 50

5. $X_1 - 1 = X_2 - 2 = 0$.

Exercises 12, p. 52

3. Foot of perpendicular is $(3, 8, 29)$.

Exercises 13, p. 56

1. Point on line is (1, 3, −2). Equation is $X_1 - 1 = 0, \dfrac{X_2 - 2}{1} = \dfrac{X_3 - 3}{-5}$.
2. ACD is $3X_1 - 2X_2 - X_3 = 0$, ABC is $X_3 = 0$,
   Angle is $\cos^{-1} 1/\sqrt{14}$. Distance is $9/\sqrt{14}$.

Exercises 14, p. 60

2. $9X_1 - 2X_2 - 5X_3 + 4 = 0$.

Exercises 16.1, p. 66

1. (*a*) [3, 14, 12]; (*b*) [−32, −30, −2]; (*c*) $[-3p, 4p, p/2]$.
3. (*a*) $\mathbf{X} = t[5, -6, 2] + (1 - t)[1, 3, 4]$.
   (*b*) $\mathbf{X} = t[0, 8, 10] + (1 - t)[-2, 9, 7]$.

Exercises 17.2, p. 76

1. $x:y:z:t = 2:-1:5:1$.
2. $x:y:z:t = 4:-2:1:1$.

Exercises 17.3, p. 82

1. $x = 0, y = 3, z = 3$.

Exercises 21, p. 105

1. $X_1 = 3/2, X_2 = 1, X_3 = -1, X_4 = 2$.

Exercises 22, p. 110

1. $k = 1, \mathbf{X} = \mathbf{Y}_1 + 3\mathbf{Y}_2 + 2\mathbf{Y}_3$.
2. $\mathbf{Y}_3 = 5\mathbf{Y}_1 - 3\mathbf{Y}_2$.

Exercises 25, p. 123

1. $\mathbf{E}_2^* = [35, 42, -61], \mathbf{E}_3^* = [6, -5, 0]$.
3. Third, fifth. Yes.

Exercises 27.2, p. 136

1. If $p + q \geqslant n$, greatest dim. $U + W$ is n, least dim. $U \cap W$ is $p + q - n$.
   If $p + q < n$, greatest dim. $U + W$ is $p + q$, least dim. $U \cap W$ is 0.

Exercises 27.3, p. 139

1. $W = L\{[0, 0, 1]\}$ or $W = L\{[1, 0, 0]\}$ will do.
2. Projection on $U = -15[1, 0, 3] + 6[2, -1, 6] = [-3, -6, -9]$,
   Projection on $W = 7[1, 1, 1] = [7, 7, 7]$.
3. When $\mathbf{X} \in W$.

Exercises 28.1, p. 147

3. $W = L\{[-1, -2, 1, 0], [0, 0, 0, 1]\}$.
4. A complementary subspace is $L\{[-5, 2, 1, 0], [0, 0, 0, 1]\}$ and

$$[1, -2, 3, 0] = -\frac{8}{5}[0, 1, -2, 0] - \frac{1}{5}[-5, 2, 1, 0]$$

so that the orthogonal projection is $\left[0, -\dfrac{8}{5}, \dfrac{16}{5}, 0\right]$.

Exercises 29.3, p. 159

1. $\mathbf{A}^* = \begin{bmatrix} 3 & -4 \\ -2 & 3 \end{bmatrix}, \quad \mathbf{B}^* = \begin{bmatrix} 2/10 & -1/10 \\ -8/10 & 9/10 \end{bmatrix}.$

2. $\mathbf{A} = \begin{bmatrix} a & a^2/b \\ -b & -a \end{bmatrix}.$

Exercises 30.1, p. 167

5. Inverse is $\begin{bmatrix} -25 & 26 & -33 \\ 4 & -4 & 5 \\ 3 & -3 & 4 \end{bmatrix}, \quad X_1 = -72, X_2 = 11, X_3 = 9.$

Exercises 30.2, p. 168

4. $\mathbf{B} = \begin{bmatrix} 1 & 1 \\ -1 & 2 \end{bmatrix}$ (not unique).

$$\mathbf{A} = \begin{bmatrix} -1 & 2 \\ 4 & 1 \end{bmatrix} = \begin{bmatrix} 1 & 1 \\ -1 & 2 \end{bmatrix}^{-1} \begin{bmatrix} -3 & 0 \\ 0 & 3 \end{bmatrix} \begin{bmatrix} 1 & 1 \\ -1 & 2 \end{bmatrix}$$

giving $\mathbf{A}^n = \begin{bmatrix} 1 & 1 \\ -1 & 2 \end{bmatrix}^{-1} \begin{bmatrix} -3 & 0 \\ 0 & 3 \end{bmatrix}^n \begin{bmatrix} 1 & 1 \\ -1 & 2 \end{bmatrix}.$

If n is odd: $\mathbf{A}^n = \begin{bmatrix} -3^{n-1} & 2 \cdot 3^{n-1} \\ 4 \cdot 3^{n-1} & 3^{n-1} \end{bmatrix}.$

If n is even: $\mathbf{A}^n = \begin{bmatrix} 3^n & 0 \\ 0 & 3^n \end{bmatrix}.$

Exercises 31.1, p. 172

2. Both = 3.

Exercises 31.3, p. 182

1. $\begin{bmatrix} 0 & 1 & 2 \\ 1 & 0 & 2 \\ 1 & 2 & 0 \end{bmatrix}^{-1} = \begin{bmatrix} -2/3 & 2/3 & 1/3 \\ 1/3 & -1/3 & 1/3 \\ 1/3 & 1/6 & -1/6 \end{bmatrix},$

$$\begin{bmatrix} 1 & 5 & 2 \\ 1 & 1 & 7 \\ 0 & -3 & 4 \end{bmatrix}^{-1} = \begin{bmatrix} -25 & 26 & -33 \\ 4 & -4 & 5 \\ 3 & -3 & 4 \end{bmatrix}.$$

Exercise 32.4, p. 188

1. $\begin{bmatrix} \cos\alpha & -\sin\alpha & -\cos(\alpha-\beta+\gamma) & \sin(\alpha-\beta+\gamma) \\ \sin\alpha & \cos\alpha & -\sin(\alpha-\beta+\gamma) & -\cos(\alpha-\beta+\gamma) \\ 0 & 0 & \cos\gamma & -\sin\gamma \\ 0 & 0 & \sin\gamma & \cos\gamma \end{bmatrix}.$

Exercise 33, p. 192

1. $\mathbf{X} = \lambda[1, -2, 1, 0] + \mu[2, -3, 0, 1].$

Exercises 36.1, p. 205

1. (*b*), (*c*), and (*d*).

Exercises 37, p. 212

1. $T(\mathbf{X}) = [3X_1 + X_3, X_1 + X_2 + X_3]$. Null space is $L\{[1, 2, -3]\}$. Range is V_2.

3. $$\begin{bmatrix} X_1' \\ X_2' \\ X_3' \end{bmatrix} = \begin{bmatrix} 1 & 0 & 1 \\ 1 & 1 & 5/3 \\ 0 & 0 & 1/3 \end{bmatrix} \begin{bmatrix} X_1 \\ X_2 \\ X_3 \end{bmatrix}.$$

Index